Frequently Asked Questions
about
Sexuality,
the Bible,
and the Church

Ted A. Smith, editor

COVENANT
NETWORK
OF PRESBYTERIANS

2006

Cover design by Antra Kitts
Book design and production by Rosemary Bledsoe

ISBN-10: 0-9791027-0-7
ISBN-13: 978-0-9791027-0-7
Second printing

The Covenant Network offers these essays as a gift to the church to help deepen and broaden our conversations about faith and faithful living. Each essay represents the views of its author and not necessarily those of the Covenant Network or its Board of Directors. Authors have followed a style of citation and reference modeled on the standard for the *Christian Century*.

The Covenant Network is a national group of clergy and lay leaders seeking to maintain the Presbyterian Church's historic, progressive vision, to promote faithful dialogue among all parts of the church, and to work for a fully inclusive church.

www.covenantnetwork.org

Table of Contents

Reprinted from previous publications

*With thanks for the ministries
of Sue Goodrich and Andy Robinson,
and prayers for a church that can welcome them.*

- T.A.S.

What are the questions? And what is this booklet?

Ted A. Smith ✣
Vanderbilt Divinity School

This booklet is an offering to the church in a season of discernment. It comes from 26 scholars who care deeply about the church. Twenty-four of us are members of the Presbyterian Church (USA), and most of us are ordained. We serve at 19 different academic institutions, including eight seminaries affiliated with the denomination. We write because we love the church and long to help it live more faithfully as the body of Christ.

This booklet grows out of a realization – a confession – that many of our debates about sexuality and ordination have grown thin, stale and mean. We need something more than slightly better answers to the questions we already have. We need questions that help us find better ways of listening together for the Word of God. We need answers that lead us not just on to victory for one side or another, but back more deeply into the heart of the Gospel. And we need to find ways of praying, thinking, writing, talking, and listening together that are themselves a sign of that Gospel.

The short essays in this booklet do not pretend to answer those needs completely. But they represent a good-faith attempt to deepen the church's discernment of the work and will of God. They begin with the assumption that discernment will require questions and answers that are thoroughly theological, widely accessible, intentionally diverse, and open to further conversation.

These essays seek to take debates about ethics, policies and practices and restore them to a broader theological context. Christian discernment requires theological thinking, for it recognizes that lives of faith unfold in response to what God is already doing. Reformed churches have therefore insisted that we cannot begin with the question, "What is the right thing to do?" Instead, as theologian H. Richard Niebuhr argued, the first question of Christian ethics must be, "What is God doing?" Only in light of that question can we begin to ask, "How shall we respond?"

Our debates go sour when we forget the priority of God's gracious action in Jesus Christ. Both liberals and conservatives have slipped into proclaiming ethical principles that float free from larger understandings of who God is and what God is doing. Conservatives have too often recited a law prohibiting same-sex love without connecting that prohibition to Jesus' table fellowship with people the Pharisees called sinners (Luke 5:27-39), the early church's realization that the Holy Spirit moved among those the law declared unclean (Acts 10-15), and Paul's reminder that "all have sinned and fall short of the glory of God" (Rom. 3:23). Liberals have too often insisted on a free-floating mandate for inclusivity without connecting that mandate to Jesus' insistence on the enduring significance of the law (Matt. 5:17) or Peter's reminder that God is working to form a holy people (1 Peter 2:9). And both sides have appealed to ideas of what is "natural" without adequately considering the Reformed tradition's deep wariness about appeals to the natural order as a revelation of the will of God. When we forget that we are seeking to discern what God is doing and how we might respond – when our conversations cease to be theological – our debates become shallow and spiteful, like church versions of political talk shows.

It seems easier to debate "abomination" versus "inclusivity" than to seek to name the work of God in the world. And attempts to say what God is doing can end in foolishness and arrogance. But God's ways with the world are not an utter mystery to us. In Jesus Christ the Word became flesh and lived among us, eager to know and be known. And we trust that by the Holy Spirit, the Scriptures are "the unique and authoritative witness to Jesus Christ," and that the confessions offer "authentic and reliable expositions of what Scripture leads us to believe and do" (Book of Order, G-14.0405). That Word, that witness, and those expositions do not invite us to glib and all-knowing speech. They lead instead to patience and to prayer. They lead us to test interpretations in Christian community.

They call for penitent listening – even as they demand that we risk bold proclamation.

Our listening and our proclamation are best when they engage the whole of the gospel. Even theological discernment goes wrong when we consider tiny slices of Scripture and doctrine apart from our best sense of the whole. The essays in this booklet therefore range more widely than many recent discussions of sexuality and ordination. The essays here address both questions that are in fact "frequently asked" and questions that should be frequently asked. They ask questions about the short list of Bible verses around which so many debates have revolved. But they also ask questions about parts of Scripture these debates have neglected, like the Wisdom literature and, remarkably, the Gospels. The essays take up familiar questions in theology, like ordination and the authority of Scripture. But they also ask questions about relevant topics that our debates have neglected, like sanctification, baptism and marriage. This broader range of questions can enrich the church's discernment, for discernment demands that we think in light of all that we know about God and God's ways with the world.

Discernment is not the work of a few experts, but of the whole church. And so the essays here are accessible to a wide readership. They are all fairly short. They use minimal jargon. They reach out to readers from many different backgrounds. While the essays are clear, they cannot be reduced to soundbites. Readers who want to skim and pick up a few "talking points" will be disappointed. The essays aspire to the very best of contemporary scholarship, and they do not back away from complexity. But these careful, scholarly essays remain accessible because the authors understand the issues so well that they can consider complex questions clearly.

Because faithful discernment requires attention to many voices, the essays in this booklet reflect many kinds of diversity. All the authors believe the church should affirm the ministries of gay and lesbian Christians with ordination, but we differ in significant ways. We differ not only in gender, race, ethnicity, age, sexual orientation, and institutional location, but also in the ways we understand sexuality, ordination, Scripture, and the church. We use different language, and we work out of different traditions within an overlapping Reformed heritage. The booklet concludes by reprinting two important statements in which scholars speak with unified voices, but it offers no single statement in itself. Instead it serves as a sign of hope that church people need not agree on every point in order to find ways of living together that recognize the gifts of all those God calls to ministry.

The diversity within this booklet is significant, but it only begins to present the whole of the church's conversation. It invites and even requires other voices. This collection of essays makes no claim to be complete in itself. It lacks the voices of people who are opposed to ordaining gay and lesbian Christians. It lacks the deeper racial and ethnic diversity of the church we hope for. It lacks the wisdom of people who do not teach in seminaries, universities, and colleges. And it includes too few Christians who identify themselves as lesbian, gay, bisexual, and transgendered. But the authors of the essays make room, I think, for voices that respond and even disagree in good faith.

As the booklet invites other authors, it also invites other questions. Beginning to expand the questions we ask only shows how much more work there is to do. This booklet features an essay on baptism but not on the Lord's Supper, on the Wisdom literature but not on the prophets. The booklet is not a final word, but an invitation to deeper and broader conversation about what God has done in Jesus Christ and how we are called to respond.

In its openness to more conversation this booklet presumes that the Holy Spirit still rests upon the body of Christ. It is offered in trust that God is already moving in the church, already drawing into the great work of redemption all the grace, violence, pettiness and loveliness of our life together. Offered in that confidence, these essays do not seek to end discussion and make irrelevant the deliberative bodies of the church. Instead they seek to build up those bodies in a season of discernment, that we may all respond to the Gospel with more faith, hope and love.   ✤

Ted A. Smith teaches ethics and preaching and directs the Program in Theology and Practice at Vanderbilt Divinity School. He formerly served as pastor of Weston Presbyterian Church and the First Presbyterian Church of Dundee, two small-membership churches in rural New York State.

What do Presbyterians believe about the authority of Scripture?

William C. Placher ✢

Wabash College

The most honest answer would be: different Presbyterians believe many different things. People in our church today have different understandings of Scripture's authority, and that's not a new development; it has been in some degree true throughout the history of our tradition. But there is a core of shared beliefs. What follows are some fairly consistent themes, drawn particularly from Calvin and the *Book of Confessions* (most of the language is not at all inclusive, but I've left it as it is in the interest of historical accuracy).

Necessity. We will not understand God rightly if we do not turn to Scripture. Calvin believed that creation itself ought to reveal God to us, but that sin so distorted our vision that we could not see how clearly the world points to its creator. We need the Bible to function like eyeglasses, to help us see God at work in the world. The light of nature, the *Westminster Confession of Faith* explained, is "not sufficient to give that knowledge of God, and of his will, which is necessary unto salvation" (*Book of Confessions*, 6.001), and therefore we need the Holy Scripture to guide us.

Sufficiency. In the face of Catholic appeals to the authority of the church and its tradition alongside Scripture, the *Scots Confession* emphasized that the Scriptures alone are "sufficient to instruct and make perfect the man of God." (3.19). Likewise, the *Second Helvetic Confession* began by declaring that in Scripture the church "has the most complete exposition of all that pertains to a saving faith, and also to the framing of a life acceptable to God." (5.002). We do not need other authorities to provide additional information. Moreover, we do not need any human authorities to vouch for Scripture's authority—its authority (quoting the *Scots Confession)* comes "from God" and does not "depend on men or angels" (3.19).

The Witness of the Spirit. The Holy Spirit, Calvin taught, inspired those who wrote Scripture, and the decisive reason to accept Scripture's authority comes not from "human reasons, judgments, or conjectures" but from "the secret testimony of the Spirit." Just as "God himself spoke to the fathers, prophets, [and] apostles," the *Second Helvetic Confession* confirmed, so God "still speaks to us through the Holy Scriptures." (5.001). "Our full persuasion and assurance of the infallible truth and divine authority thereof," according to the *Westminster Confession of Faith*, is "from the inward work of the Holy Spirit, bearing witness by and with the Word in our hearts." (6.005).

Interpreting Scripture by Scripture. If the meaning of one biblical passage is obscure, and it's something important for us to know, the point will always be made more clearly somewhere else in Scripture. *The Second Helvetic Confession* asserts that the best way to interpret the Scriptures is "gleaned from the Scriptures themselves (from the nature of the language in which they were written, likewise according to the circumstances in which they were set down, and expounded in the light of like and unlike passages and of many and clearer passages)" (5.010). Likewise the *Westminster Confession of Faith* maintains that "the infallible rule of interpretation of Scripture is the Scripture itself" (6.009). When something isn't clear, we should look for other passages which address the matter more clearly. *Westminster* again: "Those things which are necessary to be known, believed, and observed, for salvation, are so clearly propounded and opened in some place of Scripture or other, that not only the learned, but the unlearned, in a due use of ordinary means, may attain unto a sufficient understanding of them" (6.007).

Correct Translation. Obviously, in believing what the Bible says, we have to make sure we get its meaning right. As a scholar influenced by Renaissance humanism, Calvin carefully sought correct texts and accurate translations. Sometimes, of course, translation is a complicated issue. In the United States before the Civil War, for instance, defenders of slavery noted that many admired Old Testament figures had slaves and that Paul sent the runaway slave Onesimus back to his owner Philemon. Thus, they said, the Bible approves of slavery. Critics of slavery, however, pointed out that the institution the Bible calls "slavery" was very different from what existed in the United States: it was not based on race, slaves could often achieve their freedom, and so on. Eventually, that recognition of historical difference carried the day among Presbyterian interpreters. We recognized that the slavery of biblical times was a different thing from slavery in the United States. The Bible wasn't approving the latter. Correct translation of words describing human activities and institutions involves understanding what those activities or institutions really were in their original context.

Accommodation. Calvin's doctrine of "accommodation" stated that the Bible often expresses things in simple form so that its original readers could understand them—like parents speaking "baby talk" to their children. Thus there are biblical passages that assume that the world is flat or that the sun and moon are the two great lights in the sky (though of course the stars are really much bigger than the moon). In such cases, Calvin wrote, their author "did not treat scientifically of the stars, as a philosopher would; but he called them in a popular manner, according to their appearance to the uneducated, rather than according to the truth." No need to explain several thousand years of scientific theory in order to make a simple point: "He who would learn astronomy, and other recondite arts, let him go elsewhere." When the Bible takes the worldview of its original audience for granted as background, accepting the authority of the Bible need not mean accepting the truth of that worldview.

Focus on Teaching. Calvin recognized that the biblical writers "were not very exact as to the order of dates, or even in detailing minutely every thing that Christ said and did." Their concern was to teach their readers about who Jesus is and how he saves us; they were not much worried about chronological details. He thought, for instance, that Matthew had probably drawn together material Jesus had preached on a number of different occasions to form the Sermon on the Mount, rather than reporting exactly a sermon delivered at one time. As Charles Hodge, the greatest theologian of Princeton orthodoxy, would say centuries later, the Bible is trustworthy in what it teaches, not in everything its human authors may have believed or assumed. They took for granted the beliefs of their time and place; such things were not the faith they were teaching.

Conclusion. We must not pick out the parts of the Bible we like and ignore the rest. Scripture speaks with *authority*. But we should be sure we understand what it means. Sometimes we translate terms which referred to an activity or institution in biblical times as if they referred to a very different activity or institution in our time; that leads to misunderstanding. Sometimes Scripture presupposes the view of the world that would have been taken for granted by its original readers so they could understand; such presuppositions are not what it *teaches*. When we have doubts about such matters in a particular case, we should use Scripture to interpret Scripture — we should look at any one passage in the light of the rest of the Bible, not in isolation.

With respect to current debates on homosexuality, for instance, we should start by looking at the biblical passages where the Bible talks, or seems to talk, about this issue. What exactly do the words mean? Are the activities or institutions being discussed the same as activities or institutions today? Is what is said about homosexuality what the passage means to teach, or something assumed in order to make a point about something else? When we have doubts about such matters, what do we learn from setting these passages in the larger biblical context – the whole story of covenant, redemption, and bringing more and more outsiders into the covenant? In asking questions like these, we are faithful to the Presbyterian tradition with respect to biblical authority. ✢

William C. Placher is LaFollette Distinguished Professor at Wabash College. An elder at Wabash Avenue Presbyterian Church in Crawfordsville, Indiana, he served on the committees that drafted both the Brief Statement of Faith and the current Presbyterian Catechism. **Callings***, the latest of his dozen books, examines Christian vocation.*

What does Genesis 1-3 teach about sexuality, and how should we live in response?

Patrick D. Miller   ✢
Princeton Theological Seminary

The first three chapters of Genesis do not directly address the church's questions about sexual relations between persons of the same sex. But the creation narratives do say much about God's hopes and purposes for the world. And they do begin to suggest the shape of faithful human responses to God's great, generative act of love in creation – especially when read as part of the whole canon of Scripture. In particular, they describe the centrality of relationships between men and women in the created order. These crucial chapters of Scripture therefore offer important indirect guidance for questions about same-sex relations. But what do they teach?

Genesis depicts a created order in which women and men are created good and placed in relationship with one another and with all of creation. Maleness and femaleness belong to this created order. The image of God is found in the human being as male and female (1:26-27). And the Genesis story clearly joins man and woman together in responsibility for filling and ruling the earth, for procreating and controlling God's creation (1:28-30).

I take that Genesis story very seriously. But taking seriously what it says does not immediately tell us what it teaches. The history of the church and of the larger society gives us good reason to pause for reflection before assuming that we know the moral meaning of God's created order. Church and society both have appealed to scriptural accounts of a created order to fix norms for roles and relationships. We have read scripture as declaring that God created a world in which women should be subordinate to men, men should cut their hair and women should not, women should not speak in church, subjects should obey their kings, and slaves should submit to their masters and obey them with the same fear and trembling with which they obey Christ.

The church is still in the process of repenting of its collusion with these systems that claimed to be grounded in God's created order. And we are right to do so. The church has heard in the gospel and in the prophetic and liberating words of both Old Testament and New Testament a counter word that does not fix people in roles and relationships and does not let cultural and social mores become final definitions of who and what we are in the church and kingdom. In this counter word we have heard what the scriptures teach.

A church that takes scripture seriously therefore faces today the same task that has faced communities of faith in every generation. We must interpret the stories of creation as guides and direction for our thinking and acting. But the presence of interpretive questions does not mean that we are bereft of answers. God does not leave us alone for each one to do what is right in his or her own eyes. For generations Reformed Christians have confessed our hope that the Holy Spirit quickens faithful reading. And we have taken as our guides the rule of faith and the rule of love.

The Rule of Faith and the Rule of Love

Interpretation of scripture in the church should not happen without attention to the rule of faith and the rule of love. The **rule of faith** suggests that our individual interpretations are placed against the community's understanding of scripture in past and present. In the Reformed community, that interpretive backdrop is found particularly in the creeds and confessions, though not only there. The subject of homosexuality has not been a special focus of attention in these documents, and the contemporary possibility of committed same-sex partnerships runs beyond what they can imagine. But it is also the case that the majority of Christian thinkers over time have regarded same-sex sexual activity as sinful. The tradition thus places the present interpreter in a kind of tension. On the one hand, there is inattention to the issue; on the other hand, where the tradition has dealt with the matter, it has generally condemned the practice of same-sex activity.

In that context, it is important that the present interpretive activity of the church be a communal one, that our efforts to think about this issue afresh and in reference to what has been thought already be a corporate engagement and not simply a matter of individual proposals for reading texts. Our interpretation happens in community, and what the community experiences in faith is more significant than the experience of any individual. What we say and do together is more to be attended to than idiosyncratic readings of texts by one or a few individuals. This means listening to a broad range of interpretive judgments in the church, including its gay and lesbian members.

The **rule of love** reminds us that our interpretation of scripture stands under the divine command to love God and neighbor. Thus, what we hear from scripture should not lead us away from the expression of love for others. Or, in the words of the document, "Presbyterian Understandings of the Use of Holy Scripture," adopted by the General Assembly of the Presbyterian Church ((USA) in 1983,

> *All interpretations are to be judged by the question of whether they offer and support the love given and commanded by God. When interpretations do not meet this criterion, it must be asked whether the text has been used correctly in the light of the whole Scripture and its subject ... No interpretation of Scripture is correct that leads to or supports contempt of any individual or group of persons either within or outside of the church. Such results from the interpretation of Scripture plainly indicate that the rule of love has not been honored (pp. 19-20).*

Measured by the rule of love, the church has fallen far short in its use of scripture in dealing with homosexuality – including those texts that deal with the topic indirectly, like Genesis 1-3. The rule of love, which says that our interpretation is correlative with the way we live, raises serious questions about what we have done with the plain sense of scripture. If it is a means by which we inflict pain and put down other Christians – or other human beings of any stripe – then our interpretation is under question.

We therefore need to ask about the preeminence of the gospel and of the grace of God as a guide for our proper response to scripture. That response may not be the same as what the plain sense of some texts would indicate. We are not to lose sense, however, of what it is that "the Scriptures principally teach," as the Catechism puts it *(Book of Confessions, 7.003)*. The *answer* to that question is what we are to believe concerning God and what duty God requires of us. It is no accident that the verses accompanying the Westminster documents are Micah 6:8, John 3:16, and John 20:31. These are fundamental formulations of the gospel, of the love of God revealed in Jesus Christ, and of our responsibility to "do justice and love kindness and walk humbly with your God." It is precisely the manifestation of justice and kindness that in this, as in all instances, is a fundamental criterion of our interpretation of scripture. What is ultimately at stake is the triumph of grace in the church.

A foundation, not a limit

Genesis 1-3 gives no direct, plain-sense teaching about contemporary same-sex relationships. But how might the church understand its indirect teaching, if we read in ways that are guided by the rule of faith and the rule of love?

The Genesis stories picture an ideal of enduring companionship of man and woman – one that features sexual relationship for procreation – as central to the human story. The Apostle Paul will articulate a different vision, but the Genesis stories tell us something very fundamental about who and what we are. The defining relationship in the human community is man and woman. That relationship often is manifest in the establishment of a commitment between a man and a woman that perdures and is fruitful in every respect.

Of course, for many human beings that particular ideal is not their experience. They may be single and so do not know the man-woman relationship as one of enduring and intimate companionship, sexual and otherwise. They may be childless and so do not know the procreative fruit of the relationship that God intends. They may be homosexual and so do not know the experience of existing in sexual relationship with a companion of opposite gender. Yet all of these persons, whose numbers are legion, are truly members of the human community God has made and of the community of faith. As persons who in their varied ways and relationships live out lives of service to God, lives of faithfulness, love, and justice, caring for one another and loving God, their place in the community of faith and my judgment of them are not determined by their conformity to the kind of relationship given central place in Genesis.

In *The Decalogue and a Human Future*, Paul Lehmann acutely perceives the different possibilities for receiving and drawing upon the Genesis account of the creation of man and woman. His comments are indicative of the fact that what the text says does not yet tell us what it teaches; that happens only when the text is perceived from some angle of vision. For Lehmann, as it should be for us all, that angle is the gospel, which he described as what God was and is doing to make and keep human life human. Lehmann teaches us how to read Genesis from the angle of the gospel, guided by the rule of faith and the rule of love.

Lehmann reads Genesis 1-3 as giving a norm in the form of what he calls a *foundational instance*. Lehmann describes a foundational instance as a normative center. He contrasts it with what he calls a *limiting instance*. If a foundational instance establishes a center, a limiting instance draws a boundary. Lehmann argues that Genesis describes a created order in which a generative, enduring sexual relationship between a man and a woman plays a central role. *But the centrality of one kind of relationship does not imply the sinfulness of every other kind of relationship.* The sexual relationship between woman and man provides a foundational instance – but not a limiting one. If the woman-man relationship were a limiting instance, it would draw a line that excluded every other kind of relationship from participating in God's great work of love. But there is nothing in the Genesis narrative to demand that we read a heterosexual relationship as a limiting instance.

On the contrary, the story of creation stresses plurality, fullness, and the rich variety of God's creative power. The man-woman relationship instead appears as a foundational moment, what Lehmann calls "the liberating instance in relation to which divergent possibilities may be pursued and assessed" (174). Read in light of the gospel, under the rule of faith and the rule of love, Genesis depicts a created order in which procreative sexual relationships between women and men are a central – but not the only – faithful response to God's work of keeping human life human.

Because we read by the rule of faith, I am glad to place my interpretation in conversation with other readers, past and present. But however we interpret Genesis 1-3, we must read the story of creation by the light of the gospel and by the rules of faith and love. For me, it is no less than the power of the gospel in the church that is at stake.   ✤

Adapted from "What the Scriptures Principally Teach," in *Homosexuality and Christian Community*, edited by Choon-Leong Seow. Copyright 1996 Westminster John Knox Press. Used by permission. Revised for this booklet by Ted Smith.

Patrick D. Miller is Charles T. Haley Professor of Old Testament Theology Emeritus at Princeton Theological Seminary. A Presbyterian minister and former President of the Society of Biblical Literature, he also taught Bible at Union Theological Seminary in Richmond. His numerous books of biblical commentary include most recently **The God You Have: Politics and the First Commandment.**

For what sin did God destroy Sodom and Gomorrah?

Christine Roy Yoder ✣
Columbia Theological Seminary

The destruction of Sodom and Gomorrah is the first text that many people think about when we talk about homosexuality and the Bible. This is striking because the narrative is not, in fact, about homosexuality, and certainly not about private, consensual acts of same-sex love. Rather, Genesis 19 illustrates the sin of Sodom and Gomorrah as sexual violence against men and women, as brutality against persons the community ought to protect. Such behavior reveals a society that no longer observes "the way of the LORD" — namely, righteousness and justice (Gen 18:19) — and thus receives God's judgment.

Genesis 18 sets the stage. The chapter opens with a depiction of Abraham as gracious host to three angelic messengers. Abraham runs to meet them, offers them shelter and the best food he has available, stands alongside them as they eat (18:1-8), and accompanies two of them on their way (18:16). His behavior exemplifies hospitality, an eagerness to serve others, even, and here particularly, unexpected strangers. That hospitality continues when God, who lingers after the meal, reports there is a great outcry against Sodom and Gomorrah and invites Abraham to help adjudicate the gravity of the sin (18:16-21). Without missing a beat, Abraham intercedes for the sake of the righteous (18:22-33). His questions of God are direct and relentless: "Will you indeed sweep away the righteous with the wicked?" "Will not the judge of all the earth do justice?" Seven times he refers to the righteous. Twice he cautions God "far be it from you to do such a thing!" He is so persistent that God ends their exchange and departs, leaving Abraham standing there. We readers stand with him, wondering as we turn to Genesis 19 what grave sin we will find at Sodom and

Gomorrah and whether there are enough righteous to save the cities. Will there be ten? Will God find even one?

The description of Abraham's hospitality in Genesis 18 heightens the inhospitality and injustice we discover at Sodom and Gomorrah. When the two angelic messengers arrive in Sodom, they meet Abraham's nephew Lot. Lot initially welcomes them with hospitality like Abraham's, but his graciousness falters and ultimately fails amid the shouts of a gathering crowd. "The men of Sodom, young and old, all the people to the last man" (19:4) surround Lot's house and demand he bring out his guests "so that we may know them" (19:5). The Hebrew verb "to know" may refer to sex (e.g., Gen 4:1, 17, 25; 1 Kgs 1:4), and Lot indicates that he understands their demand as such when, much to our horror, he offers instead his daughters who have not yet "known" a man (19:8). The scene is replete with threat and chaos: Lot with his back to the door and pleading with the crowd ("I beg you, my brothers, do not do this evil," 19:7), his guests cornered inside, the crowd's increasing stridency, the men pushing and shoving against Lot in an attempt to break down the door, the messengers' last minute rescue of Lot. With each verse, the volatility of the crowd intensifies. No consent is asked for. No consent is given. This is not a matter of private, consensual homosexual sex. The mob's demand—their intended evil—is gang rape.

The mob's demand for homosexual gang rape is paralleled by Lot's disturbing counterproposal: the heterosexual gang rape of his two virgin, betrothed daughters (19:8). In his efforts to protect the male guests inside his house, he suggests he bring the women of his house outside—where they will be without physical protection and arguably, because he offers them to the men to rape, without legal recourse (Deut 22:22-27; cf. Judg 19-20). Telling the mob to "do to them as you please," Lot exemplifies the very depravity about which he has just admonished the Sodomites. He offers his daughters as sexual objects (ironically a fate soon to be his own, cf. 19:30-38). If we hoped that Lot might be the one righteous person (so 2 Pet 2:5-8) who would motivate God to spare Sodom and Gomorrah, we now know there is no hope. The society is utterly corrupt. Indeed, God spares Lot and his family because God remembers Abraham (19:29).

Whereas Genesis 19 depicts the sin of Sodom and Gomorrah as sexual violence, other biblical texts that refer to the cities charge them with inhospitality and injustice generally. Notably, not one mentions the homosexual aspect of the mob's demand. (The obscure reference to "strange flesh" in Jude 7 suggests the sin is men violating angels.) Isaiah, for example, likens Judah to Sodom because they practice injustice ("crushing [God's] people...grinding the face of the poor") and, in their arrogance, do not even try to hide it (3:1-15). Ezekiel similarly identifies Sodom's sin as arrogant disregard of those in need: "[Sodom] and her daughters had pride, excess of food, and prosperous ease, but did not aid the poor and needy" (16:49). Jeremiah warns that prophets have become like Sodom and Gomorrah because "they commit adultery, walk in lies, and strengthen the hands of evildoers so that no one turns from wickedness" (23:14). Matthew names the sin of Sodom as inhospitality (10:5-15; cf. Luke 10:1-12) and attributes its destruction to unrepentant disobedience of God (11:23-24). This larger tradition with regard to Sodom and Gomorrah suggests that Genesis 19 points to just one example (i.e. gang rape) of how egregiously the community was out of step with the "way of the LORD". That such inhospitality and injustices persist in our own communities should give us pause if we ever locate ourselves alongside Abraham early in the morning, looking down at the smoldering landscape that was Sodom and Gomorrah, thinking God's justice has been rightly served against "them" (19:27-29).   ✤

Christine Roy Yoder serves as Associate Professor of Old Testament at Columbia Theological Seminary, Decatur, GA. She is a minister member of Greater Atlanta Presbytery, in which she serves on the Committee on Ministry. She is also the Associate Editor of the Bible Content Exam, Presbyteries' Cooperative Committee.

What does Leviticus teach about same-sex relations, and how should we live in response?

Robert B. Coote ✢
San Francisco Theological Seminary
and Graduate Theological Union

Some laws in Leviticus are important to all of us. The commandment to "love your neighbor as yourself" (Lev 19:18), for example, was essential to Jesus and remains so for us. On some others we may not agree. One example would be, "You (a man) shall not lie with a male as with a woman: it is an abomination" (18:22). (An "abomination" was an act that violated the categories that Leviticus used to make sense of the world, an impurity; for example, since bleeding made a woman impure, a man who had intercourse with a menstruating woman committed an abomination – 18:19, 24-30.)

There are many laws in Leviticus that practically no Presbyterian follows. The law that comes immediately after the command to love your neighbor forbids wearing clothing that mixes different kinds of material, such as a shirt made of cotton and polyester (19:19). Another law prohibits clipping one's beard at the edges (19:27). Others prohibit cross-breeding animals (19:19 – leaving unclear what constitutes a "breed"), eating meat with blood in it (17:10-13), eating pork or lobster (11:7, 10-12), ordaining anyone who can't walk or has poor eyesight (21:17-20), and much more that we would probably regard as irrelevant or contrary to an ethical life. Some might appear positively abhorrent. Leviticus imposes the death penalty on children who dishonor their parents (20:9). And on a man lying with another male, in the only other verse in Leviticus on the subject: "they both shall be put to death" (20:13).

On what basis do we decide to obey one verse in Leviticus and not another? Selecting only the verses we agree with seems arbitrary. Some have suggested that we should keep laws in Leviticus that are reaffirmed in the New Testament. But the church does not apply this standard consistently. In Acts 15, early church leaders waive most of the Jewish dietary restrictions for Gentile Christians, but they agree that Gentiles should not eat any meat with blood. This law from the covenant with Noah (Gen 9:4) and from Leviticus is reaffirmed in the New Testament, but we don't believe it is necessary for holiness.

Even if we accepted all of the Levitical prohibitions reaffirmed in the New Testament, they would not include the prohibition of same-sex love. Jesus makes no mention of same-sex relations, and Paul's apparent censure of homosexuality in Romans 1 differs significantly from the prohibition in Leviticus. Paul writes about same-sex relations among Gentile men and women. But the Levitical prohibition of same-sex relations applies only to Israelites, only to males, and only to the land of Canaan. Whatever Paul intends, he does not mean to reaffirm a few favorite passages of the law in Leviticus. This should come as no surprise: Paul's entire life was turned upside down by the realization that God's new covenant does not depend on the laws of the Torah, even though as a Jew he continued to honor them.

The purity laws in Leviticus were developed out of the priestly account of creation in Genesis 1 and the categories that unfold there, beginning with the disposition of blood and the unqualified command to procreate. (For example, Leviticus does not mention lesbianism because it involves no waste of male "seed.") Other than the eating of blood as described in Acts, however, Paul rejects the notion that the Mosaic food restrictions derived from the blood taboo apply to Gentiles, and he like Jesus urges celibacy, not procreation. The capstone of both creation and the laws of the Mosaic covenant in Leviticus is the Sabbath. But Jesus subordinated even this treasured mark of holiness to doing good.

Presbyterian Christians affirm Jesus' emphasis in our Book of Order. "Truth is in order to goodness; and the great touchstone of truth, its tendency to promote holiness, according to our Savior's rule, 'By their fruits ye shall know them.'" Like Jesus and Paul, this Historic Principle of Church Order (G-1.0304) takes the measure of holiness to be goodness defined by love of neighbor, not the structural abstractions of Leviticus. Such abstractions – male vs. female (what about the intersexed?), same vs. different (what about "interracial" marriage and offspring?), saved semen vs. lost semen (is shared sexual pleasure not a mark of a strong marriage?), with blood vs. without blood (should women be defined by menstruation?) – will not serve a church committed to holiness defined by love of neighbor. Calvin called holiness "our advance in piety through the course of our life." Holiness is to be gauged by the ethics of love and justice, not by categories and patterns tied to a tabernacle, altar, blood sacrifice, temple, city, and holy land that have ceased to define the Christian life.

The law against same-sex love fails the test of holiness laid down by our church's Constitution. It arises not out of response to God's command to love your neighbor as yourself, but out of a need to organize the world into categories of clean and unclean. The belief system that categorizes people on the basis of an identification of sex and gender, exploiting the binary nature of sex to provide a spurious moral righteousness, is still dominant among us. Not only has the church continued to embrace this aspect of the dominant culture's modern-day moral pollution code, but we have remained its chief advocate. The church's appeal to purity and pollution categories to support the continued disparagement of same-sex love serves the same purposes that anthropologist Mary Douglas (*Purity and Danger*) described for pollution thinking in any culture. Pollution beliefs function culturally to uphold a moral convention in the midst of moral uncertainty or a perceived shortage of moral indignation.

Intolerance or moral uncertainty and disagreement may provide a cultural excuse for unfair discrimination, but it scarcely represents fidelity to the Lord who triumphs over all barriers of status, intolerance, and inequity. As the earliest church avowed, "In Christ there is neither Jew nor Greek, neither slave nor free, not male and female – for all are one in Christ Jesus" (Gal 3:28). The church has betrayed this baptismal ideal many times over, but it remains the ideal.   ✢

Robert B. Coote is professor of Old Testament at San Francisco Theological Seminary, where he has taught for 30 years. He was baptized and raised a Presbyterian and is at present a member of First Presbyterian Church in San Anselmo, California. He has served on the Presbyteries' Cooperative Committee on Examinations for Candidates.

On matters of sex, what kind of "textual orientation" does the wisdom literature provide?

William P. Brown ✚
Columbia Theological Seminary

The wisdom literature is perhaps the most open-ended yet thoroughly didactic corpus of the Old Testament. Even the books themselves are remarkably diverse: Proverbs, Job, and Ecclesiastes. They are the product of centuries of accumulated wisdom and insight, the result of sustained inquiries into the nature of reality, its anomalies as well as its regularities, for the purpose of figuring out how we are to lead our lives in "righteousness, justice, and equity" (Prov 1:3b). In their quest for wisdom, the sages were not reluctant to extend their investigations *beyond* the particularities of their faith. They, in fact, borrowed from the wisdom of surrounding cultures, adapting it and transforming it. Case in point: Proverbs 22:17-23:11 is actually an adaptation of the Egyptian "Instructions of Amen-em-ope" (ca. 1100 BCE). The biblical sages were convinced that *all* truth came from God, even truth at odds with itself.

The diversity of approaches espoused in the wisdom literature is the result of the sages' struggle with the wisdom of the past (tradition) and the truth of present experience. Job, for example, resists the wisdom of his friends, who have sold their souls to a rigidified tradition, for the sake of the truth he knows from his own experience, namely, that he remains righteous before God and neighbor, despite all evidence to the contrary. The sage behind Ecclesiastes quotes traditional sayings and then contradicts them with his own experience-based insights. In short, within biblical wisdom itself there resides a generative tension between tradition and experience. Neither can be dismissed.

Although the wisdom books do not specifically address contemporary concerns about sexual identity and conduct, specifically homosexuality, they may provide a helpful "textual orientation" for gaining insight into such matters.

Proverbs is a collection of collections of didactic sayings, from extended lectures to pithy apothegms, brought together in self-correcting ways. The search for wisdom, according to Proverbs, is a dynamic enterprise, one based on observation and study in which no final word concludes, once and for all, the quest for understanding. As testimony to this, Proverbs bears its own self-critique, indicated in part by the myriad incompatible sayings it contains (see, for example, Prov 26:4-5). The book describes wisdom as both contextual and dynamic. Wisdom is a "pathway," and a pathway is formed by the passage of many feet.

As for appropriate sexual conduct, the book of Proverbs is unequivocal on at least one matter, sexual fidelity. Proverbs calls people to spousal fidelity not through the language of law or sanction, but through the language of pleasure and blessing:

> *Drink water from your own cistern,*
> > *flowing water from your own well.*
> *Should your springs be scattered abroad,*
> > *streams of water in the streets?*
> *Let them be for yourself alone,*
> > *and not for sharing with strangers.*
> *Let your fountain be blessed,*
> > *and rejoice in the wife of your youth,*
> > *a lovely deer, a graceful doe.*
> *May her breasts satisfy you at all times,*
> > *may you be intoxicated always by her love.*   (5:15-20)

Within the marital context of lifelong commitment, sex is deemed a gift to be enjoyed by both partners. (Sex as the means of procreation is not mentioned in these texts.) Those who break the covenant of marriage through adultery are deemed "strange" and are to be avoided at all costs (2:16-19; 5:3-6; 6:24-29, 32, 35; 7:6-25). (The phrase translated as "loose woman" in the NRSV is better translated as "strange woman.") If one could reduce Proverbs' view of sexual fidelity to a motto, it would be "Adultery is dangerous." It is dangerous not because it incurs the wrath of God—nowhere does Proverbs cite the Seventh Commandment (Exod 20:14; Deut 5:18)—but because adultery is a betrayal, one that results in confusion, mistrust, anger, vengeance, and even violence. Whereas adultery is dangerous, fidelity is delightful and life-sustaining!

Neither Job nor Ecclesiastes espouses a sexual ethics. But they do broach larger issues that relate to the topic. **Job** is demonized by his friends and family; he is found to be morally anomalous and physically repugnant (19:15-17). His friends impugn him with all manner of moral perversion (22:5-11), to which Job proclaims his innocence by taking an oath of moral purity that includes sexual fidelity (31:1-40, see vv. 9-12). Before he reaches that climactic point, however, Job struggles mightily with who he is in the wake of both his sense of being godforsaken and the "friendly fire" of his accusers: "I am blameless; I do not know myself; I loathe my life" (9:21).

> *My relatives and my close friends have failed me;*
> > *the guests in my house have forgotten me;*
> *my serving girls count me as a stranger;*
> > *I have become an alien in their eyes.* (19:14-15)

Whereas Proverbs castigates the "strange woman" for her marital betrayal and sexual promiscuity, relegating her beyond the bounds of normative conduct, the central character of the book of Job is himself the quintessential "stranger." Condemned by his friends, who accuse him of "doing away with the fear of God" (15:4a), Job insists that "I have understanding as well as you" (12:3). Job finds from his own experience a repository of truth, a truth that his friends and family cannot accept, namely, that he is innocent. Indeed, it is Job's growing realization of his innocence, his persistence in righteousness, that ultimately renders his friends speechless. Job has become a hopeless, irredeemable alien to them.

The resolution of Job's plight is found in God's answer, which reveals a world full of strangeness. God proudly points out exotic creatures from the margins, from ostriches to onagers, a wild kingdom unaffected by human norms and influence yet legitimated and cared for by God. Though Job is decentered in this strange world, God shows him to be in solidarity with the wild animals in their fierce freedom, dignity, and dependence upon God. God cares for the stranger, whether animal or human. Whereas Job once lamented that he had become a "brother of jackals, and a companion of ostriches" (30:29), God shows him that he is actually in good company! Job has found himself sharing company with strange beasts, with the denizens of the margins, shunned by the human community yet dignified and sustained by God.

For **Ecclesiastes**, wisdom remains out of reach: "That which is, is far off, and deep, very deep; who can find it out?" (7:24). Despite his concerted efforts of inquiry, the "Teacher" (aka Qoheleth) comes to the realization that God's purposes are ultimately inscrutable. Both world and God remain impenetrable to mortal eyes. Life is full of uncertainties; it is ephemeral and futile (NRSV "vanity"; Hebrew hebel), and even the most meticulous planning cannot anticipate, much less control what may come next. For all the ingenuity and power exercised by human beings, there are some things that cannot be changed:

> *Consider the work of God;*
> *who can make straight what he has made crooked?* Eccl 7:13 (cf. 1:15)

Qoheleth's theological rationale is clear:

> *I know that whatever God does endures forever; nothing can be added*
> *to it, nor anything taken from it; God has done this, so that all should*
> *stand in awe before him* (3:14).

What appears "crooked" to us may not be to God. God makes the "crooked" as well as the "straight," and all attempts to straighten "what God has made crooked" will only meet in failure and frustration, so Qoheleth confesses.

Qoheleth does not provide specific examples about what constitutes "crookedness," but he is specific about how to live amid the "crooked" and the "straight," and that is to cultivate a life of acceptance and gratitude for life's simple joys, fleeting though they may be, including a good meal, moments of warmth and intimacy (4:11; 9:9), and enjoyment in one's work (2:24-26; 3:12-14, 22; 5:18-29; 8:15; 9:7-10; 11:9-10). In short, what truly makes life worth living need not be discerned by extensive inquiry and meticulous planning. It may be right in front of our nose, and everything else, including our anxieties over sexuality, pale in comparison. ✠

William P. Brown is an ordained minister of the PC(USA) and has taught Old Testament at Union-PSCE in Richmond for thirteen years before joining the faculty of Columbia Theological Seminary in Decatur in 2004. He is the author of several books, including a commentary on Ecclesiastes in the Interpretation series published by WJK.

What do the Gospels say about sex and sexuality?

Margaret P. Aymer ✛
Interdenominational Theological Center

Those who seek guidance from the Gospels about sex and sexuality may be surprised to discover their relative silence on these matters. Where we moderns are preoccupied with sex, the Gospels seem little interested. Seekers will find these ancient writings to be quite forceful on questions about duties within heterosexual marriage. On questions about people marginalized because of their sexual status, however, they show both compassion and a readiness to affirm their place in the work of God. And one of the strongest themes in the Gospels is the extent to which the requirements of biblical law come under consistent questioning by Jesus himself.

Heterosexual marriage is the "default" sexual relationship in the New Testament. It is not so much argued for as presumed. John's Gospel reports Jesus' attendance (and wine-making) at a wedding (John 2:1-11). While this text is frequently used to avow Jesus' approval of such legal contracts, Jesus expresses neither approval nor disapproval in this story. If anything, the larger example of Jesus' own life as an unmarried person, coupled with the itinerancy to which he calls his disciples, calls into question the centrality of heterosexual marriage for Christian life.

More forceful directives on the matter of marriage – or, better, on the matter of divorce – can be found in Mark 10:2-12 (with parallels in Mt. 19:3-9 and Lk 16:18). In this frequently cited text, Jesus – in response to a question posed to him by religious men – cites Genesis as the basis for his injunction against divorce. Jesus argues that the joining of the created beings into "one flesh" is an act of God that should not be torn apart by any human being. Here Jesus is not advocating that all should marry; rather, he is arguing against the divorce of those who do. And he is arguing against a practice that, in the ancient world, was overwhelmingly the prerogative of the husband, and overwhelmingly risky to the economic and social well-being of the wife. Far from prescribing marriage as a legalistic norm for all people, Jesus is, as usual, arguing against interpretations of the law that crush the ones who are most vulnerable.

The question of divorce is accompanied by that of adultery. The Gospels seem to presume the accepted definition of their day, considering as adultery sexual intercourse between any man and a woman who is either betrothed or married to another man as a wife or concubine. Because a wife or concubine became the property of her husband, adultery became a matter of grand theft, and of shaming (thus Absalom rapes David's concubines as a means of shaming him (2 Sam. 16:19-23)). Adultery was thus potentially a capital offense, as is evident in the narrative of the woman caught in adultery in John's Gospel (8:1-11). While Jesus refuses to cast a stone at the woman, he does not endorse adultery. On the contrary, in Matthew's Gospel, at least, he internalizes and intensifies the definition of adultery. Even a man who looks at a woman with lust in his heart could be guilty of adultery (5:27-32). (Ironically, nowhere does Jesus counsel against male lust toward other men or against any female lust whatever.)

Closely related to adultery is *porneia*, frequently translated as "fornication." *Porneia* is like adultery, in that it is an action perpetrated by men on women. The difference here is that these women are not married or betrothed to another man. *Porneia* is generally not deemed as serious an offense as adultery. In Deuteronomic law, a man committing such an act with an unattached young woman must marry her and pay her father fifty shekels (Deut. 22:28-29).

The New Testament also uses *porneia* to describe sexual acts with prostitutes. In the ancient world, prostitution was a common, established practice. This was particularly the case in temples of the fertility goddesses of the ancient world. *Porneia* and its cognates all refer to prostitution. A *porneion* is a brothel; to *porneu_* is to prostitute; a *porn_* is a prostitute; the *pornikos* was the tax normally paid by brothel-keepers; to *pornoboske_* is to keep a brothel; the trade of "brothel-keeper" was known as *pornoboskia*; and a man who loved harlots was known as a *pornophilas*. Any translation of *porneia*, then, should include not only "fornication," which has come to take the meaning of any sex outside of the legal contract of marriage, but also a particular association with "engaging in prostitution." The Gospels say very little about *porneia*, except that it comes out of the heart of a person (Mk 7:21; Mt. 15:19) and can thus defile that person. There is no clear directive about whether what defiles the person is the thought of sex, the desire to exploit another person for sex, or something else.

Given the Gospels' strong stances on divorce and adultery, and to some extent on prostitution, it may come as a surprise that the Gospels show great sympathy for first-century sexual minorities (that is, persons who live outside of reproductive heterosexual marriage). In fact, sexual minorities and sexually marginalized persons figure prominently in positive roles in the Gospels.

Matthew's genealogy (1:1-17) features four women, the only four women in either genealogy of Jesus in the Gospels. All of these women are known for dubious sexual morality: Tamar, who gets pregnant by her father-in-law after playing the prostitute; Rahab, a prostitute and traitor to her nation; Ruth, a foreign woman who "lies down at the feet" of a strange man while he is drunk in order to obtain financial security for herself and her mother-in-law; and the wife of Uriah, who is raped by King David, is forced to marry him, and bears him Solomon. These four women, along with Mary, whose pregnancy looked for all the world to be adulterous, are the mothers and grandmothers of the Christ.

Another category of sexual minorities and marginalized people is unattached and/or infertile women. Unattached women were considered to be "loose," whether or not there was any evidence to support that allegation. Infertile women were considered cursed by some sin they had committed. Yet Luke, in a clear parallel with the stories of Sarah and Hannah, holds up barren Elizabeth as one who is righteous exactly in her barrenness. She goes on to become the mother of John the Baptist (1:1-25). All three of the Synoptic Gospels hold up widows – particularly widows who have no sons – as models of faith (Mk 12:42-44; Lk 21:1-3) and as persons for whom Jesus particularly cared (Mt. 7:11-17).

And Mark shows the clearly unattached Gentile woman, the one he calls the Syrophoenician, in a toe-to-toe argument with Jesus for the life and sanity of her daughter. She not only challenges Jesus, but also wins the argument – even after Jesus dismisses her with the slur "it is not right to take the food of the children and feed it to the dogs" (Mark 7:24-31). Indeed, Matthew's Jesus quips that prostitutes would enter into the kingdom of heaven before the religious leaders of his day, because the women, at least, believed John. (Mt 21:31-32). The pattern is clear: Unattached and infertile women may have been marginalized in the wider society because of their sexual status, but they play essential roles in the Gospels' vision of the work of God in the world.

On the subject of same-sex sexual activity, Jesus says nothing – either positive or negative. Some scholars have argued that Jesus encounters a same-sex sexual relationship when he is asked to heal the *entimos pais*, the beloved male "servant" or "slave" of the centurion. The *entimos pais* may or may not have been having a sexual relationship with his boss/owner. Such relationships were common at the time, but there is no specific evidence here. When confronted with the request for healing, Jesus cures the slave/servant without comment about or investigation into the nature of the relationship between this centurion and his *entimos pais* (Matt 8:5-13; Lk 7:1-10). Where modern readers might be full of questions, Jesus and the Gospel writers are silent.

Other scholars have detected a hint of homoeroticism in talk of "the disciple whom Jesus loved," the one privy to secrets to which even Peter has no access and to whom Jesus gives over care of his mother after his death (John 13:23, 19:26-27). There is no evidence of any sexual dimension to this relationship. At the same time, though, there is no special effort in the Gospel to explain, clarify, or justify the relationship. Once again, the authors of the Gospels are far less concerned about how such a narrative might appear than we moderns might be if we were to write these narratives ourselves. Questions about same-sex relations simply are not very important to writers trying to pass on the Good News.

What does concern the Gospel writers is the question of what it means to be a faithful servant of the living God, especially in light of the destruction of the Temple in Jerusalem in 70 C.E. All four Gospels were penned in the wake of this catastrophe. In light of such massive destruction, what did it mean to faithfully follow the law? What parts of the law were relevant and what parts had been superceded by events of the recent past, or – in the case of the Jesus movement – by the teachings of Jesus? With these questions in mind, the Gospel writers remember Jesus not as a pious, scrupulously lawful, religious man, but rather as a man in constant conflict with the religious establishment about the meaning and purpose even of such central tenets as Sabbath and the laws of *kashrut*. (Cf. Mat 12:1-14; 15:17-19 ; Mk 2:23-3:6; 7:17-23; Luke 6:1-10; 13: 10-17; 14:1-6; John 5:2-18; 9).

The Gospels remember that in the midst of great social chaos, Jesus was asked what the most important law was. He responded, as have Jews for generations before and since, with the words of the great *Shema*: "You shall love the Lord your God with all your heart, and with all your soul, and with all your mind." And then, without missing a beat, he added a second: "You shall love your neighbor as yourself" (Matthew 22:37-39). Perhaps, finally, even on this issue of sexuality, that is all that needs to be said.   ✛

Margaret P. Aymer is Assistant Professor of New Testament at the Interdenominational Theological Center in Atlanta, GA, where she serves as Secretary of the Faculty Council and sits on the Task Force for Curriculum Revision. She is a Minster Member of the Presbytery of Greater Atlanta and serves on its Examinations Committee. She is affiliated with Central Presbyterian Church.

What does Romans 1 teach about homosexuality, and how should we live in response?

Beverly Roberts Gaventa ✦
Princeton Theological Seminary

In the first chapter of Paul's letter to the Romans, we find an extended attack on humanity for its failure to live in a properly creaturely relationship to God. Among the things Paul says in this long accusation is that "their women exchanged natural intercourse for unnatural, and in the same way also the men, giving up natural intercourse with women, were consumed with passion for one another. Men committed shameless acts with men and received in their own persons the due penalty for their error" (Romans 1:26-27). Understandably, these lines prompt many Christians to regard Paul as unequivocally opposed to homosexual relationships.

As with any text, however, whether an e-mail message or the Gettysburg address, we need to examine the literary context in which these verses appear. Having opened the letter by characterizing the gospel as God's own power for the salvation of all human beings, Paul in this section begins a relentless indictment of humanity. The indictment, which he puts forth in 1:18-23, is that human beings rejected the very godliness of God: they suppressed God's truth (1:18), they did not honor God or give God thanks (1:21), they worshipped things of their own making instead of worshiping God (1:22-25). This, in Paul's analysis, is the fundamental sin of humankind.

Because of humanity's implacable refusal to acknowledge its own creatureliness in the face of the God of heaven and earth, God "gave them up." Three times Paul repeats this terrifying assertion that God handed humanity over (1:24, 26, 28) to a whole series of actions. The behaviors include out-of-control passions, such as those mentioned in vv. 26-27, but they also include all the attitudes and actions itemized in the remainder of the chapter, such as envy, murder, gossip, foolishness, faithlessness, and a host of others. In their literary context, then, vv. 26-27 depict same-sex relations as the *result* of human sinfulness, a sinfulness involving all humanity, a sinfulness rooted in human rebellion against God. What Paul is writing here constitutes a sweeping depiction of fallen humanity; this is not an exhortation, much less an early church order.

New Testament scholars – highly learned individuals of good will who are deeply shaped by these texts and who strive to serve the gospel faithfully – have serious disagreements about the cultural and historical factors that influence Paul's comments in Romans 1. Out of the complex discussion, a few points are crucial.

First, Paul does not operate with a notion of a homosexual (or heterosexual) "orientation" in the contemporary sense; instead, his language reflects the Greco-Roman world's understanding of sexual relations among people of the same gender as discrete acts rather than a homosexual orientation or lifestyle. A number of ancient writers speak of same-sex acts not as indications of an orientation or a preference, but as symptoms of passion that has simply gone out of control. For instance, they would not say that a man who was married to a woman but also enjoyed sex with men was bisexual, or wrestling with two different orientations. They would say that he had a super-abundance of what they took to be a single, gender-indifferent, sexual passion. We need to understand that Paul is addressing a different question than the ones we are asking.

Second, when Paul speaks of "natural" and "unnatural" actions, he reflects the rigid hierarchy of Greco-Roman understandings about gender and sexuality. To put the matter directly, the sexual penetrator is regarded as superior to the one who is penetrated, so that a man who allows himself to be penetrated is regarded as unnaturally passive and women who engage in sex with one another are regarded as unnaturally active. Before finding ourselves compelled by this argument, we would do well to remember that what seems "natural" or "unnatural" is not fixed for all people and all times.

In 1 Corinthians 11, Paul claims that it is "unnatural" for women to have their heads unveiled and for men to have long hair, but few contemporary Christians feel compelled to agree with Paul's understanding of nature in that case.

Third, and perhaps most important, in this passage Paul seems to be playing, perhaps even deliberately, on some stereotypical Jewish accusations about Gentiles. For example, most annotated Bibles will refer to the Wisdom of Solomon 13-15, a Jewish text of the late first century B.C.E., which in several important ways parallels Romans 1. There also the author claims that Gentiles should have known about God from observing the world around them, that they instead made their own gods, and that the result is that their lives are mired in wickedness, including sexual promiscuity.

Addressing gatherings of Jewish and Gentile Christians in Rome, gatherings in which there may have been conflicts both theological and ethnic, Paul appears to be using this stereotype of the godless, wicked Gentile to draw in his audience. As the chapter proceeds, the audience will surely understand that the "they" to whom Paul refers are those outside the congregation, and the audience will imagine itself to be siding with Paul in his sharp attacks on godlessness and immorality. By the time he reaches the end of the chapter, with its declaration that those who commit such acts deserve death itself, the audience may have reached a frenzy of outrage.

In an instant, however, the outrage is undone, for Paul's next comment is this: "Therefore you have no excuse, whoever you are, when you judge others; for in passing judgment on another you condemn yourself, because you, the judge, are doing the very same things" (2:1). No longer does the indictment point outward to "those people over there," now it points directly to the Roman congregations who have joined him in condemning others. Paul has pulled the rhetorical rug out from under the audience, equating their judgment of others with the rest of the godless rebellion depicted in Romans 1.

Where does Romans 1 leave us with the question of homosexuality? The passage does not address homosexuality as an orientation, and it certainly does not address ordination or leadership in Christian communities. In common with many of his contemporaries, Paul assumes (but never actually argues) that same-sex relations are symptomatic of human sinfulness. Even those who conclude faithfully that this text requires Christians to condemn contemporary forms of same-sex relations must nevertheless hear in Romans 2:1 a powerful word of caution: we too stand under judgment, especially when we stand in judgment of others.   ✤

Beverly Roberts Gaventa is Helen H. P. Manson Professor of New Testament Literature and Exegesis at Princeton Theological Seminary. An ordained elder, she currently serves on the Session at Nassau Presbyterian Church. She is the author most recently of **Acts** *in the Abingdon New Testament series.*

What does 1 Corinthians 6:9 teach about sexuality, and how should we live in response?

Robert L. Brawley ✣
McCormick Theological Seminary

In 1 Cor. 6: 9-10, Paul gives a long list of "wrongdoers [who] will not inherit the kingdom of God." Presbyterian New Testament scholars Paul Achtemeier and Marion Soards, whom I hold in high esteem, think that when 1 Cor 6:9 uses the Greek terms *malakoi* and *arsenokoitai*, Paul *clearly* is speaking about same-sex erotic behavior among males and excluding such people from being heirs of God's kingdom. Thus, in the contemporary debate about the ordination of non-celibate gays and lesbians, they use this text to limit the issue to "homoerotic practice" aside from any other criteria that make people hold interpersonal relationships dear.

But is it really so clear that 1 Cor 6:9 is about "homoerotic practice" and is it really so clear who is excluded from being heirs of God's kingdom? I suggest that there is actually a lack of clarity. The lack of clarity shows up in several ways. One is in the variety among translations. Another is the difficulty we have in making direct correlations between biblical texts and the way we construe reality today. Most importantly, however, the argument about clarity does not adequately consider the context in 1 Corinthians 6, and this context is eye-opening with respect to how Paul deals with sexual behavior among the Corinthians.

Translations. Though *malakoi* literally means soft, it is often used in Greek to describe effeminate men, and many interpreters suggest that this identifies receptive partners in same-sex erotic behavior among males. One would be hard pressed to deduce any-thing about a receptive partner from the King James translation which simply says "effeminate" or from Luther's translation quite literally as "weakling." The Revised Standard Version combines the two terms *malakoi* and *arsenokoitai* into one translation as "sexual perverts," a questionable move in translating, which the New Revised Standard Version tries to "correct" by reverting to two terms. With respect to *malakoi* the NRSV translation is "male prostitutes." When the transla-tion tradition moves between the extremes of "weakling" and "male prostitutes," this indicates lack of clarity in our understanding of the term. Simply the variety in translations is one indication that the church has no sustained tradition of clarity about the meaning of *malakoi* in 1 Cor 6:9.

The problem of clarity is perhaps even more difficult with *arsenokoitai*. 1 Cor 6:9 is the first place we know of in all of Greek lit-erature in which this term is used. Paul apparently coined it. So how does one know what a word means the first time it ever appears? Granted, we know some things from the formation of the word. It is compounded from a term for "bed" and a term for "male" with an agency ending—implicitly one who beds a male. Again, a quick review of translations shows the uncertainty in the meaning. The King James Version has "abusers of themselves with mankind"; Luther has an equivalent of "violators of boys," perhaps implying pederasty; and the NRSV introduces "sodomites," an astonishing innovation in the translation tradition.

Correlation. A further difficulty is attempting to correlate our interpretations of the biblical text with the way we interpret reality. For example, the list in 1 Cor 6:9-10 includes the word *methusoi*, trans-lated in the NRSV as "drunkards." But what kind of present reality are we able to correlate with Paul's word *methusoi*? People who drink alcohol in any quantity? People who occasionally drink to excess? People who drink too much on a regular basis? Further, how much is too much? The text itself does not enable us to know with certainty what present reality we should correlate with *methusoi*. Similarly, it is not at all clear how we should correlate *malakoi* and *arsenokoitai* with realities of our time. Do the words refer to men who engage in promiscuous sex with men? Do the words refer to women at all? Can they be stretched to include men and women in same-sex relation-ships marked by mutuality and covenant fidelity in sickness and in health, in joy and in sorrow – relationships that Paul could scarcely imagine? The church faces uncertainty not only in translating *malakoi* and *arsenokoitai* but also in knowing how to correlate these terms with sexual behavior today.

Context. The context is eye opening. 1 Cor 6:9-10 lists categories of human beings who are excluded from being heirs of God's kingdom. But in 6:11 Paul says that even though some of the Corinthians used to belong to these categories, they no longer do: "And this is what some of you used to be. But you were washed, you were sanctified, you were justified in the name of the Lord Jesus Christ and in the Spirit of our God." At first glance it appears obvious that when the Corinthians became believers, they changed their behavior. But as true as this may be, Paul spends the rest of the chapter dealing with the sexual behavior of some heterosexual males in the Corinthian Christian community. Even after being washed, sanctified, and justified, some of the Corinthian believers were still engaging in sexual intercourse with prostitutes.

The remainder of the chapter is Paul's attempt to deal with their behavior. His argument is triadic. He reminds the Corinthians of their relationship to Christ, to the Holy Spirit, and to God. "Do you not know that your bodies are members of Christ?" he asks (6:15). In order to deal with sexual behavior that Paul considers to be problematic, he first reminds the Corinthians of their relationship with Christ.

But then he reminds them also of their relationship with the Holy Spirit: "Do you not know that your body is a temple of the Holy Spirit within you, which you have from God, and that you are not your own?" (6:19). Unfortunately, this has often been interpreted only in individualistic terms, as if each believer's body is a temple of the Holy Spirit. But this is all in the second person plural, so that the emphasis is on the community as the body of Christ, as is evident elsewhere in 1 Corinthians (e.g. 11:29 with respect to the Lord's supper). The meaning is something like: "Do you not know that your [corporate] body is a temple of the Holy Spirit who [lives] among you." Not only does Paul remind them of their relationship with the Spirit but also of their place in the corporate body of believers.

Paul's thought then moves to the third part of the triad:

". . . [your corporate body is a temple of the Holy Spirit who lives among you], which you have from God, and that you are not your own? For you were bought with a price; therefore glorify God in your body" (6:19-20). Here Paul reminds the Corinthians of their relationship with God. This is not altogether apparent because Paul uses a divine passive. That is, he expresses "you were bought with a price" in the passive voice, but had he expressed it in the active voice, he would have said, "God bought you with a price." Here again the "you" is plural, and Paul's exhortation to glorify God in "your body" is also plural, that is, it is addressed to the corporate body.

In sum, when Paul is faced with sexual behavior from some believers in the Corinthian congregation which does not fit his own expectations, he does not fit these Corinthian believers into the categories of 6:9-10, which would exclude them from being heirs of God's kingdom. On the contrary, his way of dealing with their behavior is to remind them of their relationships with Christ, with the Holy Spirit, and with God with the expectation that they would live out their sexuality as members of a community that lives in dependence upon the grace of God.

1 Corinthians 6 distinguishes two groups of people – those who are excluded as heirs of God's kingdom in 6:9-10 and those who in the community of believers stand in a relationship with Christ, with the Spirit, and with God (6:12-20). Surprisingly, some Corinthians whose sexual behavior does not fit Paul's expectations are still included in the second category.

The analogy to our own struggles about sexuality is strong. Even if this text suggested that all same-sex erotic activity were sinful – and it is by no means clear that it does – it still would not offer grounds for a categorical exclusion of non-celibate gay and lesbian Christians from the ministries of the church. As with all Christians, gay and lesbian Christians live their lives as part of a community in relation to Christ, to the Spirit, and to God. All of our lives, including our sexual lives, are caught up in and transformed by this relationship. 1 Corinthians 6 reminds us of this good news. It reminds us of the importance of sexual ethics. It calls us to glorify God in our bodies. But it offers no support to our attempts to exclude from ministry those whom God has bought with a price and joined to the body of Christ. ✢

Robert L. Brawley is Albert G. McGraw Professor of New Testament at McCormick Theological Seminary in Chicago. A Presbyterian minister, he taught New Testament at Memphis Theological Seminary for 13 years before joining the McCormick faculty in 1992. His books include the edited collection **Biblical Ethics & Homosexuality: Listening to Scripture.**

Since the Bible seems only to condemn same-sex relations, how can some Christians affirm same-sex marriage or the ordination of openly gay and lesbian Christians? Where is there any support for this approach in the Bible?

Jeffrey S. Siker ✛
Loyola Marymount University

This is a crucial question that calls for a constructive response. A *constructive* response is one that helps to build and to edify the church as the body of Christ (see, e.g., 1 Cor 12-14). A *constructive* response also means that as faithful Christians we are seeking precisely to *construct* an answer that addresses competing claims that we feel must be included in any response. What does it mean for us to discern God's Spirit as we seek to construct a faithful response to the question of the status of lesbian and gay Christians in our midst?

We are not the first ones to ask comparable questions about a constructive response that seeks to discern God's Spirit in addressing controversial and divisive issues. The history of the church is full of such struggles, whether we look to the Apostle Paul, the split between Eastern Orthodoxy and the Roman Catholic tradition, the fights between the Protestants and Catholics, or the debates in the United States over slavery and the status of women in the church. In all of these debates both sides appealed to the witness of Scripture, church tradition, reason, and experience in light of God's Spirit to argue positions that were exactly the opposite of one another. As we address the current crisis regarding the recognition of openly gay and lesbian clergy and same-sex relationships, we must do so in light of the church's long history of heated debates over discerning the leading of God's Spirit. It is our challenge, our responsibility, and our opportunity to be engaged in such discernment where, to be sure, we do our best to see through a glass darkly as we work out our salvation in fear and trembling.

To the question at hand, then. Since the Bible seems to condemn same-sex relations, how can some Christians on the basis of Scripture argue that the church should endorse same-sex relations of any kind, whether by celebrating gay marriage or by ordaining openly gay clergy?

There are basically two responses to this question, both grounded in Scripture. First, we must be clear about what Scripture condemns and why. We must be aware that the notion of "homosexual orientation" is a modern notion (as is sexual orientation in general), and that the term "homosexual" is never found in Scripture – even though some translations anachronistically and misleadingly render the original Hebrew and Greek words from Scripture as "homosexual." Such translations read our modern understandings back into Scripture and fail to understand Scripture on its own terms. For example, in Paul's letters, the passing references that condemn same-sex relations (Rom 1; 1 Cor 6) are addressed to the context of Paul's day, where same-sex relations were typically and understandably seen as exploitive, especially given that pederasty and slave-prostitution were the primary forms of same-sex relations with which Paul would have been familiar.

To condemn all modern-day homosexual relationships on the basis of the exploitive same-sex relations of Paul's day would be the same as condemning all modern-day heterosexual relationships on the basis of David's adulterous relationship with Bathsheba. Just as there is no blanket condemnation of all heterosexual relations because of some inappropriate heterosexual actions (rape, incest, adultery), so also we may ask if it is correct to issue a blanket condemnation of all same-sex relations because those referred to in Scripture were exploitive and thus inappropriate relations (e.g., rape and pederasty).

Further, in Paul's time such homoerotic expressions were viewed as being against nature (cf. Rom 1). But what counts as natural or unnatural varies from age to age and culture to culture. (Consider Paul's comments on hair length in 1 Cor 11.) In our present age we have come to understand that individuals are born with a sexual orientation of which they become aware as they mature. Sexual orientation is as natural and unchosen as left-handedness or brown eyes. It is simply part of the rich diversity of God's creation.

Thus, first and foremost it is important to understand Scripture on its own terms, with its own cultural assumptions and perspectives – some of which views we regard as inapplicable in our time. Perhaps the best example of this is the Presbyterian Church's stance on the role of women in church leadership. Scripture is quite explicit in its rejection of women for such leadership positions (1 Cor 14; 1 Tim 2), and yet the modern church argues (correctly) that the Spirit of God has led us to recognize that women have been gifted by God just as men, and therefore are appropriate candidates for positions of ordination and church leadership. This current position stands in significant tension with many biblical evaluations of women as being subordinate to men and of less value than men. And yet we are confident as a church that we are being faithful to the call of God's Spirit, even though the inclusion of women in leadership roles caused tremendous conflict in the church.

This observation leads to the second biblical response to the question posed above. It is one thing to say that the Bible's passing references to practices significantly different from modern practices do not amount to an outright ban. But does Scripture provide any reasons to affirm same-sex relations or ordination of openly gay/lesbian Christians? I think it is important to state clearly that Scripture offers no *direct* evidence for such a case. But this is not the end of the story, as Scripture does not offer direct evidence for any number of concerns crucial to Christian faith and practice (e.g., various issues of modern bioethics).

Scripture did not provide Paul with all he needed to know, nor did he always have a "word from the Lord" regarding important new situations. But Paul did think he was able to discern the Spirit. For example, Paul appeals to the Galatians to reflect on their own communal experience of God's Spirit (Gal 3:1-5) as the most important guide regarding whether or not they should observe the Jewish ritual law. Paul broke with established custom and even, arguably, with the teachings of Jesus in this regard (cf. Matthew 5:18-19). But Paul felt himself led by the Spirit and believed that the experiences of Gentile Christians confirmed their reception of the Spirit apart from the law.

The author of the Acts of the Apostles made the same kind of argument in his narrative of God's inclusion of the Gentile Cornelius in Acts 10. Cornelius did not have to become a law-observant Jew in order to have proper faith in Christ. This went completely against early Christian tradition, as the controversy of Acts 10-11, 15, and Galatians 2 richly attests. God startled Peter with the rooftop vision and the firm declaration, "What God has made clean, you must not call profane" (Acts 10: 15). God was doing what appeared to be a new thing. Paul and Peter were calling on the church to acknowledge what God was doing, even though it scandalized the church and seemed to go against scripture and tradition.

In short, then, while Scripture does not provide direct testimony of God's blessing of same-sex relationships or of gay clergy, Scripture does provide clear and direct testimony of God's call to pay attention to the inclusion of the faithful whom the church has often failed to see as welcomed by God. Peter paid attention to Cornelius' faithful response to God's Spirit, even though he was a Gentile. Paul paid attention to the Galatians' faithful response to the Spirit, and made a point that their experience was to guide them in matters of faith and practice even against the testimony of time-honored interpretations of Scripture and tradition.

Scripture calls upon us in the church today to pay attention to the testimony of God's Spirit as we have experienced the profound faith of gay and lesbian Christians in our midst. As Peter told the Jerusalem assembly, "If God gave [Cornelius's household] the same gift that he gave us when we believed in the Lord Jesus Christ, who was I that I could hinder God?" (Acts 11: 17). Surely we must see them first of all as brothers and sisters in Christ who are baptized in the same Spirit that all Christians share, brothers and sisters who do not cease to be gay or lesbian by virtue of their Christian faith.

So does the Bible provide positive evidence for the inclusion of gay and lesbian Christians in the church? Does the Bible give Christians reason to affirm same-sex relationships and the ordination of gay/lesbian Christians? In my view the answer is a resounding *yes*. We need to listen to the voices of our sisters and brothers in Christ whose sexual orientation in no way hampers their ability to form loving and committed relationships, just as it in no way hampers their capacity to serve God and the church in ordained ministry. To this Scripture, tradition, reason, and especially Christian experience bears witness as we seek to discern and to embody God's loving and healing Spirit in a broken world. Let us welcome all to the community of faith and the community of ministry in this Spirit.   ✤

Jeffrey S. Siker is Professor and Chair of the Department of Theological Studies at Loyola Marymount University, Los Angeles, CA. He has served churches in Michigan and New Jersey, and has been Parish Associate at Covenant Presbyterian Church in Los Angeles for the last 18 years. He has also served on and chaired the Committee on Preparation for Ministry in the Presbytery of the Pacific. He edited **Homosexuality in the Church: Both Sides of the Debate.**

What does Christian baptism have to do with the current controversy in the church about sexuality and ordination?

Thomas G. Long ✛
Candler School of Theology

To see how the theology of Christian baptism speaks to a contemporary issue like sexuality and ordination, we must first understand baptism itself, and to do that is to grapple with the symbols of water and fire. Whether in a font, a pool, or a river, water is the central symbol of baptism, just as bread and wine are the central symbols of the Lord's Supper. But to the symbol of water, Jesus added the symbol of fire. John the Baptist said that his baptism was of water, but that Jesus would baptize with "the Holy Spirit and fire" (Matthew 3:11).

Water and fire. What do these two basic symbols mean? They point to the deep truth that baptism means not one thing, but many things. Water is the fluid that surrounds us in the womb, water makes an oasis of life in the desert, water slakes our thirst in a parched land, and water washes us clean. So it is with the water of baptism. Baptism is about birth, and to be baptized is to signify that we are "born again," that we have become a new creation in Christ. The life-giving water of baptism is a living spring in the midst of the wilderness, and to be baptized is to be brought into the place of true life in Jesus Christ. "Give me this water," said the Samaritan woman to Jesus, "that I may never be thirsty…" (John 4:15). Baptism is also about being washed clean in the pure water of God's mercy, and to be baptized is a sign that by the grace of God we are forgiven, cleansed of our sins, and called into the fellowship of the redeemed.

As one of the Presbyterian confessions, the Second Helvetic, beauti-fully states it, "We are baptized with water...washed or sprinkled with visible water. For the water washes dirt away, and cools and refreshes hot and tired bodies. And the grace of God performs these things for souls, and does so invisibly or spiritually" (*Book of Confessions* 5.188).

Christian baptism is not only about water, though; it is also about fire, which means that it is about the power of the Holy Spirit to bring energy, power, warmth, and light to our lives. It is the Holy Spirit who stirs up the love of God, burning in our hearts. It is the Holy Spirit who fills us with fiery passion for the gospel, it is the Holy Spirit who causes good gifts to flame up in our lives, and it is the Holy Spirit who lights up the way of Christ and beckons us to follow. When Jesus was baptized, the Holy Spirit descended like a dove upon him, and the voice of God announced that Jesus was "my Son, the beloved." Our baptism is a sign that the same Spirit falls upon us, declaring us to be the beloved daughters and sons of God. "Baptism signifies...being sealed by God's Spirit," states the Presbyterian *Book of Order* (W-2.3004), a statement that draws upon the language of Ephesians: "When you heard the gospel of your salvation...you were marked with the seal of the promised Holy Spirit; this is the pledge of our inheritance toward redemption as God's own people, to the praise of his glory" (Eph. 1:13-14). To understand baptism is not only to think about water, but also to think about fire.

Putting together the meanings we discern in these two sym-bols, water and fire, we see two important insights about the relation-ship between baptism and the debate about ordination. First, the pure water of baptism reminds us that this sacrament is about God's puri-ty and not ours, God's grace and not our righteousness, that it is about something that God does toward, for and with us, to which our Christian lives are a response. As Calvin insisted, "Christ's purity has been offered us in [baptism]; his purity ever flourishes; it is defiled by no spots but buries and cleanses away all our defilements." This means that all baptized Christians stand on the same moral ground, namely the righteousness of God. We are, as the old hymn puts it, "standing on the promises of Christ" and not on our own good works.

We are able, then, to see every baptized person as a treasure, as one who has been claimed by the mercy of Christ, and as one whose flourishing and whose full participation in the church is our duty and delight. We are called to help each other grow into our baptismal identity, to help each other along the way of discipleship and obedience as fellow pilgrims who have been graced by light along the path, to find together as brothers and sisters how to allow our lives to conform more and more to the way of Jesus Christ. Any talk in the church of who belongs and who doesn't, of who is in the circle and who is out of the circle, of who is morally pure and who is impure, is not mere political incorrectness. It is instead a denial of the deep truth of baptism, a denial of the promise of God to Israel and to the church: "I have called you by name, you are mine. When you pass through the waters, I will be with you..." (Isaiah 43:1-2).

Perhaps even more pointedly, the symbol of fire and the promise of the Holy Spirit remind us that the sacrament of baptism is itself an ordination service. All baptized people are already ordained. Through baptism, God creates a new community, a priesthood of all believers, a nation of ordained ministers. In the words of 1 Peter (a letter that many scholars think contains portions of an early baptismal sermon), "But you are a chosen race, a royal priesthood, a holy nation, God's own people, in order that you may proclaim the mighty acts of him who called you out of darkness into his marvelous light" (1 Pet 2:9).

It is well known that in the worship of the early church, those who were not baptized were dismissed before the sacrament of the Lord's Supper. When they were eventually baptized, they would then be welcomed to the feast of the faithful. But it is less well known that, as Presbyterian church historian Catherine Gunsalus González notes, the non-baptized were dismissed not only before the Lord's Supper but also before the prayers of the people. Praying this prayer, she says, was considered to be a priestly act, and "baptism gave a priestly role in intercession that has been lost" (*Reformed Liturgy and Music*, Winter, 1994, 5). In other words, the early church knew that baptism was not only an act of initiation into the church; it was also an act of ordination into priestly ministry.

The issue before the church is not whether persons of this or that sexual orientation can be ordained to ministry. They are already ordained to ministry by virtue of baptism. As is the case with ministers of the Word, elders, and deacon, all baptized Christians have had hands laid upon their heads as a sign that they are set apart as ministers of Christ and as a sign of the presence, power, and blessing of the Holy Spirit. That same Spirit has given to the baptized all the gifts and graces the church needs to sustain its life and engage in its mission, and the whole church is called to be good stewards of these charisms and gifts.

So the real question that baptism places before us is not who shall be ordained. That one has already been decided at the font. The real question is one of the stewardship of gifts. If the Holy Spirit gives to this one among us the gift of teaching, and to another among us the gift of preaching, and to still others the gifts of discernment, leadership, and care, who are we to turn these spiritual gifts away? What we are truly summoned to decide is not who among the baptized receives these spiritual gifts or who is entitled to exercise them. The Holy Spirit decides that. We are summoned, rather, to receive these gifts with joy and gratitude and to be the kind of church that orders its life in such a way that these gifts are honored, exercised, and nourished to the glory of God and the blessing of the world. ✛

Thomas G. Long is Bandy Professor of Preaching at Candler School of Theology, and earlier taught at Columbia and Princeton Seminaries. A Presbyterian minister, he served on the task force that developed the original text of the current Presbyterian Directory for Worship. His recent books include **Testimony: Talking Ourselves into Being Christian** *and* **The Witness of Preaching**, *2nd ed.*

What do the Confessions teach about sexuality? And how do they inform the ethical commitments of Presbyterian Christians?

Christopher Elwood ✛
Louisville Presbyterian Theological Seminary

In Presbyterian debates over the inclusion of non-heterosexual persons it is often assumed that the *Book of Confessions* gives unequivocal support to traditionalists and thus is entirely bad news for those who want to see a more welcoming church. Many believe that the *Book of Order*'s call for candidates for ordination to repent of all practices "which the confessions call sin" (G-6.0106b) effectively excludes "self-affirming, practicing homosexuals" from the church's ministry. But in fact same-sex relations are by no means at the center of the practices "which the confessions call sin." By some counts there are more than 600 such practices, including forming a visual or mental image of God or Jesus (4.097, 7.219), opposing government policy on taxation or war (5.258), and working or playing on Sunday – or causing others to do so (7.229). Amid the many words of the eleven documents of the *Book of Confessions*, there are very few references that can be construed as pertaining directly to same-sex relations. We can look briefly at these.

1. *"Homosexual perversion"*? A passage in the *Book of Confessions*' version of the Heidelberg Catechism (which was written in 1563) suggests that those guilty of "homosexual perversion" will not be saved (4.087). The problem is that this passage does not appear in the catechism as originally written. Nor does it appear in any

translation other than this one, produced in 1962. In 1997, when it came to light that the original version had been tampered with, one of the translators defended inserting these words because, in light of the sexual revolution of the 1960s, "it would be well to be more specific ... than [the author] had been in his day." Edward Dowey, professor at Princeton Seminary and chair of the committee that brought this catechism to the Presbyterian General Assembly (which adopted the entire *Book of Confessions* in 1967) was appalled to discover, too late, that his committee had missed what he called an "illicit change." Because the church never deliberated over the "updating," it is unclear what force the translators' unorthodox rendering has for Presbyterians.

2. *"Sodomy"*? The Westminster Larger Catechism (of 1647) lists "sodomy, and all unnatural lusts" among a great many specific sins forbidden by the seventh commandment (including "the keeping of stews," or public baths; 7.249). In understandings of sodomy common to the 17th century, this ban would include sexual relations between two men (and possibly between two women). But it would include a good deal more than that, including any form of sexual expression (even heterosexual) that violates "nature's aim" of procreation.

3. *"One man and one woman"*: The Westminster Confession defines marriage as between "one man and one woman" (6.131, 6.133) so as to exclude the possibility of polygamy (of which there are plenty of biblical examples). Its authors did not mean to address same-sex marriage (hardly conceivable in the 17th century). And yet this definition does show the way that many confessions assume that the Bible establishes monogamous heterosexuality as the norm for human relations. The cultures out of which the confessions were produced could not have conceived of the moral possibility of healthy, stable, committed and covenanted relationships between partners of the same sex. Is such an assumption binding in a very different context – one in which there is no longer general agreement about the "facts" that were once thought to uphold the assumption? This is not clear. For a parallel example: The confessions' accounts of the creation of the universe include assumptions that today could be called "creationist" (e.g., 6.022-23). But they were written well before the advent of modern biological science. Do these accounts require Presbyterians to oppose evolution?

As we can see from these few examples, when we turn to the confessions for proof-texts to support one or another position on the moral standing of same-sex relations we end up with little to show for our efforts. That is because it is only very recently that the church has seriously confronted new questions about sexual partnerships, and it is unreasonable to expect our confessions to yield direct answers to questions that did not arise in any serious way in the times for which they were written.

Perhaps, then, another approach is called for – one that asks after the larger theological convictions that guide our ethical reflection on sexuality in our time. Here are a few broad themes that pertain to our current reflections on sexuality:

1. **The limitations and necessity of confessional witness:** Presbyterians resist any slavish dependence on the prejudices of the past. Our confessions themselves subordinate their authority to that of "Jesus Christ, the Word of God, as the Scriptures bear witness to him" (9.03). They require us to look critically at all human doctrines, to continue to reflect together on the way the Holy Spirit speaks to us in scripture, and in this way to contribute to the Spirit's work of continually reforming the church (6.010). This is one reason why we have a *Book of Confessions*: no single human document witnesses to God's Word perfectly and this witness needs to be done afresh for the new challenges of new days.

2. **A guide to reading scripture:** On the basis of the confessions, Presbyterians reject narrow, literalistic readings of the Bible. They take account of history, language, and culture in interpretation; they seek to ground their reading of the Bible in the overarching story of God's work of reconciling the world to Godself in Christ (the rule of faith); and they work to understand scripture so as to increase the love of God and neighbor rather than diminish it (the rule of love). They recognize, also, that understanding scripture requires the illumination of the Spirit and the shared insights of a faithful community of readers.

3. **The primacy of grace:** Presbyterians believe that we are entirely dependent on God's grace for salvation. Therefore they reject interpretations of scripture or the human condition that serve self-righteousness, or the false confidence that we do not require God's forgiving and reconciling work in every aspect of our life.

4. **The tendency to idolatry:** Our confessions sensitize us to a primary way in which we experience sin: our inclination to place our trust in ourselves or our condition of life or in anything else that is not God. Whenever we elevate one element of our experience – be it our race, nation, culture, gender, class, or sexual orientation – and give it ultimate loyalty or see it as the mark of special divine favor, we reject the whole claim of God on our life.

5. **The good gift of human sexuality:** Confessions written by Protestant reformers rejected the idea that human sexuality was a necessary evil. Almost all persons have a sexual urge. To encourage anyone to deny this fact or to require a celibate life was viewed as potentially disastrous. Indeed, the Larger Catechism forbids "entangling vows of single life" (7.249). Therefore, it is best to make use of God's gift of marriage, which should be open to as many persons as possible; and not only for the purpose of procreation and child rearing, but for the sharing of love and comfort (5.246, 7.248). Marriage is a treasured sign of God's intention for life together (9.47). Some persons, however, may have a special gift of celibacy. But the confessions are adamant that celibacy should not be imposed on anyone as a requirement for ministry, and those who choose to be celibate should not view themselves as holier than others (5.245). Sexuality, as a good gift, calls for wise use; what we do with our bodies matters and thus all, whether married or single, sexually active or abstinent, are called to a chaste or pure life (4.108).

6. **Discipleship as the thankful glorifying of God:** Presbyterians do not seek to be saved by a moral life. Rather, the quest to live morally comes through our thankful obedience to the God who has already embraced and redeemed us. Our chief end is to glorify God in all we do. But how do we do this given the mystery of our complex desires and affections? Obviously, this requires careful discernment. Reformed confessions treat the law, in the form of the ten commandments, as a primary means to test our progress in discipleship. The law aids us in loving God and loving neighbor. It does not cause us to ask, Do I have the right affectional and sexual orientation? But rather, Am I, through God's grace in Christ and as enabled by the Spirit, living out through the capacities and orientations that are God's gift to me a witness that contributes to the glory of God and that embodies God's care for the world?

The confessions give no final answers on matters of human sexuality. That is not their purpose. But they do provide us with historic principles of interpretation that may help Presbyterians become better attuned to the Reformed Christian witness in its breadth and diversity, and perhaps also help us speak together despite our differences.

✤

Christopher Elwood is Professor of Historical Theology at Louisville Presbyterian Theological Seminary, which he joined in 1996 after teaching at Harvard Divinity School and Davidson College. A Presbyterian minister, he served two churches in Massachusetts. His latest book is **Calvin for Armchair Theologians.**

What has ordination implied for Reformed Christians, and how might Reformed theologies of ordination inform our current debates about ordination and sexuality?

Dawn DeVries ✤
Union Theological Seminary-PSCE

The theology of the Reformation fundamentally reshaped the doctrine of ministry, and the practices surrounding ordination in Reformed churches. In the Roman Catholic as well as the Eastern Orthodox Churches, ordination as a sacrament ritually distinguished one group of people from another within the church. Priests, it was argued, by virtue of an "indelible character" conferred on them through valid ordination in the apostolic succession, were elevated to the role of mediators on behalf of the laity. Especially in their consecration and offering of the sacrifice of the Mass, which was said to "represent" the sacrifice of Christ on the Cross, those holding ordained office were viewed as a special class of members within the Body of Christ.

For the Roman Catholic Church, the unity of the church's whole ministry is secured by the Bishop of Rome – the Pope – who is the ruler over the whole Church, standing in the place of Christ, and as the successor to St. Peter. Under the Pope, the entire leadership of the church is hierarchically organized, with metropolitans over bishops, bishops over priests, priests over deacons.

A quick glance through our *Book of Confessions* will confirm just how completely the Reformed churches rejected this theology of the ministry. In the first place, they did not recognize a fundamental distinction between priests and the laity. On the contrary, they saw the church as a communion of the faithful who have all been made priests and kings in Christ and are therefore able to offer up spiritual sacrifices to God through Christ. Thus understood, the priesthood includes all believers. This was a crucial insight, because it undercut the hierarchical understanding of ministry inherited from patristic and medieval times. The priestly work of interceding before God on behalf of others is a common work of the people of God.

If every believer can function as a priest before God, then ordained ministry must not be primarily about such priestly mediation performed by a special class of hierarchs. In the Reformed understanding, ministry is conceived rather as service. Ministers are servants of the Word of God, stewards of the mysteries of God, and shepherds or pastors of the people of God. They are not a separate class of citizens in God's Kingdom, set apart by an indelible mark. They are those who receive a call and are set apart for a special work of leadership in the church, of which they too are simply members. They are set apart for the sake of good order in the church, and no one minister stands "over" another.

Our confessions also explicitly reject the claim of any person to stand in the place of Christ in the church. As the Second Helvetic Confession puts it, "Christ the Lord is, and remains, the only universal pastor, the highest Pontiff before God the Father; and . . . in the Church he himself performs all the duties of a bishop or pastor, even to the world's end; and therefore does not need a substitute for one who is absent. For Christ is present with his Church, and is its life-giving Head" (5.131).

In Reformed understandings of ministry, the notion of a *call* to ministry is crucial. John Calvin and the Reformed Confessions speak of two parts of a call to ministry: the "internal call" or "secret call" that the individual receives from God in his or her conscience, and the "external call" that the candidate receives from the church.

In general, far more emphasis is placed on the importance of this latter external call. That is because the Reformers rejected the notion that anyone could simply appoint himself or herself to leadership in the church. The call to leadership ultimately comes from God the Holy Spirit. It comes in recognition of the fact that a particular individual is blessed with certain gifts that could be used for the benefit of the broader community and for the glory of God.

"Hearing" a call to ministry, therefore, is a complex process of discernment. Faithful discernment involves prayer and obedient discipleship from the candidate, but also thorough examination of that person by the broader church – examination that can culminate in the public recognition of the candidate as a deacon, elder, or minister in ordination. This is why our *Book of Order* outlines such a long and complex process of candidacy – especially for those who are to be ordained as Ministers of Word and Sacrament. The many steps in this process allow ample opportunities for both the candidate and the church members who know him or her best to "discern the call."

It is clear in our confessions that ministry is not a sort of "civil right" of baptism. Not all members of the church are blessed with the particular gifts needed for ordained office. On the other hand, the doctrine of the priesthood of all believers would seem to overrule any attempt to consider a particular group of people categorically ineligible for ordained ministry simply because of some aspect of their human identity (such as age, disability, gender, or sexual orientation). If all believers are called into the Body of Christ through baptism, and joined in the royal priesthood, then surely it is possible that the Holy Spirit can raise up ordained leadership from anyone within the Body.

In the process of candidacy and examination that all ordained officers go through, the church's judicatories rightly consider whether individuals appear to possess gifts for the particular office to which they are to be ordained, and the right kind of educational preparation and formation to use their gifts wisely and effectively. The session and presbytery also rightly examine candidates on their moral integrity. We are all aware that scandals involving the church's leadership can seriously damage its ability to bear witness to the Gospel of Christ in the world. So church leaders must be persons seeking to live lives of earnest and exemplary faithfulness. Finally, the judicatories examine candidates on their understanding of the faith, since they will be entrusted with the task of instructing others in the faith, and ordained leaders maintain the church's identity through their use and application of Scripture and the liturgical, confessional, and theological resources handed down from our forebears.

Given the Reformed tradition's great emphasis on thorough examination and its complex process of discerning God's call to ministry, it is not surprising that our church order has traditionally entrusted this task to the closest relevant judicatory – to the session in the case of deacons and elders, and to the presbytery in the case of ministers. This makes very good sense, because only those who are closely familiar with a candidate will be in a good position to make sound judgments about the subtler qualities necessary for effective leadership. While church-wide standards for ordination are also demanded and upheld (for example, an M.Div. degree, knowledge of biblical languages, knowledge of the church's constitution and liturgy as demonstrated in ordination exams), it is hard to judge from a test (or from a great distance) things like a person's holiness of life or earnest obedience to the call of God. These equally important standards require the kind of knowledge that only close and long-term acquaintance can afford.

The Reformed churches slowly came to recognize that the Holy Spirit's call went out to a wider group of people than they originally imagined in the 16th century. Our Scots Confession strongly rejects any kind of ordination of women. In the Scots Confession's view, the mere fact that women are allowed to baptize (under certain very special circumstances) by the Roman Catholic Church provides sufficient proof of the total corruption of the ministries of that church (3.22). But our most recent confession, the Brief Statement of Faith, explicitly affirms that God calls both women and men to all the ministries of the church (10.4).

This expansion of who might be considered for ordination may be an important lesson to remember from our own history. As the Westminster Confession states, "the Supreme Judge, by which all controversies of religion are to be determined, and all decrees of councils, opinions of ancient writers, doctrines of men, and private spirits, are to be examined and in whose sentence we are to rest, can be no other but the Holy Spirit speaking in the Scripture" (6.010). As Reformed churches, we have had the experience – always somehow surprising – that the Holy Spirit may have a new thing to say to the church, if only we will listen attentively.   ✤

*Dawn DeVries is the John Newton Thomas Professor of Systematic Theology at Union-PSCE in Richmond. Her books include **Jesus Christ in the Preaching of Calvin and Schleiermacher**. She has served as a member of the General Assembly's Special Committee on Catechism from 1994-1998, and a representative at ecumenical gatherings such as the Fifth World Conference on Faith and Order in 1993, and the Eighth Assembly of the World Council of Churches in 1998.*

What do Presbyterians say about marriage?

David H. Jensen ✠
Austin Presbyterian Theological Seminary

Biblical Foundations

For Presbyterians the primary resource for understanding marriage is Scripture. The creation story implies one purpose of marriage, companionship: "it is not good that the man should be alone; I will make him a helper as a partner" (Gen. 2:18). This purpose is connected, though not synonymous, with the earlier injunction for humanity to be fruitful and multiply. The subsequent forms of marriage recorded in the Old Testament are surprisingly wide. Many OT writers, for example, assume polygamy as part of God's blessing for humanity. Some marriages occur as the result of morally reprehensible actions, such as abduction (Judg 21). And, in the longest sustained passage of human relationship in Scripture, the Song of Solomon celebrates the sexual love between a man and a woman without referring to marriage directly. These varied depictions suggest that God's blessing is not confined to particular forms of marriage, but extends across culture and redeems fallen relationships whenever persons live in faithfulness to God's covenant together. As God redeems humanity, no one cultural form of marriage emerges as normative for all others.

The New Testament specifically blesses singleness and marriage, at times favoring the former. Jesus' own singleness does not come at the expense of binding personal relationships, but intensifies them as they are directed to God's Reign. Paul prefers singleness to marriage in much of his writing because God's Reign is imminent: "So then, he who marries his fiancée does well; and he who refrains from marriage will do better" (1 Cor. 7:38). Jesus' sayings against divorce are stronger than anything found in the Old Testament (Mk. 10:11-12), indicating that the bonds of marriage endure throughout time. Yet Jesus also claims that the demands of the gospel may pit family members against one another (Mt. 10:35-7). However strong the covenant of marriage is between partners, the covenant between God and humanity initiated in Jesus Christ is primary and may cause ruptures in the former. In the NT, the promises of marriage are always provisional in comparison to the promise of God's Reign.

Reformed Confessional and Theological Heritage

Reformed theology serves as aid in interpreting the primary witness of Scripture, yet an overarching theology of Christian marriage does not exist in our tradition. Calvin and the Reformers rejected the notion of a *sacrament* of marriage, because it is not a "visible word" by which God expresses the promises of grace and communion in and through Jesus Christ. They preferred to call marriage an *ordinance* instituted by God, profitable for God's people (Second Helvetic, 5.171). One way of approaching a Reformed theology of marriage is to claim that its traditions understand marriage as both a *sign* of grace and a *response* to grace already given. Marriage represents a journey shared by two persons, in covenant before God and the community of faith, pledged over a lifetime. In this sense, a married couple, in the Reformed tradition, is always *on the way* to Christian marriage.

John Calvin devotes surprisingly few words to marriage in his *Institutes*. He married somewhat late in life, and wrote comparatively little – and then only reservedly – about his own marriage and family life. Calvin celebrates marriage as a blessing for human happiness and as an antidote to sin: "Man has been created in this condition that he may not lead a solitary life, but may enjoy a helper joined to himself...Therefore, the Lord sufficiently provided for us in this matter when he established marriage, the fellowship of which, begun on his authority, he also sanctified by his blessing...The companionship of marriage has been ordained as a necessary remedy to keep us from plunging into unbridled lust" (*Institutes* 2.8.41). For Calvin, the *restraint* of marriage is also a joy.

Following Calvin, the Westminster Confession of Faith contains a clear endorsement of marital union as a public good: "Christian marriage is an institution ordained of God, blessed by our Lord Jesus Christ, established and sanctified for the happiness and welfare of mankind, into which spiritual and physical union one man and one woman enter, cherishing a mutual esteem and love, bearing with each other's infirmities and weaknesses, comforting each other in trouble, providing in honesty and industry for each other and for their household, praying for each other, and living together the length of their days as heirs to the grace of life" (6.131).

Notably absent from this ringing chorus are injunctions of procreation. The good of marriage is not tied directly to the rearing of children. Its underlying purpose is neither to propagate the species, nor to establish a seal of sexual union. In this sense, Westminster de-mystifies both sexual intercourse and the raising of children, anchoring both in the public goods of happiness and human welfare. Sexual union and children are the fruits of that wider good rather than their source. They are gifts that may occur in the context of a marriage. Indispensable gifts, however, they are not. In our age that glorifies sex as a means of spiritual union and overburdens children as means of parental happiness, this Reformed emphasis is a decidedly counter-cultural strain.

Contemporary Reformed theology has extended Westminster's emphasis on the public good, intimating the healing of brokenness and heralding the relationship that God establishes with creation. Shirley Guthrie suggests an analogy, where marriage is "a partnership that reflects the covenant relationship between God and the people of God." Glimpsed in this light, the covenant of marriage extends not only to the couple, but to the entire community of faith. As Guthrie writes, "Marriage is never a purely private relationship between two individuals…[It] is thus a social and communal matter…and a wedding is the public recognition, acceptance, and commitment to this fact." A Christian marriage attests to neither the private choice of one couple, nor the apotheosis of courtly love. Rather, a marriage expresses public claims of God's covenantal love, witnessed in mutual human love.

A Christian marriage, then, is an anticipatory event, offering a foretaste of the heavenly banquet and assurance of our present participation in Christ's covenant with the world. A prayer from the Presbyterian *Book of Common Worship* expresses this hope for marriage, not only for the church, but for all creation: "Make their life together a sign of Christ's love to this sinful and broken world, that unity may overcome estrangement, forgiveness heal guilt, and joy conquer despair."

Interpreting Our Heritage Today

The biblical authors and Reformed heritage both assume that a marriage covenant is between a man and a woman. The question of same-sex marriage simply does not enter their interpretive world. Since the church must continually re-interpret its heritage in light of new questions in the attempt to be faithful to the Good News of Jesus Christ, Presbyterians are warranted in asking whether or not the distinctive strands of our tradition would allow for or prohibit same-sex unions or marriages. The burden for either side, in my opinion, lies in whether proposals for same-sex unions meet the theological criteria for marriages outlined in our tradition: May such unions, as Westminster stresses, serve the common good? Are they dim reflections of God's covenant with humanity, as the Old Testament suggests? Do they direct human persons to one another and to the ultimacy of God's Reign as the New Testament upholds? Do they, as Calvin urged, model restraint from sin *and* joy in companionship? Do they, however imperfectly, anticipate God's communion with all creation in Christ, as our liturgy celebrates?

If the church refuses to entertain these questions, then we fall under the judgment outlined in the Confession of 1967: "The church comes under the judgment of God and invites rejection by man when it fails to lead men and women into the full meaning of life together, or withholds the compassion of Christ from those caught in the moral confusion of our time" (9.47). Marriage, in the Reformed tradition, stresses covenant, God's desire for communion with all persons, mutual restraint and joy, the response of God's people, and the public good. Whenever we debate same-sex marriage, those themes – not sex, procreation, and gender roles – demand our greatest attention.   ✤

David H. Jensen is Associate Professor of Constructive Theology at Austin Presbyterian Theological Seminary. His most recent book is **Graced Vulnerability.**

Is gender complementarity essential to Christian marriage?

Mary McClintock Fulkerson ✤
Duke University

With the movement to legalize same-sex marriage, much discussion has centered on what defines marriage. Some have argued that marriage is an unchanging tradition. Historically, however, this is simply not accurate. The U.S. definition of marriage, for example, has changed radically over the centuries. This is especially so for women, who have suffered the most from traditional definitions. In colonial times marriage was an economic and political arrangement between families. For centuries in the South it was a legal privilege only available to whites. One of the most enduring traditions of marriage has been the husband's right to his wife's body, which only changed recently when the marital rape exception was removed in the 1980's. And these examples are only the beginning. The meaning of marriage has changed over time, even in the relatively short history of the United States. And changes have typically enhanced the moral character of marriage.

Opponents to gay marriage, however, would say the real unchanging requirement for marriage is gender complementarity - the idea that men and women are different from one another in essential ways, and that Christian love depends on the pairing of just those differences. "Adam and Eve, not Adam and Steve," as the expression goes. Since Scripture can be made to support both sides of the debate, it is useful to think about the implications of this notion that a covenant relationship can only be made between two persons of different genders. Not only does gender complementarity require male and female, it means that without these two halves, there cannot be a whole. As a model for human wholeness, gender complementarity is a dangerously exclusive one. On its terms a person who devotes his or her life to service of God - Jesus, Paul, Mother Teresa - is only half of a person, i.e., is not fully created in the image of God. To be sure, a man and woman are necessary for biological procreation. However, Protestants eliminated procreation as the defining purpose of marriage in the 16th century.

Another implication of gender complementarity - that there are fixed natures for masculinity and femininity - is also troubling. To begin with, this notion is historically inaccurate. Just as the definition of marriage has changed, so have accounts of masculinity and femininity. Early Church Fathers defined women's nature as less rational and more easily corrupted than men's. By contrast domestic images for U.S. white women at the turn of the century represent them as naturally more spiritual than (white) men. Accounts of male and female natures have always differed according to a subject's race and class position in society. An African American woman in earlier centuries was expected to drive mules and pick cotton. Seen as a natural-born breeder, not a mother, her young could be sold just like animals. Her white upper class counterpart, by contrast, was cast as a spotless, pure mother, fragile and in need of protection.

The identification of nurturing and relational skills with females may seem intuitively true. Centuries of assigning childrearing to women has enabled many women to develop the skills that support human development. However, as historically caused rather than biologically essential traits, capacities to nurture, to love and support the young are traits that Christians should covet for their male children as avidly as their female. Dividing up these traits not only idealizes stereotypes to which few people actually conform, it refuses to honor the unique gifts and potential of each child of God.

Then there is the problem that few people actually fit the idealizations. Countless boys and men have internalized images of what it means to be a "real man" that they are never able to live up to. A boy who is smart in math and science (as opposed to poetry and social work) will be lauded in our culture. A boy who prefers classical music to football, who is diminutive in size, or who would like to care for children, however, will inevitably be labeled a "sissy." By insisting upon gender complementarity, his church will continue to underwrite his fear that he is not a "real man."

Speaking of embarrassing failures to "measure up" to gender complementarity ideals, there is Jesus. On complementarity's terms the Biblical portrait of Jesus of Nazareth makes him something of a misfit. Having never married, he would have been only half a person. Several of Jesus' character traits are typically "female" - caring compassion, strength in weakness, and sacrifice. These images have so worried gender complementarians that more than once in U.S. history they have attempted to rescue Jesus from "effeminate" representations. "Muscular Christianity," a turn-of-the-century movement, remasculinized Jesus by imaging him as a red-blooded and virile, manly man - the opposite of a wimp. More recently Promise-Keepers insist upon calling Jesus a "Tender *Warrior*" to keep his style of caring from sounding too feminine. But if Jesus doesn't fit our notion of what a man should be, we would be better off broadening our understanding of gender roles than trying to change the story of Jesus.

If cultural definitions of maleness and femaleness cannot be essentialized, neither should the match of male and female sex organs be taken as proof that God only blesses heterosexual matings. Biologists now know that there are not just two kinds of people. The so-called "natural divisions" of humanity into those with XY sex chromosomes and those with XX is no longer accurate. Over 5.5 million people on the globe are not "male" or "female" according to these chromosomal patterns, and many of them cannot be defined by genitalia. To ignore such science is akin to agreeing with Aristotle that women are physiologically misbegotten males.

But what about complementarity *without* sex/gender essentialism? As the balancing of one person's strengths and weaknesses by those of another, complementarity can truly enhance Christian marriage. It means that differences harmonize, not that only certain differences are allowed (I Cor.12-13.) An outgoing personality in one partner might be complemented by the analytical skills of his shy partner. Rightly understood, complementarity suggests that differences can function to supplement and enhance, not divide people.

Jesus never defined sexuality. Indeed, his singleness, admiration of eunuchs (Mt.19:12), and admonition to give up family (Lk.11:27f) are good grounds to call the heterosexual nuclear family arrangement into question. However, Jesus does call us to God's radical vocation of love. This vocation requires honoring the unique gifts of everyone. It calls us to repent of this new form of "works righteousness" where I must be a "real woman" married to a "real man" in order to be saved. ✤

Mary McClintock Fulkerson teaches theology at Duke Divinity School. Ordained in 1978, she is a member of New Hope Presbytery in North Carolina, has chaired New Hope's task force on sexuality, and is one of the presbytery's commissioners to the 2006 General Assembly. She has written on Presbyterian women in **Changing the Subject: Women's Discourses and Feminist Theology** *and is the author of a forthcoming book on an interracial church.*

Can God use sex for our sanctification?

Eugene F. Rogers, Jr. ✢
University of North Carolina- Greensboro

Conservative Christians object to same-sex marriage because they want marriage to show visible holiness. That idea is useful because it prompts all Christians to reflect on the sort of holiness that marriage teaches and displays. Here I reflect on the theology of marriage under the rubric of sanctification. This approach owes much to the tradition of the Orthodox Church, which regards marriage as a way of participating in the divine life not by way of sexual satisfaction but by way of ascetic self-denial for the sake of more desirable goods. Theologically understood, marriage is not primarily for the control of lust or for procreation. It is a discipline whereby we give ourselves to another for the sake of growing in holiness – in short, for God. Marriage is a way in which God can train human beings – bodies and all – to "glorify God and enjoy him forever," as Westminster puts it.

In this respect marriage and monasticism are two forms of the same discipline, as the Orthodox writer Paul Evdokimov has argued. They are both ways of committing ourselves to others – a spouse or a monastic community – from whom we cannot easily escape. Both the monastic and the married give themselves over to be transformed by the perceptions of others; both seek to learn, over time, by the discipline of living with others something about how God perceives human beings.

Rowan Williams has written, "Grace, for the Christian believer, is a transformation that depends in large part on knowing yourself to be seen in a certain way: as significant, as wanted. The whole story of creation, incarnation, and our incorporation into the fellowship of Christ's body tells us that God desires us, as if we were God, as if we were that unconditional response to God's giving that God's [Son] makes in the life of the Trinity. We are created [and we marry] so that we may be caught up in this, so that we may grow into the wholehearted love of God by learning that God loves us as God loves God." Like all forms of asceticism, this is a high-risk endeavor. It can expose the worst in people – so that it can be healed.

Sexuality, in short, is for sanctification, that is, for God. It is to be a means by which God catches human beings up into the community of God's Spirit and the identity of God's child. Monogamy and monasticism are two ways of embodying features of the triune life in which God initiates, responds to and celebrates love.

Monasticism is for people who find a bodily, sexual sanctification first and foremost in the desirous perception of God. Marriage is for people who find themselves transformed by the desirous perception of another human being made in God's image. In a marital or monastic community, the parties commit themselves to practicing faith, hope and charity in a situation in which those virtues get plenty of opportunity to be exercised.

This way of understanding the Christian life obviously takes seriously the embodied character of human life. And embodiment implies diversity. The Holy Spirit characteristically rests on bodies: the body of Christ in Jesus, in the church, in the sacraments and in the saints. As the Spirit forms the bodies of human beings into the body of Christ, she characteristically gathers the diverse and diversifies the corporate, making members of one body.

We can see the Holy Spirit working for a harmonious diversity as she hovers over the waters in creation. Let us suppose that "Be fruitful and multiply" applies to the commands "Let the earth put forth vegetation" and "Let the waters bring forth swarms" and "Let the earth bring forth everything that creeps upon the ground" (Gen. 1:26,1:11, 1:20, 1:24). In all these cases, the earth and the waters bring forth things different from themselves, not just more dirt and more water. And in all these cases, they bring forth a variety of things: one might almost translate the phrase as "Be fruitful and diversify."

What kind of diversity or otherness does the Spirit evoke? Does it evoke the diversity represented by homosexual persons? Clearly, the majority opinion of the church has said no – that sort of diversity in creation is not the work of the Spirit. But it is not at all clear that such a judgment is necessary.

Conservatives will suppose that by invoking the diversity of creation I am begging the question. And yet, if the earth is to bring forth not according to its kind (more dirt) but creatures different from dirt and from each other, then the burden of proof lies on the other side. It needs to be shown that one of God's existing entities somehow cannot do its part in communicating and representing God's goodness and do so precisely in its finitude, by its limitations. What are the limits on accepting diversity as capable of representing God's goodness? Conservatives and liberals would agree that a diversity evoked by the Holy Spirit must be a holy diversity, a diversity ordered to the good, one that brings forth the fruits of the Spirit, primarily faith, hope and charity.

Given that no human beings exhibit faith, hope and charity on their own, but only in community, it is hard to argue that gay and lesbian people ought to be left out of social arrangements, such as marriage, in which these virtues are trained. In the words of Gregory of Nazianzus, our human limitations are intended for our good. So too, then, the limitations ascribed to same-sex couples, or for that matter cross-sex couples: in Gregory's words, their "very limitations are a form of training" toward communicating and representing the good. The trick is to turn these created limits toward the appreciation of the goods represented by others. Our differences are meant to make us yearn for and love one another. Difference is for blessing.

Under conditions of sin, otherness can lead to curse rather than blessing, to hostility rather than hospitality. Certainly there has been enough cursing and hostility to go around in the sexuality debates. But as created, otherness is intended for blessing and hospitality.

For large sections of various Christian traditions, blessing does not float overheard. Sanctification comes through concrete practices of asceticism, a discipline or training through which lesser goods serve greater ones. To reflect Trinitarian holiness, sanctification must involve community. It involves commitments to a community from which one can't easily escape, whether monastic, nuptial or congregational.

Gay and lesbian people who commit themselves to a community – to a church, or to one another as partners – do so to seek greater goods, to embark upon a discipline, to donate themselves to a greater social meaning. Living out these commitments under conditions of sin, in a community from which one can't easily escape – especially a community such as marriage and monasticism – is not likely to be straightforwardly improving. The community from which one can't easily escape is morally risky. It tends to expose the worst in people. The hope is that community exposes the worst in people in order that the worse can be healed.

Christians will see such healing as the work of Christ. Many Christian traditions portray Christ as a physician who must probe people's wounds in order to heal them. The probings of Jesus, the Great Physician, occur most readily in communities to which people bind themselves. The healing work of Christ in community brings both great risk and the promise of holiness.

For the risk of commitment to be worth it and to have the best chance of success, the community must have plenty of time and be made up of the right sort of people. Growth takes a lifetime. The right sort of people are those who will succeed in exposing and healing one another's flaws.

For gay and lesbian people, the right sort of otherness is unlikely to be represented by someone of the opposite sex, because only someone of the apposite, not opposite, sex will get deep enough into the relationship to expose one's vulnerabilities and inspire the trust that healing requires. The crucial question is, What sort of created diversity will lead one to holiness?

The answer is no doubt as various as creation itself. But certainly same-sex couples find the right spur to vulnerability, self-exposure, and the long and difficult commitment over time to discover themselves in the perceptions of another – they find all this in someone of the same sex. Theologically, says David McCarthy, a homosexual orientation is this: "Gay men and lesbians are persons who encounter the other (and thus themselves) in relation to persons of the same sex." Some people, therefore, are called to same-sex partnerships for their own sanctification. Opposite-sex partnerships wouldn't work for them, because those would evade rather than establish the right kind of transformative vulnerability.

The difference between members of a same-sex couple is not "merely psychological," but also an embodied difference, if only because sexual response is nothing if not something done bodily. But even embodied difference cannot be reduced to male-female complementarity, because that would leave Jesus a deficient human being. Jesus did not need a female other half to be fully human. (This point raises the issue of what singleness is for, but that's a question for another day.)

If this account is correct, then it turns out that conservatives wish to deprive same-sex couples not so much of satisfaction as of sanctification. But that is contradictory, because so far as I know no conservative has ever seriously argued that same-sex couples need sanctification any less than cross-sex couples do. It is at least contradictory to attempt in the name of holiness to deprive people of the means of their own sanctification.

Conservatives often claim it's dangerous to practice homosexuality, because it might be a sin. I want to propose that the danger runs both ways. It is more than contradictory, it may even be resisting the Spirit, to attempt to deprive same-sex couples of the discipline of marriage and not to celebrate same-sex weddings. As the king asks a guest in the parable of the wedding feast, "Friend, how did you get in here without a wedding garment?" (Mt. 22:1-13).

✣

Eugene F. Rogers, Jr. was raised in Shandon Presbyterian Church of Columbia, SC and educated at Princeton, Tuebingen, Rome, and Yale. He has been Eli Lilly Visiting Professor of Christian Thought and Practice at Princeton University and Chair of the Program in Theology, Ethics, and Culture at the University of Virginia. Now Professor of Religious Studies at the University of North Carolina at Greensboro, he is author of **Thomas Aquinas and Karl Barth, Sexuality and the Christian Body, Theology and Sexuality,** *and* **After the Spirit.**

What can we learn about the texture of Christian ethics by observing how African American congregations have historically dealt with issues related to sexuality?

Gayraud S. Wilmore ✢
Interdenominational Theological Center

It should be clear to anyone who keeps up with such things that the majority of African American Christians, if asked to vote yea or nay tomorrow on the ordination of lesbian and gay people to the ministry or to important lay offices, would vote nay. Most Blacks in all-Black denominations (comprising about 80% of all African-descended Christians in the U.S.) and most (but perhaps a smaller percentage) in predominantly white denominations are strangely traditional and almost puritanical when it comes to imposing formal, even stringent, moral and ethical standards upon those who are presumed to be emissaries of Jesus Christ in his church.

I consider my mother and father, both deceased, and most of my relatives of their and my generation (strong Presbyterians, Baptists, and Methodists), fairly typical in this respect. Mother and Dad were strong on civil rights and justice for the poor, the incarcerated and disabled; passionately concerned about equal and non-segregated public education; supporters of soldiers, sailors, and marines, but wary about wars; committed to legislation for welfare mothers, full employment, controlled abortion, open and affordable housing, the prudent regulation of laissez faire capitalism, government sponsorship of universal medical care, health insurance and social security. But they were also believers in an inerrant Bible that, to all intents and purposes, condemned the sexual behavior of lesbians, gays, bi-sexual, and trans-gendered persons – albeit, God love them all!

That is the kind of Christianity some of us assimilated from the right wing of the Great Awakenings of the 19th century. That's what the white Baptists and Methodists of the South, the Quakers from Pennsylvania, and the doughty Congregational and Presbyterian missionaries from New England and Ohio taught us in the church-sponsored schools and mission stations below the Mason-Dixon Line. We learned that cleanliness was next to Godliness, and that sex was dirty – even between a married man and woman – so you know what it had to be between people of the same gender! Our preachers found the inerrant proof-texts in the big pulpit Bible and the congregation nodded its heads and said, "Amen, Reverend. Ain't that the truth!"

Nevertheless I will always admire those courageous white women and men who followed the Union army and gathered the newly freed slaves into make-shift congregations, one-room school houses, boarding schools, and who were frequently members of the faculties of our first fledgling colleges and universities. They taught us more than reading, writing, and arithmetic. They taught us middle-class manners and morals. Many an awkward and timid young Black boy or girl caught a glimpse of a wonderful life as a freeborn, full-fledged American citizen. Some of these young people became eager, enterprising migrants to the cities of the South and North because of the band of Northern missionaries and teachers, both white and Black, who told the white population of the former Confederacy what Joseph told a man in Shechem: "I am seeking my brothers."

But for all the good they did, they also messed us up. They overlaid the pragmatic spirituality of our African inheritance with the unctuous, privatistic, feel-good, and moralistic religiosity of an evangelical Protestantism that the missionaries themselves didn't practice. They made us feel guilty about sex. They loaded us with biblical laws and ordinances, and conventional Anglo-Saxon mores that they themselves abrogated whenever it suited them. Throughout the 20th century some of our boldest and brightest religious leaders sought to free us from bibliolatrous piosity and helped some of us to adopt a faith that defined and sanctified our experience of a continuous struggle for humanity in the face of unremitting dehumanization and indignity.

But the effort has borne little fruit thus far. What is called the Black Church in America is, for the most part, a hyper-conservative institution when it comes to human sexuality and recognition of the amazing grace and responsible freedom in the bedroom that all Christians have been given in Jesus Christ.

However, this conservatism of the mainline Black churches, and their sisters and brothers who remained in the predominantly white denominations, is nuanced in some peculiar ways that even Black scholars are aware of but do not fully comprehend. The churches made notable exceptions when communal values overrode moralistic constraints. Here, a gay assistant pastor or choir director was cherished and people kept their thoughts to themselves, their mouths shut, and turned their heads so as not to see. There, an old maid lesbian Sunday School teacher and the young college girl who lodged with her during the school year were discreetly ignored if they made no open display of affection. Here, a preacher who was known to be sleeping with a woman leader in the congregation was quietly persuaded by a group of husbands to mend his ways or give up the church. There, a bisexual artist or musician who was suspected of promiscuity with men and women was spared from having the matter dragged into public view. Rather than ruin the lives of everyone involved and shame the community, the church chose to quietly remove him from his position and recommended that he seek private counseling. Different cases were resolved in different ways. The point is that Black churches have many times let communal values override moralistic legalism.

This kind of finely discriminated and nuanced observance of Biblical literalism regarding matters of sexual impropriety points to a deep-lying humanism, and even pragmatism, in African American religion. To those on the outside it may smack of hypocrisy (and often it can be explained in no other way), but I think more frequently it shows that in the windy interstices of a rigid structure of conservative Christian ethics, built up over years of Bible-thumping sermons on Sunday mornings, sawdust trail revivals, and unrelenting prayer bands and evangelistic efforts of all kinds, there is a common sense and unsanctimonious realism in the faith of African Americans that tends toward the *shalom* of the community, toward forgiveness, toward inclusivity and prudential tolerance.

That is what Black liberation theology, which flourished in the latter days of the civil rights movement and came to full throttle with the rise of Black Power between 1964 and 1970, attempted to reinstate and unleash as a counterpoint to the influence of white theology in the institutional Black churches. The effort has not been abandoned. Today more Black clergy are graduating from seminaries where they have learned that justice, liberation, and inclusiveness are at the core of the gospel and the Black religious experience. Large national gatherings of Black ministers, unencumbered by ecclesiastical certification and oversight – like the annual Hampton, Virginia pastors' conference and the Samuel DeWitt Proctor Pastors and Lay Convocations of the past three years – are beginning to listen to Black biblical scholars and theologians. Today a new breed of scholars in religion are cautiously pressing for an orthodoxy that avoids consigning the LGBT community to hell. They are reminding Black church members to "Remember that you were a slave in the land of Egypt, and the Lord your God brought you out from there with a mighty hand and an outstretched arm. . . " (Deut. 5:15).

Nevertheless, the reinterpretation of human sexuality in the Black church moves slowly against the currents of Protestant fundamentalism. But the commitment to cultural autonomy and radical freedom in Christ espoused by 20th-century Black liberation and womanist theologians reinforces the ethos of a Black Christianity which naturally resists any form of orthodoxy connected to exclusivity and racism while still clinging to many traditional values. There is nothing particularly Black about this theological and ethical inconsistency, but it at least gives the lie to the allegation that born-again African Americans are inflexible Bible-idolaters and wholly bound to an outmoded orthodoxy. We have introduced some significant changes to American churches and to this society in the past, and may again in the future.   ✢

Gayraud S. Wilmore was executive director of the United Presbyterian Council on Church and Race (CORAR) during the civil rights movement. Since then he has been a seminary professor. He retired in 1990 and is Emeritus Professor of Church History at the Interdenominational Theological Center in Atlanta.

If the church accepts homosexuality, what is to keep us from accepting sins like adultery, incest, bestiality, and sex with children?
Don't we have to draw the line somewhere?

Mark Douglas ✤
Columbia Theological Seminary

This question raises a legitimate concern that all Presbyterians ought to take seriously: if we accept one form of sexuality that is sinful, what's to keep us from accepting other sinful forms of sexuality? Yet while the question is legitimate, the assumption behind it may not be. For the question assumes that one form of sexuality – namely heterosexuality expressed within the context of marriage – is nonproblematic while other forms are sinful. But if the Reformed tradition teaches us anything, it is that sin pervades every part of our lives – including all our sexual lives. Or, said more directly, there are *no* sinless expressions of sexuality.

And here, examples from divorce and adultery to pornography are so easy that we need to get beyond them without forgetting them. Think, instead, about all the frustrating awkwardness of trying to know what one's lover is thinking and trying to please him or her without asking mood-shattering questions; all the vulnerable embarrassment we feel in exposing our bodies to others; all the maddening frustration of unfulfilled or – perhaps even worse – partially fulfilled desire; all the absurd psychological games we play with ourselves, our lovers, or those we hope may one day be our lovers, all the selfish motivations that are so likely to drive human actions while intimate; that abrupt realization that sex and intimacy and orgasms may be absolutely splendid but sometimes seem hardly worth the trouble it takes in getting to them. Where do all these feelings come from if not from a deep sense that what sex is and what we imagine sex should be aren't the same? What do all these examples point toward if not sin? How could any of us be so filled with *hubris* as to think that our sexuality is sinless sexuality?

So while the concern behind the initial question is legitimate, it needs to be reframed: If we recognize sinfulness in all sexual relations, how are we to distinguish between those that the church finds room for and those that the church rejects? Or, to frame that question a bit more theologically: Given that God created us in love and for love but that all of us have sinned by attempting to deny, refuse, contort, or abuse that love, how are we, as the church, to engage sinners and sins? Framing the question theologically in this way opens it up to the church's rich, deep, and broad vocabulary for thinking about engaging sin and sinners: the vocabulary of sin and grace, justification and sanctification, gospel and law. Using this vocabulary is neither automatic nor easy, and its use leads to neither automatic nor easy answers. However, if the church is to think as a church rather than some other type of gathering of persons, it is vital that it speak through its native theological language. Toward that end, let me make two initial – and initiating – comments about what I understand God to be doing in dealing with sin and what I believe the church is called to do in response.

First a word on justification. For those within the Reformed tradition, God's work of redemption must be the starting point for our thinking about sin and grace. The witness of the New Testament is that God deals with sin by being born as one of us, living with us and teaching us, dying for us, and being resurrected that we might have new life and, eventually, so that we might become like God. Or, said differently, God deals with sinners neither by accepting us nor by damning us but by redeeming us because we cannot redeem ourselves. The one who could condemn all of us has chosen to redeem us instead. In God's desire for us, he used the cross and the empty tomb to restore intimacy with us.

And all this happens to us in our bodies. Redemption does not remove us from our bodies, but restores them to us so that we can use them for the purposes for which they were created: to glorify God and enjoy God forever. Whatever moral lessons we sinners might learn from God's great act of justification and no matter how much we might disagree about those lessons in their particulars, it seems to me that the way we deal with ourselves and other sinners ought to bear some coherent relation to the way God has chosen to deal with sinners: with an eye toward neither acceptance nor damnation, but redemption.

Second, a word on sanctification. If it is true that the purpose for which we are embodied is to glorify God and enjoy God forever, then that purpose pervades all the ways we use our bodies – including the ways we use them sexually. It follows that the purpose of sex isn't procreation or intimacy per se – though those things are gifts that may come with sex – but a way in which we work with God because God is working in us so that we might become closer to God. In sanctification, we learn to trust our bodies to the one who is sovereign Lord of them – and to refuse to trust our bodies to anyone or anything other than God. Said differently, having sex – theologically understood – should, like all other acts by which we relate to others, become a way we learn to express through our bodies the desire God feels for us and has created us to feel for each other. And this desire, at least according to Scripture and the Reformed tradition, is a desire shaped by and revealed in publicly affirmed, non-breakable covenants of mutual love. (This is, I think, the very reason that the church has, can, and must continue to relate sex to marriage and the reason the church, like Jesus, should be deeply troubled about far-too-easy understandings of marriage and the far-too-common event of divorce.)

All of which returns us to the legitimacy of the initial question. For while thinking of some expressions of sexuality as sinful and others as not sinful is an error, we are right, I think, to recognize that some sinful expressions of sexuality are far more problematic than others because while all expressions of sexuality fail to live up to their primary purpose, some expressions cannot live up to that purpose because they stand in opposition to it. Or, to say that more affirmatively, some expressions of sexual desire at least begin to mirror the way God expresses divine desire – and thereby become part of the process by which we learn to become holy — while others do not.

Since God has expressed God's desire for us by covenanting with us, so our sexual lives ought to conform to covenantal patterns of commitment. Since God has made these covenants public, so the covenantal patterns of our sexual lives ought to be public. And since God's desire for us is that "we will be like him for we shall see him as he is" (1 John 3:2), so our sexual lives ought to be shaped by visions of mutuality and equality.

Where desire is allowed to come and go without commitment, where it must remain private, where it cannot be mutually expressed: these expressions of sexuality actively inhibit our ability to participate in our sanctification. These criteria clearly exclude the kinds of sins – adultery, incest, pederasty, bestiality – that some fear would necessarily follow on acceptance of covenanted same-sex relationships. Where desire can be publicly expressed in binding covenants of mutual love: there we find persons learning to use their bodies to love God and enjoy God forever.   ✦

Mark Douglas is Associate Professor of Christian Ethics at Columbia Theological Seminary and an ordained minister in the Presbyterian Church (U.S.A.). He is the author of **Confessing Christ in the 21st Century.**

How does the struggle for full inclusion of gay and lesbian Christians relate to the civil rights movement and other struggles for freedom and equality?

J. Herbert Nelson, II ✢
University of Memphis

Growing up in South Carolina, my male peer group and I measured our maturing into manhood on the basis of girls and sports. We often talked about our likes or dislikes for certain girls. Some boys boasted about losing their virginity. (In retrospect, it is clear that many of the stories were contrived; nonetheless, they were always fascinating.) The rest of us talked about sports. Our recent performance in high school athletics or the latest playground "juke" of an opponent served as validation for our stories.

In our own strange way we never became preoccupied with hatred of gay or lesbian people. Our uncomplimentary names for them were most often used to reassure ourselves and others that we were not gay. We did not understand much about them, but lesbian and gay people were our grade school companions. They lived next door, down the street, and around the corner from us. We knew their parents and played sports with their older brothers and dated their sisters. Therefore, the relationship waters were muddied and many connections remained in place. We simply viewed the obviously gay brother as different. I did not realize at the time that this was the accompany these childhood friends for the remainder of their lives in this society.

The Gospel of John's account of the woman caught in adultery (John 8:1-11) describes relationships of power that are reminiscent of the power structures in our own society. Forget for a moment that this woman is an adulteress. I ask you to forget, because it is obvious that the men who bring her to Jesus and raise the question regarding the right to stone her based on the Law of Moses have forgotten. If sin was the major issue, some man or men caught in the act with her would also be facing capital punishment. However, the text represents a male-dominated, hierarchical context in which men are exempt from the death sentence based on the power structure of their culture. Categorized as an adulteress and alienated from power, this woman's sin is now to be punished by a march to death. The emerging religious leader's approval is now needed as a cursory nod to the established powers before the crowd performs the execution. Wait! Jesus writes on the ground. Did he write the names of the accusers who had been with this woman? If so, was it the son of one of the Pharisees who had not sown all of his wild oats? Or was this woman the unacknowledged daughter of one of the men in the crowd? Although we will never know what Jesus wrote on the ground that day, we do know that the men dropped their rocks and went home when confronted with their own sinfulness. Jesus' writing changed the way power was construed in that particular situation.

As we discuss ordaining lesbian and gay Christians, it is important that we too remember power as a central issue. Although traditional interpretations of the story of the woman caught in adultery focus on sin and Jesus' openness to grace, both power and gender construction are also central issues. Male domination is also at issue, because the participation of the man in an adulterous relationship is overlooked. Just so, the question of whether or not to ordain gay and lesbian Christians is not just a question about what counts as sin or grace. It is also a question about power. And so it is related to other struggles for freedom, equality, and full participation.

We have to remember that slavery and the refusal to ordain women were both defended on biblical and theological grounds. But I shudder to think what the Presbyterian Church (USA) would have become had we not fought for women to be ordained fifty years ago. Or, what would have happened to our denomination if the leadership of the Presbyterian Church in the United States had not taken a stand on principle to move the 1965 General Assembly meeting from Memphis, Tennessee to Montreat, North Carolina? The meeting was moved because the session of the local church (Second Presbyterian) that was to host the General Assembly prohibited African Americans from being admitted to worship. We have shown at least some ability to name the power issues at work in biblical and theological conversations. And we need to do the same thing now.

The Church of Jesus Christ has participated in gender and race domination and exclusion throughout history. Therefore, we must view the biblical record and our interpretation as to who is in and out with both theology and history in mind. Theology presses our faith perspectives to higher and better hopes. But history reminds us of our frailty in accepting God's expectation for an inclusive Christian community based on love for all humanity. We must examine how our interpretations of scripture have led to the acceptance of some and the alienation of others. We need to study who gains from exclusion. We need to ask who desires power and who is genuinely seeking righteousness. We need to trace the ways that questions of sin hide questions of power.

Jesus repeatedly rejects human attempts to exclude people who get labeled as "sinful." Blind Bartimaeus receiving his sight (Mk. 10: 46-52) is another example of grace pressing against the edges of society's power arrangements. While the established host guides Jesus through the polished main streets, an inappropriate beggar cries out for healing, disrupting the hospitality committee's tour. The crowd rebukes him, but Jesus confronts the established theology that legitimates the blind man's segregation and exclusion. Jesus heals him. In so doing, Jesus raises a community's awareness of redemption by lifting the veil of historical domination of the poor and proclaiming a new ethic of restorative justice. He reaches beyond the boundaries of the established order to redeem Bartimaeus and forces the community to view Jesus, Bartimaeus and itself differently. As an old parishioner told me a few years ago, "When you really see Jesus, you cannot see yourself or the world the same anymore." Presbyterians must bring Jesus into our present arrangements of power constructed by white males so that we may unbind ourselves from the categorization, alienation, and separation that has caused centuries of pain.

Oftentimes we struggle with the word "power" in the church. We like to pretend that there is no exercise of power in the household of God. But power is a reality that exists even in the church. And lesbian and gay Christians have discovered the real obstacles that power poses to their broader participation in the Church. They are not the first to do so, and they will not be the last. Lesbian and gay activists sometimes compare their struggle to the struggles for women's suffrage and racial desegregation against a prevailing power structure. But many persons who fought in older movements for freedom and equality find it difficult to see the correlation between these struggles. It can be difficult to see the connections for at least three reasons.

First, none of these movements has been built on a consciousness of the intersections of various kinds of oppression. Many African-American women would argue that the civil rights movement and its leaders were sexist and chauvinist. Similarly, women's suffrage was concerned with women and their rights as human beings and not translated to the larger society as a movement that also included lesbian women. Our movements have focused on one use of power or another, sometimes to the neglect of the "intersectional" nature of exclusion.

Second, many persons in older civil rights movements do not believe in extending the rights of gay and lesbian persons. As Gayraud Wilmore has aptly stated in his article for this booklet, African Americans have not understood the lesbian and gay struggle for inclusion in Christendom in the same vein as the civil rights movement. Although we African-Americans live in the contradictions in church life by hiring church personnel and ordaining clergy and officers who are lesbian and gay persons, our theology remains stagnant with regards to full public acceptance. But why should this be? We can support a movement against exclusive power structures even if we do not think it is exactly like our own struggle as African-Americans.

Finally, it is difficult to connect the struggles because each movement has a tendency to slip into the "empire thinking" that has been born out of Western theological construct of oppression. Simply put, the empire mind believes that someone has to be left out so that the powerful may prosper. The imperial mindset leads excluded groups to compete with one another, as if full acceptance of gay and lesbian people would come at the cost of real equality for African-American Christians. But the imperial mindset serves only the empire. The truth is that we're all in this struggle together.

People involved in *every* struggle for freedom and equality should ask questions about the power relations at stake in this debate. Is this issue really about sin – or is it centered on maintaining the "good ole boys" club through conservative control of the denomination? Can liberal ideals of inclusion be accomplished through passive-aggressive strategizing? Will moderate waffling raise effective ways of declaring Jesus' real desires for the Church, or simply appease both sides with watered-down rhetoric in the name of Church unity? What do opponents to lesbian and gay ordination have to gain? And in what ways can proponents of lesbian and gay ordination use their power so that it is effective for the gospel and promotion of the Church? How can we make stronger connections – practically, politically, and theologically – between these movements for equality and inclusion?

In retrospect I know that my friends and I teased and demeaned the gay boys we grew up with because we needed to affirm our own superiority. Sports and girls were simply mechanisms by which we affirmed our maleness as it had been defined by our culture, society and rearing. It was a poor choice and I was wrong! Women were also degraded in our boyish conversations. Even when I did not participate, I stood by and quietly or laughingly approved "kiss and tell" stories or demeaning characterizations. Growing older has allowed me to both experience and witness the ways that cultural power constructs have damaged and scarred the souls of human beings through labeling, categorizing and defaming. I have committed myself not to participate in power mongering that debilitates the possibilities for a community that embraces all of God's children.

Judgment can be harsh in this world we live in. And it can be a tool for the already powerful against the already powerless. I believe that is why judgment and exclusion remain God's business.

Participating in the building of the Kingdom of God with all the weaknesses, frailties and human faults that all of us possess is the business God assigned to me. And that is difficult enough. I believe I will leave the business that belongs to God in God's hands. Jesus had the formula correct. The wheat and the weeds are to be separated at the harvest. And it is not harvest time yet!   ✤

J. Herbert Nelson, II is pastor of Liberation Community Presbyterian Church in Memphis, TN, a tent-making new church development that evangelizes the poor into PC(USA) membership. Dr. Nelson is Co-Founding Coordinator of the Southern Faith, Labor and Community Alliance and was formerly Associate Director of the Benjamin L. Hooks Institute for Social Change at the University of Memphis.

What do Presbyterians teach about sexuality?

Su Yon Pak ✢
Union Theological Seminary

Education happens everywhere, intentionally or unintentionally. It happens in church basements, in the pews, in Session meetings and in women's gatherings. Education happens in positive as well as in negative events. As educator Lawrence Cremin asserts, "What is taught is not always what is desired, and vice versa; what is learned is not always what is taught, and vice versa. Moreover, there are almost always unintended consequences in education; indeed, they are frequently more significant than the intended consequences. Hence, educational transactions are often marked by profound irony." It is because of this all-pervasive and surprising nature of education that it is important to pay special attention to the *process* of education. If we want to know what Presbyterians teach about sexuality, we will have to look at the whole process: curriculum, practices, and silences.

Curriculum. The word "curriculum" comes from the Latin word *currere* which means "to run." The work of the curriculum is the forming and re-forming of the course the church will run. There are three types of curricula operating in any educational situation: explicit, implicit and null. The *explicit* curriculum is what is explicitly being taught – the written and the spoken contents. It refers to things like sermons, the Book of Confessions, and written Sunday School materials. The *implicit* curriculum is less obvious. It refers to elements such as the location of the Sunday School class, organization of the room, what gets rewarded, and whose opinions are valued. The *null* curriculum is a paradox. It teaches by way of not teaching. It refers to what is absent, left out, and silenced. Whose stories are not heard? Who is not present in the leadership? What are "taboo" subjects never talked about in churches? The null curriculum teaches as powerfully and formatively as the explicit curriculum. What are some of the null curricula of your church?

Practices. Christian practices are an important part of the church's curriculum. In fact, Craig Dykstra would say that curriculum itself is "the practice of a people." Many communities through many generations have participated in Christian practices, not only as a way to embody faith, but also, and perhaps more fundamentally, as a way to come to faith. Why? Practices are activities that people do together over time. They form a way of life that is lived out in the world in response to God's reconciling love. Christian practices address fundamental human needs in ways that reflect God's purpose for humankind. These human needs – the need for healing, the need for community, and the need to be fed and cared for, for instance – are fundamental and universal for every living human being. At the same time, different historical, political, racial, economic, cultural and social contexts create different and particular ways in which the needs are met. And certain needs are more urgent and prominent in one community than others. What are the urgent practices necessary in your community?

Silences. Sexuality – Null Curriculum of the Church? For many Presbyterian churches, the topic of sexuality belongs in the category of null curriculum. That is, Presbyterian churches teach about sexuality by not teaching about it. What does that silence teach?

First, it teaches that sexuality is not in the realm of the sacred – that it is not considered to be even potentially holy. In this way, the Church teaches that our spirituality does not include sexuality and sexual desires. But if we believe that the whole person is made in the image of God, we should embrace sexuality as an essential aspect of what it means to be human. In this null curriculum, the church gives up its opportunity and responsibility to form a member to be a whole embodied person. In the absence of explicit teaching and formation from the church about sexuality – except in the form of "don't do it before marriage" – people are forced to look outside of the church. The point here is that by not teaching about sexuality, except in limited and negative ways, the church loses its voice and therefore its authority in this central aspect of human life.

Second, the church's silence teaches that sexuality is shameful. Shame has a role in making a person aware that certain actions betray their personhood. But when it is used as a tool to make sexuality forbidden or dirty, it has a detrimental effect on a person's human development. When the church speaks about sexuality, it does so in the context of morality, usually in terms that define sexuality as shameful, disgraceful and embarrassing. The church's null curriculum teaches that all sexual acts are shameful. This shroud of shame clouds our clarity about what is good and what is not good.

But here is the irony: While sexuality is usually a null curriculum of the church, it becomes an explicit curriculum in practices and teaching that condemn homosexuality and bisexuality. The broader background of a null curriculum of silence and shame does much to shape the ways the church talks about homosexuality. When the topic of sexuality is "taboo," practices and sexualities different from what is considered to be the norm challenge people to think about their own sexuality. This makes us uncomfortable. And this discomfort with sexuality breeds discomfort with homosexuality.

We should also think about the implicit curriculum of the church's teaching about same-sex relations. Dedicated and committed persons of homosexual and bisexual orientations are explicitly and implicitly prohibited from leadership positions, from ordination, and from creating a family through Holy Unions. What does this teach? What does this teach our young people? It teaches implicitly that there is a double standard operating in the church. While all are called in baptism to service to God, and some are called to serve the community in ordained capacity, these calls are not affirmed as valid for gay and lesbian Christians. While the labor of gay and lesbian people in the church is acceptable and even encouraged, public leadership affirming that labor is not acceptable. While joining together in love to form a committed relationship and a stable family is considered a virtue, when persons are of the same gender, that same desire is considered to be an abomination. The double standard implicitly teaches that some Presbyterians are of more value in the eyes of God and the church community than others. And this becomes an explicit curriculum of discrimination.

What can the church do? The church must affirm sexuality as an important aspect of what it means to be human. One powerful way to affirm sexuality is to promote Christian practices for honoring the body. Providing an open space and hospitality where young people's bodies and their desires are welcomed, honored and discussed as a practice of honoring the body can be one way to affirm sexuality. As Stephanie Paulsell writes in *Honoring the Body*, "It is only through learning to honor the body in every aspect of our embodied life that we will be able to honor our bodies' sexual feelings and desires." Sexual desires are part of other desires which need to be checked and harnessed. Just because we have desires does not mean that we should act on every desire that comes to mind. This balance of openness and boundaries is taught and learned so that it can become a moral compass for young people negotiating their own sexualities. This is especially important for young gay and lesbian people trying to come to terms with their sexualities in a world that is hostile to their being.

The church also needs practices and rituals that mark and affirm sexual development. The church ritualizes various markers in a person's life: birth, first communion, marriage and death. What would it mean for the church to recognize markers of sexual development such as the onset of menstruation, the changing of a boy's voice, and menopause? For many people these changes bring much shame and embarrassment. Ritualizing the celebration of sexual development could turn a sense of shame into a sense of what is holy, sacred. It would affirm that sexuality is indeed holy, a part of the realm of God.

In sum, teachings about sexuality cannot be left by default to be an unintended consequence of the church's education. The church needs to educate explicitly and implicitly that the body and its desires can be good and are a fundamental part of life as a human being. This message can then help to focus the church community to think more positively about gay and lesbian issues. If sexuality can be good and positive, then homosexual acts done within the same moral guidelines can be seen as good and positive. ✣

A cradle Presbyterian, Su Yon Pak received her M.A. in Christian Education from Princeton Theological Seminary and Ed.D. in Religion and Education from Teachers College Columbia Univer-sity and Union Theological Seminary. For the last 7 years, she has worked at Union, 6 years as Dean of Students and currently as Associate Director of Development. She is a co-author of **Singing the Lord's Song in a New Land: Korean American Practices of Faith.** *She has also written young adult curriculum for the United Church Press, and contributes to Horizons magazine.*

Is there room in the PC(USA) for those of differing orientations?

Jeanne Stevenson-Moessner ✣
Perkins School of Theology

Anne Lamott tells of a seven-year-old child who was lost one day in the big city. She was frantic and confused until a police car stopped to assist. The officers offered to drive her around adjacent neighborhoods until something looked familiar. Suddenly the small child recognized a steeple. With relief, the child instructed the officers to stop the car at the building with the steeple. Happily she announced: "You could let me out now. This is my church, and I can always find my way home from here" (*Traveling Mercies*).

This story brings life to Webster's definition of "orientation" as a "homing faculty or instinct." The hushed question that we are cautious to articulate is whether the church will be able to give bearings to and accommodate those of differing orientations. Will you and I and those who differ from you and me be able to find our way home from the landmark of our church? Is there room in our church for those of differing orientations, particularly differing sexual orientations?

Webster's also defines "orientation" as "the planning of church architecture so that the altar is in the east end." Facing the east positioned the worshipper for the rising of the sun. This definition reminds me of being positioned in just such a way at a Good Friday service many years ago in a retreat center outside Basel, Switzerland. The retreat center was the home of the Schwestern von Grandchamp, the female counterpart to the Brothers of Taizé; the retreat center was called *Sonnenhof*, meaning "halo around the sun." I made the retreat in an attempt to heal from some ostracism I had encountered. The hostile exclusion had come from some men who did not believe women should complete advanced degrees in theology, nor become ordained. I was very angry with their theological orientation and with them.

On this silent retreat, one of the Dominican nuns kept following me to ask, "Would you like to come talk?" My repeated negative replies did not deter her. Eventually, I gave up and met with her in the garden. As we say in clinical parlance, I ventilated. She heard my raw anger for one hour without saying a word. When I had finished, she made one comment about these hurtful men: "Christ died for them, too." I became angrier, and the anger did not subside until I found an ikon in the gift shop, an ikon of Mary Magdalene before the risen Christ in the garden, near the empty tomb (John 20). Mary Magdalene called him *Rabboni* or Teacher. I found my mandate to continue in my doctoral program and to-wards ordination; my orientation was towards the Teacher, towards the risen Son. On Good Friday at Sonnenhof, we knelt at the base of a large cross in the sisters' chapel. My struggles did indeed look different from that vantage point. I have gone back many times to that vantage point, in times of challenge and times of anger. Is there room in our church for those of differing orientations?

Orientation is adapting or adjusting to a particular situation. Dis-orientation occurs when we cannot adapt or adjust to a particular situation or person or position. Sociologist Georg Simmel dealt with the complicated cultural/sociological dynamics of the "stranger" or "wanderer" or "sojourner" always in a figure-ground relationship to the home or host country (*Soziologie*, 1908). In a 1977 article Donald N. Levine developed Simmel's thought in a typology of "stranger" relationships which included the following: guest, sojourner, newcomer, intruder, inner enemy, marginal man or marginal woman. Varying degrees of "social distance" are involved with the various categories, from the vantage point of those in the home country.

Varying degrees of theological distance occur in the church, when the stranger or intruder or enemy is considered in a figure-ground relationship with the host theology. This phenomena can be dis-orienting. When I encounter someone who is resistant to my position on an emotionally-laden topic, I ask myself silently the question Dr. Letty Russell taught me to ask: What is at stake here? What would the individual have to lose if he/she saw the issue from my vantage point? This exercise and the insight that can ensue has often assisted me, not in agreement with, but in compassion for "the stranger."

Orientation is technically "a position with relation to the points of the compass." Yahweh is described in the Hebrew Bible as setting a compass upon the face of the depth (Proverbs 8:27b). Those who partake in the *basileia* and banqueting of God will come from many points of this compass: "then people will come from east and west, from north and south, and will eat in the *basileia* of God" (Luke 13:29). We may well be feasting with those who were theological and sociological strangers. The cycles of violence with which strangers or enemies or intruders have sometimes been treated will be replaced with a compass of compassion. There is an ultimate orientation like the magnetic north that supercedes proximate orientations. H. Richard Niebuhr spoke on the distinction between proximate goals and the ultimate goal of our faith which is love of God and neighbor (*The Purpose of the Church and Its Ministry*, 1956). Proximate goals are worthy; they include denominational issues and passionate causes involving sexual orientation. These proximate goals may even come close or very near to the ultimate goal of our faith; however, they must never be the central point or orientation of our faith, lest they become gods in themselves, and we become lost finding our way home.

Sexual orientation engenders a volatile debate in our church today. We seek desperately to understand the arguments from all angles. There are various theories as to the "why" of differing sexual orientations: socialization, genetics, and abuse. I would like to think if a sexual orientation has grown out of a reaction to abuse, the church would especially be a place in which to find safe haven. Theories regarding the source of sexual orientation are changing over time. For example, at Georgia Baptist Hospital in Atlanta, we residents were trained with the DSM III-R (*Diagnostic and Statistical Manual of Mental Disorders*, Third Edition-Revised, 1987). Homosexuality was considered a "sexual disorder not otherwise specified" (p.561). Today, residents in pastoral care and counseling train with the DSM IV. In this revised edition, homosexuality as a sexual orientation is no longer categorized as a sexual disorder by the medical/psychiatric field.

Is there room in the church for those with differing theories and orientations? I believe this is possible if we image ourselves as adopted children of God (I develop this idea more fully in *The Spirit of Adoption*, 2003). In the last three decades, social workers and sociologists have changed their understanding of families constituted through adoption. Three decades ago, families undergoing adoption were counseled to believe that an adoptive family would be the same as a biological family. That view has been called "rejection-of-differences" and led to dysfunctional and unhealthy families (David Kirk, *Shared Fate*, 1964). Adoptive parents were told by agencies that the adopted child "would be just like having a biological child." We now know that is not so. Adopted children often have a differing set of genes, heredity, physical characteristics, and abilities than the adoptive parents. Social workers and agencies now counsel families into "an acceptance-of-differences," if there is to be a healthy and functional family.

The church is a family constituted through God's adoption of us. This adoption imagery of inclusion into God's family is mentioned in Ephesians, Galatians, and Romans. The metaphor of adoption into God's family is used more often than the birth imagery, or second birth imagery, as in John 3. That means we may not look like each other, we may not vote like each other, and we may not have the same sexual orientation. However, we have been adopted as God's children through Jesus Christ, the Firstborn; our inheritance has been sealed with the guarantee of the Holy Spirit (Ephesians 1). Perhaps if we can move into an acceptance-of-differences that an adopted family must have to be healthy and functional, we can actualize some of that inheritance.

Here is my revised version of Anne Lamott's story:

There were three small children who were lost one day in the big city. They were frantic and confused until a police car stopped to assist. The two officers offered to drive them around adjacent neighborhoods until something looked familiar. The officers had a hard time believing they were from the same family; one child had been adopted from China, one from Guatemala, one from Nebraska. They looked very different. They also couldn't agree on their directions. The three adopted children, sisters and brothers, huddled together in the back seat of the patrol car. With relief, the children instructed the officers to stop the car at the building with the steeple. On this one point they finally agreed: "This is our church. As a family, we can always find our way home from here." ✛

Jeanne Stevenson-Moessner is Associate Professor of Pastoral Care at Perkins School of Theology (Southern Methodist University), an ordained Presbyterian minister, a Fellow in the American Association of Pastoral Counselors, a member of the International Academy of Practical Theology, a Henry Luce III Fellow, and Chair-elect for the Society for Pastoral Theology. She is the author of **The Spirit of Adoption: At Home in God's Family.** *Before coming to Perkins, she taught at Columbia Theological Seminary and the University of Dubuque Theological Seminary.*

Can people change their sexual orientations? Should the church require gay and lesbian Christians to try to change their orientations in order to be ordained?

Nancy J. Ramsay ✤
Brite Divinity School

In *The Spirit and the Forms of Love*, Daniel Day Williams suggested that "love has communion in freedom as its goal." Sexual orientation refers to the way women and men self-identify in our sexual attraction to others. But it is more than a matter of preferred sexual partners. Sexual orientation is part of persons' core identity. It shapes the ways we seek to satisfy deep God-given needs for communion and intimacy – sexual, emotional, physical, and spiritual. Sexual orientation is not simply sexual behavior. Persons who self-identify as gay, lesbian or bisexual in their sexual orientation are not simply naming preferences for sexual partners. Rather, many would say sexual orientation refers to a more encompassing aspect of a person's being in the world.

The best model for understanding sexual orientation acknowledges a continuum between heterosexual and homosexual orientations, despite urgent concerns for heterosexual conformity. Indeed, only about ten percent of the population of the United States think of ourselves as exclusively heterosexual or homosexual.

Sexual orientation, like other aspects of our identity, may become more complex in our self-understanding. Some adults find, for exthat their orientation is more truly satisfied in a homosexual orientation after they initially identify as heterosexual. Some studies suggest that women's sexual orientation may be more fluid, allowing them to choose a partner based more on emotional attachment, while men's orientation usually finds expression in more fixed terms. However, even this capacity for some fluidity in sexual orientation does not mean that sexual orientation ought to be reduced to a lifestyle choice.

Rather, such occasions describe a struggle to discern the relationship that will bring the most integrity to one's identity and desire. It is also the case that for some persons who move from one location on the orientation continuum to another in their behavior, this shift may reflect a growing strength to resist the oppressive environmental effects of heterosexism and homophobia that they may also have internalized. The forces of such change will vary, but the liberative dynamics of such change cannot be overlooked. They would suggest that such change is less a "choice" than a developmental freedom to be who one is despite the oppressive forces at work against valuing one's true orientation.

The question of whether persons whose sexual orientation is predominantly or singularly gay, lesbian, or bisexual should undergo conversion therapy presumes that such sexual orientations are pathological. In 1973 the American Psychiatric Association took the action of removing homosexuality from the official manual listing mental and emotional disorders after careful research confirmed that homosexuality is not an illness, mental disorder, or emotional problem. In 1975 the American Psychological Association followed suit. Since that time both organizations have advocated against stigmatizing homosexuality and have encouraged their members to become educated about sexual orientation and to correct any biases they may bring to their practice of therapy. Both organizations have focused attention on the distortions of heterosexism and homophobia as they undermine the well-being and safety of gay and lesbian and bisexual persons.

Conversion therapy advocacy groups such as Exodus International, Transforming Ministries, and OneByOne (Presbyterian Renewal Network) presume that homosexual and bisexual orientations are a matter of dysfunctional and sinful choice and disordered desires. Such groups reduce homosexual orientation to addictive disordered sexual behavior and desire. Proponents argue that changing one's sexual orientation is difficult but possible. Conversion or change therapies vary in ologies; but their primary means involve religious instruction, group counseling, and exploration of various possible psychosocial origins for distorted desire such as absent fathers or mothers or sexual abuse. These therapies also try to help participants develop heterosexual desire. If that fails, these approaches encourage abstinence.

Sexual reorientation tries to proceed in ways similar to Alcoholics Anonymous (Homosexuality Anonymous) in that it expects ongoing self-monitoring of desires and behavior. Those who seek conversion therapies are usually persons whose religious beliefs exclude the possibility of a right relationship with God if they self-identify in a homosexual orientation. For these persons there is a remarkable motivation to align their behavior with their faith. Often they have internalized homophobia and fear that their salvation is at stake in their conversion therapy.

For a relatively small number of persons, conversion therapy seems to have contributed to their ability to develop heterosexual desires and enter into lasting marriages. There are no studies that use commonly accepted scientific means to verify results. In one study of nearly 900 persons who sought to change their homosexual orientation, roughly two percent reported success in their effort to change their orientation. A larger number reported improvement in self-esteem and other relational and spiritual indicators. While numerous studies describe anecdotal reports of harm from these conversion therapies, the absence of empirical evidence of harm has kept national clinical and medical groups such as the American Psychological Association from preventing their members from engaging in such therapies.

Thus the APA's position is complex. Because there is no empirical evidence of harm, it does not forbid its members from participating in conversion therapy. But because it does not regard homosexual orientations as a disorder, it recognizes no need for conversion therapy. The American Psychiatric Association, the American Psychological Association, the American Psychoanalytic Association, the American Medical Association, the American Academy of Child and Adolescent Psychiatry, and the National Association of Social Workers all question the efficacy and utility of "change therapies."

The church does and should have standards of its own. Theologically we do well to wonder what notion of sin underlies the urgency for conversion therapy. Daniel Day Williams described sin as the refusal to effect love in life. Indeed, throughout scripture we are enjoined to look beyond a focus on form or the letter of the law and to see[1] after those practices that better assure the flourishing of love embodied in relationships marked by authenticity, mutual respect, care, and joy. Sexuality that deepens the authenticity of our communion and joy in one another helps us to glimpse God's love and hopes for us regardless of the form that sexuality takes. The evidence gathered by clinical and medical specialists of the last forty years points not to homosexuality but to heterosexism as one of the sins that has caused the most distortion and pain.

We should not encourage gay and lesbian people to undergo conversion therapy. Rather, we do well to require of all who serve as religious leaders a commitment to honor their relationships of sexual intimacy as covenantal relationships in which authenticity, joy, mutual regard, hospitality, and love flourish.

✦

Nancy J. Ramsay, a Presbyterian minister, is Dean and Professor of Pastoral Theology and Pastoral Counseling at the Brite Divinity School at Texas Christian University in Fort Worth, TX. Before coming to Brite in 2005, she was Professor of Pastoral Theology at Louisville Presbyterian Theological Seminary and an active member of Mid-Kentucky Presbytery.

How might we respond in debates among Christians on homosexuality when told to "love the sinner but hate the sin"?

Robert C. Dykstra ✛
Princeton Theological Seminary

In most every charged discussion among Christians on homosexuality, someone will rise to insist that the church's proper response is to *love the sinner but hate the sin*. This pithy saying draws from among the most potent words in the theological lexicon – *sinner* and *sin*, *love* and *hate*. Yet seldom does it further conversation or foster new insight or accord. More often it has the effect of closing down debate, in the way of the bumper sticker that declares, "*God said it, I believe it, and that settles it.*"

The injunction to *love the sinner but hate the sin* is heard so often as to lead many people to assume that God said it – that it is found in the Bible or was spoken by Jesus. Rather, the expression, or one very much like it, was penned several hundred years later – in the fifth century – by St. Augustine, the church father and bishop of Hippo. *Cum dilectione hominum et odio vitiorum*, "with love for humankind and hatred of sins," Augustine wrote in a letter chastising a group of nuns upset with their newly-installed prioress (*Letter 211*).

The particular sin he was enjoining these women to "hate" at that point in the letter where the now-familiar injunction occurs was their own looking men directly in the eyes with desire in their hearts. In the same letter, he likewise condemns their sins of hoarding secret caches of food and clothing received from relatives or friends, that is, of not sharing all things in common in Christian community. Further, he decries their not fully covering their hair with a headdress and their desire to bathe more often than once a month.

Religious women looking men in the eyes, receiving new uncovering their hair, wanting a bath: it's no wonder that giv origins contending against activities like these, Augustine's directive to *love the sinner but hate the sin* continues to be conscripted, however unwittingly, in attempts by some in the church to keep sexuality in check today. Yet even they would notice that somehow the church's collective wisdom concerning sinners and sin has changed over time.

Certainly Christians today would affirm the importance of paying attention to sinners and to sin in their lives, relationships, and churches. We would do well to love sinners, including ourselves, and to hate sin, in which we all persist. In a similar way, most of us look back with gratitude or relief to moments in our own lives when a friend or mentor was willing to take the risk of confronting, challenging, or correcting us when we may have been losing our way. We therefore have reason to assume that many, even most, contemporary Christians would be inclined to agree with Augustine, at some basic level, on the need to love the sinner and hate the sin.

On another level, the vast majority of Christians today would take exception to at least some of what Augustine reckons in his letter as sin. The circumstances and nature of what constitutes a particular sin – the broadest sense as sexuality – appear to have changed considerably since the time of his letter. We would see in a very different light issues concerning the number of baths allotted to nuns or, more tellingly, what we might understand as their struggle to appropriate their physical bodies and sexuality into their religious vocation. This gives us pause as we try to sort out and fill in the blanks of *sinner* and *sin* in our own current conversations around sexuality. How confident are we of getting our *loving* and *hating* just right? Will we know when we have loved or hated enough?

In *Heterosexism: An Ethical Challenge* (1993), Patricia Beattie Jung and Ralph F. Smith point out that while some Christians see homosexuality as the vilest example of *sin* or *depravity*, others see it less severely, as an *affliction* akin to alcoholism, with abstinence the only sufficient response. The authors go on to note that still other Christians view homosexuality simply as a *difference*, one of countless signs of the diversity of God's creation, more like being left-handed. Smith and Jung recognize that our sexuality touches the depths of our mystery as persons much re than does being right- or left-handed. But they observe that in terms systemic qualities of a world organized around the norm of hetero the analogy to left-handedness proves apt: "[W]e clearly world in favor of right-handed people. We only recently stopped advocating efforts to reorient people. We have gravely distorted our understanding of left-handedness by false myths for centuries" (see pp. 21-31).

Those who press for the full participation of gay, lesbian, bisexual, and transgendered Christians in the life of the church may find themselves *agreeing* with their critics on the value of loving sinners and hating sin. They nonetheless *disagree* with them on who or what in a specific case are sinners or sins. They remain skeptical, at a time when sexuality is viewed by many to be inseparable from who they are as persons, of anyone's faring well in actual efforts in this regard to distinguish *sinner* from *sin*.

Instead, at the point in conversations on sexuality when someone announces that one must love the sinners but hate the sin, the purported "sinners" in this instance, no doubt like the recipients of Augustine's letter, experience themselves not only as unloved but unheard. They sense that the discussion is effectively declared closed.

To acknowledge a change in perspective on what specifically comprises sin from Augustine's time to our own is not to say that there are no longer any moral truths or that there is no such thing as sexual sin. Neither does it mean that those who favor the full inclusion of gay, lesbian, bisexual, and transgendered Christians reject the principle of loving sinners and hating sin. It is instead to suggest that we as individuals, and the church as a collective body, would be wise to exercise great discretion and modesty in our claims to know, for every time, place, and circumstance, just who is and is not a sinner or precisely what is and is not a sin. When we are told, or tell others, to love the sinner but hate the sin, it would prove worthwhile to recall Jesus' own injunction to remove the log from one's own eye before attempting to take the speck from a neighbor's (Luke 6:42b). Honest self-scrutiny may be our last, best hope for a reconciling vision. ✤

Robert C. Dykstra is a Presbyterian minister and associate professor of pastoral theology at Princeton Theological Seminary. His most recent book is **Losers, Loners and Rebels: The Spiritual Struggles of Boys.**

Would inclusivity alienate our global partner churches?

M. Thomas Thangaraj ✝
Candler School of Theology and
Bishop Stephen Neill Study and Research Center

If the Presbyterian Church (USA) decides to recognize the Christian discipleship of gay and lesbian persons and offer them ordination to the ministry of the church, will it affect their ecumenical relations with their partner churches all over the world, especially the ones in the so-called Third World? I want to address this question as an individual Presbyter of the Church of South India (CSI). (I am *not* offering here any official position of the CSI). CSI came into existence in 1947 as an organic union of Anglican, British Methodist, Presbyterian, and Congregationalist churches in South India. Since then, CSI has maintained a healthy partnership with churches connected to all the four denominational traditions, including the PC(USA). CSI values greatly its relation with those churches.

How would the people in the Church of South India react to the inclusivity of the PC(USA)? Given the spiritual climate of our congregations, one may guess three kinds of reaction. A majority of members of the Church of South India may have a knee-jerk reaction to your desire to be inclusive in matters of sexual orientation. They would see your inclusivity as something contrary to the teachings of the Bible and the church. The knowledge of the Bible has been one of our priorities in the congregations in South India, especially in Tirunelveli diocese that I belong to. Many read the Bible daily and ~arry a copy of the Bible wherever they go. On every Sunday children ^morize the biblical verse assigned for that Sunday and recite it ^ the congregation during worship. Therefore, our people are ~iliar with the biblical texts that seem to prohibit homosexual relations. On the basis of those texts many would find themselves strongly condemning any attempt to be inclusive.

There are others in our churches who may be troubled by the controversy regarding sexual orientation for a very different reason. They would argue that this controversy is a distraction from what we are really called to do. The economically poor are right in our midst, and their needs are so great that we simply cannot afford to be distracted into considering matters of sexual orientation. "When people are dying of starvation and malnutrition on our streets, both in the USA and in India, can anyone possibly care about what people do in their bedrooms?" This is the kind of question they would raise. The question of inclusivity is a luxury that well-fed, well-clothed, and well-cared-for Christians can afford to have. If one takes seriously the mandate given by Jesus during his preaching in his home town Nazareth, we should be out there working for the liberation of people who suffer because of poverty, war, and oppression.

There is a small minority of people who recognize the ambiguity surrounding the biblical teaching on sexual orientation and wish to remain open on the issue. Such people want to listen more to the arguments on both sides before they make up their minds. To be inclusive, for them, is a gospel mandate, and therefore they cannot alienate a whole group of persons simply on the basis of a few selected texts from the Bible. They are also aware that homosexuality is a fact before it becomes an act – that is, it is a mode of being and not simply a way of acting. The stance against slavery and the ordination of women into the ministry of the church are instances where the church recognized the culturally conditioned nature of biblical teachings and moved away from merely depending on isolated texts. In a similar vein, perhaps the church should reinterpret the texts regarding sexual orientation taking into account the contemporary discipleship of gay and lesbian Christians.

It is clear that Christians in CSI – let alone Christians across the global South – do not all have the same kind of reaction to the issue of inclusivity. The question that we are addressing here makes an implicit assumption that the partner churches have a single monolithic view regarding sexual orientation and therefore that the decision to be inclusive will alienate the partner churches. It is important to note that Christians in different parts of the world take a variety of positions when it comes to the question of inclusivity.

Much more important in this discussion is how we view ecumenical relations. Whether the partner churches will be alienated or not is dependent on our understanding of ecumenism. We, in South India, have learnt in our own history of church union that unity is not the same as uniformity. The four denominational traditions that came together to form the Church of South India were intentional in allowing the individual traditions to thrive within the united church. Anyone who travels to the various congregations of CSI will immediately notice the rich variety of practices, worship patterns, theological stances, and church governance within the CSI. If uniformity is the goal of unity, then CSI is *not* a united church at all.

But our vision of unity makes room for difference. A decision of the PC(USA) to ordain gays and lesbians, therefore, should not alienate the CSI, because we know that we can remain united without being uniform in our expressions of Christian discipleship. Our contexts are different and therefore our expressions of Christian obedience will also be different. If the task of each church is to "read" its context carefully and prayerfully, and in the name of gospel of Christ find ways to offer love and care to all those who are alienated and oppressed in that particular context, then your decision cannot and should not affect our ecumenical relations negatively. We are together in Christ with a variety of gifts, concerns, and patterns of discipleship.

There is an irony behind the question we are addressing. Do the churches in the West really care about the opinion of churches in the Third World when it comes to matters of theology, doctrine, and Christian practice? Are the theological and ministerial resources of the partner churches in the Third World readily and enthusiastically consulted in the seminaries and divinity schools in the First World? Or is it the case that some Christians in the West want to enlist the support of those in the Third World simply because it promotes their own theological agenda? A further irony is that many of the Third World churches are still so dependent on the economic resources of the churches in the West that they choose not to be alienated even when decisions are made without any reference to them.

In all these considerations, one thing is clear to me. Our call, wherever we are, is to bear witness to the all-embracing love of God revealed in the face of Jesus the Christ. Such witness demands that we wrestle with the needs of our context and discover our particular contextual obedience to the gospel. In the Holy Spirit we are given the freedom of the children of God to choose those forms of obedience that fulfill the church's mission in our own context today. It is this freedom that unites us as one family of faith. ✛

Dr. M. Thomas Thangaraj is a Presbyter of the Church of South India. He currently splits his time between serving as Professor of World Christianity at Candler School of Theology at Emory University during the spring and as Director of the Bishop Stephen Neill Study and Research Centre at Tirunelveli, South India during the fall.

What could bring a person to change his or her mind about sexuality and ordination? What happened in your case?

Jack Rogers ✢
San Francisco Theological Seminary

In 1993, a gay man, who had earlier been elected a deacon, asked Pasadena Presbyterian Church to consider becoming a More Light Church (i.e. a congregation willing to ordain lesbian, gay, bisexual, and transgender people – LGBT). My wife Sharon and I worship at Pasadena Presbyterian Church, and I reluctantly agreed to serve on a task force charged with creating an educational program that would inform the whole congregation about the theological, social, and scientific issues involved in such a decision.

I had never before really studied homosexuality. I opposed ordination of LGBT people reflexively – it was just what I thought Christians were supposed to do. Serving on the task force challenged me to apply my Reformed theology and evangelical method of biblical interpretation to the issue of homosexuality for the first time.

I had a sabbatical coming and decided to research how the Presbyterian Church had changed its mind on other moral issues: slavery and segregation, the subordination of women to men, and divorce and remarriage. In each case the church initially selected isolated proof-texts to support a general societal prejudice. Then, over time, we learned to interpret Scripture through the lens of Jesus' life and ministry. In that way we recognized the full humanity of people and our responsibility to support equal rights for all.

Studying the Biblical texts further, I learned that, for most people, there are, at most, eight passages that are purported to discuss homosexuality. None of them are about Jesus, nor do they include any of his words. In fact, many responsible scholars on both sides of the homosexuality debate have concluded that properly understood, seven of the eight passages have nothing to do with homosexuality as we know it today. That leaves some of those who oppose equal rights for people who are LGBT relying on one text, Romans 1. So I undertook a more thorough study of Romans 1-3.

It seems clear to me that the Gospel Paul is proclaiming in Romans focuses not on the issue of sexuality but on the universality of sin, and on the free grace of salvation through Jesus Christ. That is the essence of the Christian message. In Romans 1:18-32, Paul is writing about idolatry – worshipping, giving our ultimate allegiance, to anything in the creation instead of God, the Creator. Paul's point in Romans 1 is that we are all sinners.

Then, in chapter 3, Paul articulates the central idea of our Reformed theology – we are saved, not by our own acts, but by God's grace, "as a gift, through the redemption that is in Christ Jesus" (Romans 3: 23-24). To turn Romans 1 into a law, condemning, not the pervasive idolatry to which every one of us is susceptible, but rather the sexual expression of one group of people, seems to me to misrepresent Paul's point.

How then does Romans 1 become the central passage for those who oppose equal rights for people who are LGBT? Many of those who share the general cultural bias against people who are LGBT import a variety of theories, irrelevant to Paul's point, in order to interpret Romans 1 as an anti-homosexual text. The most egregious example of this is the book by Robert Gagnon, *The Bible and Homosexual Practice: Texts and Hermeneutics* (2000). The irony is that for Gagnon, one really doesn't need the Bible, because, according to him, everything it says about homosexuality comes initially from th observation of nature.

Gagnon says what many people who are heterosexual believe: "Acceptance of biblical revelation is thus not a prerequisite for rejecting the legitimacy of same-sex intercourse" (488). Behind all of the ancient sources, including the biblical ones, for Gagnon, was "the simple recognition of a 'fittedness' of the sex organs, male to female" (364). He goes on to say that the Old Testament Holiness Code "was responding to the conviction that same-sex intercourse was fundamentally incompatible with the creation of men and women as anatomically complementary sexual beings" (157). He refers to "Paul's own reasoning, grounded in divinely-given clues in nature" (142). In each of these statements, Gagnon gives priority to nature over revelation.

Based on his observation of nature, Gagnon claims to know that people who are homosexual choose their orientation. He asserts that they are willfully idolatrous and sinful (254), and implies that they must behave like heterosexuals or be celibate in order to be saved (493 and 470). None of these theories has any basis in science or in Scripture.

In contrast to the use of non-biblical theories to oppose equal rights for people who are LGBT, the Bible contains a clear and direct analogy for our present situation. In the early days of the church, Gentiles were prohibited from becoming Christians. Jewish Christians considered Gentiles unclean by nature and polluted by idolatrous practice. But Acts 15 records the testimony of Peter and Paul that God's Holy Spirit had fallen on believing Gentiles. These Apostles accepted Gentiles into the church with no restrictions. James then read the Torah to say that God had always purposed the conversion of the Gentiles. If the early Christian church leaders could find new truth in Scripture and change their minds about something of which they were once so sure, so can we.

I had often said that I could not change my position on homosexuality unless I was convinced by Scripture. By studying the Bible in its historical and cultural context and through the lens of Jesus' redeeming life and ministry, I have now been convinced that ripture does not condemn, as such, the sexual expression of contorary Christian people who are LGBT.

My professional focus of study and teaching has been creeds ions, especially those in the Presbyterian *Book of*

Confessions. There is nothing in the authentic texts of that collection of creedal statements that forbids a loving, life-long commitment of two people to each other, whether gay or straight. The phrase, "homosexual perversion," that appears in the English translation of the Heidelberg Catechism in our *Book of Confessions* (4.087) was illegitimately inserted in 1962 by a pair of American translators who shared the general cultural bias against homosexuality – it does not appear in the original Latin or German.

The issue of granting equal rights to people who are lesbian, gay, bisexual or transgender has been a source of conflict in our denomination for 30 years. There is a biblical way to resolve the conflict in the church. Jesus said: "In everything do to others as you would have them do to you; for this is the law and the prophets" (Matt. 7:12). All we have to do is to apply the same hermeneutic, the same gracious interpretation of Scripture, to all people.

In the Reformed tradition we know that God's first word to us is grace. Our thankful response is obedience to the leading of the Holy Spirit. When we finally accept Christian people who are LGBT as full and equal members of the church – as we will – we will be wonderfully blessed. ✤

Jack Rogers, Professor of Theology Emeritus at San Francisco Theological Seminary, served as Moderator of the 213th General Assembly. He earlier taught for seventeen years at Fuller Theological Seminary. His **Presbyterian Creeds** *has taught thousands of seminarians and church officers. Dr. Rogers' tenth book, just published, is* **Jesus, the Bible, and Homosexuality: Explode the Myths, Heal the Church.**

Which side are you on? And are there more than two?

Cynthia M. Campbell ✢
McCormick Theological Seminary

In the debate about the status of gay and lesbian members of the Presbyterian Church (USA), it sometimes seems as though the only options are "for" and "against." Either one condemns homosexuality as contrary to God's will or one affirms homosexual persons and puts discussion of appropriate behavior off limits. Like most issues, this never has been as simple as "for" and "against," because in fact there are several different questions being asked at the same time ... about the nature of human sexuality as well as about what is right and wrong in sexual behavior. In this essay, I suggest that rather than two sides there is a range of responses to the issue of homosexuality, each of which is based on different theological ideas and ethical values.

At one end of the spectrum are those who see homosexual behavior as something that is always wrong. The reason most frequently given is that such behavior is contrary to nature or to the order of creation. This view holds that God created human beings male and female for the purpose of procreation. Because procreation is impossible for homosexuals, they and their relationships are "disordered" because they do not conform to God's design. The only hope for homosexual persons is to become "reordered" or restored to the proper relation to the opposite sex.

Other essays in this volume have addressed some of the problems associated with this view. Leaving aside the question of same-sex relationships, it has long been argued that although procreation is surely one important purpose for human sexuality, it is wrong to ₒduce human sexuality to reproduction. The human experience of ₁ality is also the opportunity for men and women to express val-·ch as intimacy, companionship, mutuality, fidelity and joy.

At the other end of the spectrum is a view that also begins with creation. According to this view, God created everything, and everything that God created is by definition good. As children of God, created in God's image, all persons are loved by God just as they are: male, female, gay, straight, of every ethnic or racial background, able-bodied or not. On this view, homosexuality is part of God's good creation to be celebrated without further question.

Sometimes persons who hold this view want to end the discussion at this point. That is to say, they want to set aside questions of what constitutes appropriate and inappropriate behavior. But such a position fails to recognize that all humanity and all human behavior stand not only under the gracious mercy but also under the judgment of God. Sexuality is part of God's good creation, but it is also marked by human sin in need of restoration and redemption by God's grace and subject to the ordering of God's word.

We might call these two positions "prohibition" and "celebration." Sometimes in our church's debates it sounds as if there are no other options. But these two positions do not exhaust the possibilities; they define the ends of a spectrum. Between these two poles, there are a number of other positions that can be identified. While these other views make use of the doctrine of creation, they also bring other theological considerations to bear on the issue.

One approach might be called "differentiated judgment." According to this view, the critical issue is homosexual activity. It is not who the homosexual is that is a problem; it is the behavior that is wrong. Thus, homosexual persons can be welcomed into the life of the church and even elected and ordained to office as long as they are not sexually active.

This is one way to understand the current position of the Presbyterian Church going all the way back to the first "authoritative interpretation" of the Constitution in 1978. At that time, the judgment of the church was that "avowed, practicing homosexual persons" were not eligible for office. The clear implication is that non-practicing and repentant homosexuals could be eligible. The same idea is conveyed in the phrase "chastity in singleness" found in G-6.0106b.

On the one hand, this approach seeks to recognize that all

persons are sinners in need of repentance and amendment of life. On the other hand, it can be argued that this standard assumes that all heterosexual relations between a wife and husband are right and that everything else – including all homosexual practice, whether between committed partners or not – is always wrong. But this focus on sexual behavior begs the question of whether sexuality is not something more than specific activities but also part of one's deep identity as a person. If sexuality is part of a person's identity, then this attempt to differentiate between behaviors becomes discrimination against persons.

Another approach might be called "pastoral acceptance." This view often begins from the experience of getting to know gay or lesbian persons and coming to the judgment that their sexual identity is simply part of who they are; it is "the way they are made." While this way of being may fall short of the ideal for human life, it is part of reality as we know it.

Now, the question becomes: how should the church respond to gay and lesbian persons? The response of the pastoral approach is that we should follow the model of Jesus who came to seek and save the lost, who welcomed sinners and brought hope to the broken-hearted. Church members who affirm a position of pastoral acceptance might believe that homosexual behavior is a sin, while at the same time believing that the church should welcome gay and lesbian persons and could ordain them to church office. After all, does the church ordain anyone but sinners who are less than fully repentant? Those who favor pastoral acceptance believe that the church should be for gay and lesbian persons what it is for everyone else: a community of hospitality given and received in the name of Jesus.

Yet another perspective can be called "sanctification." This view begins with acknowledgment of homosexuality as part of the way human life is and asks how Christians should live in relation to this reality. Unlike the "celebration" position, this view remembers that all Christians, of whatever sexual orientation, are sinners redeemed by the grace of God alone. As forgiven sinners, all are set free to ask: how then are we to live? The simple answer is that we are to love one another (and ourselves) as God has first loved us. Among other things, this means to take part in the ministries of the church and live in relationships (of community and family) ordered by the kind of "covenant fidelity" that we see demonstrated by God in Jesus Christ. On this view, the church would not only welcome gay and lesbian persons to membership and ministries, but also welcome and bless covenants of life-long partnership just as the church blesses and honors marriage. The church would welcome gay and lesbian Christians to ministries and faithful partnerships not so much as privileges to which they have a "right," but rather as disciplines through which, by the grace of God, sanctification occurs.

Other positions could be identified. Each of these has been stated in over-simplified terms. And other typologies of positions could and have been made. What matters is not so much the particulars of the positions, but the fact that neither a simple "for" or "against" is an adequate response to the complex set of questions involved in the issue of homosexuality. The church should continue to bring to these questions a broad range of biblical and theological ideas as we seek to discern how God is calling us to live faithfully in our day.

In our discernment, it is critically important that we recall as a church community that the question of how we as Christians understand homosexuality comes not as a "social issue" impressed upon the church from "the world." This question has come from within the church family and our own families. It is fellow believers, baptized sisters and brothers, who have come seeking to share their gifts and the fullness of their lives with Christ and the church. Perhaps it is with that reality that we had best begin. ✛

Cynthia M. Campbell is the ninth President and the Cyrus McCormick Professor of Church and Ministry at McCormick Theological Seminary in Chicago. She has also served on the faculty of Austin Presbyterian Theological Seminary and for over ten years in pastoral ministry.

What do leaders and scholars in the Black Church say about sexuality and ordination?

An Open Letter To Martin ✢
January 20, 2005

In 1963 Martin Luther King, Jr. wrote his famous "Letter from a Birmingham Jail." His words were meant for a nation that he believed could rise above its self-destructive tendencies and study racism and inequality no more. Today, much of African America — and the nation at large — is confronted with equally destructive and dehumanizing circumstances. What follows is a "Letter to Martin" that was signed by dozens of Atlanta black clergy and published in area newspapers. The letter has served as an inspiration and impetus to action for many.

Dear Martin,

Every third Monday in January history compels us to remember and reactivate your legacy. How shall we honor you? And how shall we honor our deepest and truest selves? Nearly four decades have passed since you left your legacy to us, and what a momentous legacy it was. Yours was the vision of a transformed nation, a society that dared to practice the very brotherhood - and sisterhood - that it preached. In a time of tremendous social upheaval you joined the freedom-loving and justice-seeking tradition of your people, black people, and you did so at great personal cost. Using nonviolent direct action, you challenged the existing status quo. In the presence of your enemies - citizen's councils, police dogs, fire hoses, bigoted mobs, half-hearted allies, Christian racists, the FBI - you practiced an insurgent religious faith. You modeled for others he commitment to racial justice and reconciling peace. With your very 'v and life you led us into the magnificent, multi-colored and multi- . quest of justice, peace and human community. Sore distressed, we 'le, have yet to catch up to your radically inclusive vision.

For African Americans, the cumulative effect of the last forty years has been as disturbing as it is dramatic. In the new millennium, our elusive and torturous quest for freedom and equality continues. The full repercussions of radical democracy in the United States are not yet known. The vast majority of whites see themselves as non-racist and live comfortably with little or no real contact with other racial-ethnic people. Oblivious to the obvious (and sometimes the not so obvious), the connection between white privilege and black rage is discounted, resisted, denied. In our houses of worship, in the ivory tower, in the corporate boardroom, in the halls of government, in popular culture and mass media, in states red, purple and blue, in old and new formations, racism lives on. In the U.S., racial exclusion is still second nature. Racism is who we are. It is our way of life.

Sadly, many black people now have difficulty seeing their connections to other black people. We have embraced societal distinctions that separate us by age, education, gender, sexuality and class. We have forgotten the example set by so many courageous souls a generation ago. Mose Wright, Daisy Bates, Jo Ann Robinson, E.D. Dixon, Ella Baker, Bob Moses, Diane Nash, Fannie Lou Hamer, Septima Clark, John Lewis and Bayard Rustin were part of that magnificent movement of blackness that emerged, broke beyond itself, widened the circle of humanity, and called forth women, children and men of all colors and conditions.

The painful truth is that we now often violate and oppress our own in the name of religion. Always, at the center of the heart of the historic black-led struggle for freedom was the black religious experience. Black self-love was upheld as a divine imperative. Local black churches became ecumenical networks of nurture and resistance. At those beleaguered places of our most urgent human need common ground often could be sought and found in the church. But not always. Movement women like Ella Baker, organizer of the Student Non-Violent Coordinating Committee, found themselves at odds with the sexism and sexual misconduct of male ministers. An out gay man like Bayard Rustin, architect of the 1963 March on Washington, was feared as a potential threat to the advancement of the race. Today, in the imperfectly desegregated post-civil rights era, religiously inspired leadership continues to perpetuate a cruel sexual ethic, and in stark violation of their own best sacred inheritance. That black women continue to be relegated to secondary status and lesbians and gays are made to feel unwelcome, unworthy and uncomfortable in what should be the most caring, compassionate and empowering of communions is a searing indictment against all the black faithful.

Martin, like you, we are sometimes uncertain in our leadership. The dominant views on sex, sexuality and gender in the Black Church are undermining community, diminishing the faith and leading many to abandon churches out of sheer moral frustration and exhaustion. Our churches have been slow to embrace gender equality. They have largely spoken only opposition and condemnation to same gender loving people and have been unable to proclaim a sexually liberating and redemptive word. Some black churches have concluded it is in their best institutional interest to participate in "special rights" polemics against this so-called "immoral humanity." As black clergy we offer here a more hope-filled perspective.

In the spirit of Jesus of Nazareth, we the undersigned clergy extend the divine invitation of human wholeness, healing and affirmation to "whosoever" (John 3:16). In the best of the Black Church tradition we say, "Whosoever will, let her or him come." Who is included in this "whosoever?" The "whosoever" of today are the diseased and the diseased, the discomforted and the distressed, those who live on the margins of the marginalized, who are the oppressed of the oppressed, the sexually battered and the abused, the homeless and the bereft, the HIV/AIDS infected, who are the young and old, female and male, lesbian and bisexual, transgender and straight. These are they, the children of God. They are our sisters and brothers and partners and friends. They belong to all of us. And they are very much we ourselves.

As Black Christian religious leaders what more shall we do? We must help to forge a progressive agenda for the black community in which race, gender, class, age and sexuality are kept in active dialogue with one another. We must engage one another, prophetically demand more of one another, and prepare to suffer, cry, and toil with each other when it comes to matters of racial and sexual justice, economic and political empowerment, to waging peace. We must be courageous in confronting the social conditions that divide; elitism, poverty, militarism and more await our deepest response. We must continue to look to the ancestors and to Jesus, "the author and finisher of our faith." We must dedicate rselves to a world where borders can be crossed and a new consensus e found, where we call our own community beloved and celebrate people, one unique person at a time. Martin, on your day we vow to take a stand to love all black people. We vow to accept and to honor all regardless of their gender, class, age, or sexuality for we all are the children of God. The power is in our hands. This is where we must go from here.

Respectfully,

Signers (organizations for identification purposes only)

Rev. Ayanna Abi-Kyles
Candler School of Theology

Dianne Allen

Rev. Margaret Aymer, Ph.D.
Interdenominational Theological Center

Randall C. Bailey
Interdenominational Theological Center

Daniel Black (Omotosho Jojomani),
Clark Atlanta University

Rev. Edward B. Branch
Atlanta University Center

Rev. Michael Joseph Brown
Emory University

Dr. Lawrence Edward Carter, Sr.
Morehouse College

Rev. Da Vita Carter McCallister,
First Congregational Church UCC

Rev. Michelle Holmes Chaney
Emory University

William T Chaney Jr.
Chaney and Associates, LLC

Rev. Jawanza (Eric) Clark
Pan African Orthodox Christian Church

Pastor Will Coleman
Black Kabbalah Institute

Sybil Corbin, M.Div.

Rev. T. Renee Crutcher
Sankofa Ministries .

Rev. McClain Dyson
New Bethel A.M.E. Church, Lithonia, GA

Dr. Teresa Fry Brown
Candler School of Theology

Minister Ronald W Galvin, Jr.
Atlanta, Georgia

Rev. Willie F. Goodman, Jr., Th.D.
Black Pastoral Theologian

Rev. Vivian Green

Rev. Dr. Maisha I. Handy
Interdenominational Theological Center

Rev. Renee K. Harrison
Emory University, Ph.D. candidate

Dorinda Henry, MTS

David Anderson Hooker

Min. BaSean Jackson (ssc)
Ph.D Student at Emory University

Rev.Curtis Jones

Rev. Shonda R. Jones
Candler School of Theology

Emmanuel Y. Lartey, Ph.D.
Candler School of Theology

Pastor, Ghana - Interdenominational
Church, Atlanta.

Rev. Portia Wills Lee
Trinity African Baptist Church, Mableton,
GA

Stephen Lewis,
The Fund for Theological Education

Rev. Dr. Mark A. Lomax, Pastor
Interdenominational Theological Center

Herbert R. Marbury
Clark Atlanta University

Rev. Timothy McDonald, III
First Iconium Baptist Church

Rev. Veronice Miles
Greater Bethany Baptist Church

Rev. Susan C. Mitchell
Sankofa United Church of Christ

Rev. Deborah F. Mullen, Ph.D.

Reverend A. Nevell Owens

Rev. Chauncey R. Newsome
First Iconium Baptist Church

Rev. Jeanette Pinkston
Saint Philip AME Church, Atlanta

Alton B. Pollard, III, Ph.D.
Candler School of Theology

Rev. Derrick L. Rice
Sankofa United Church of Christ

Rev. Fert Richardson
Suwanee Parish United Methodist Church

Rev. Marcia Y. Riggs, Ph.D.

J. Erskine Love
Columbia Theological Seminary

Rev. Aaron Naeem Robinson

Rosetta E. Ross,
Spelman College.

Rev. Melva L. Sampson
Spelman College

Rev. Roslyn M. Satchel, Esq.
*National Center for Human Rights
Education*

Rev. Dr. Teresa E. Snorton
*st African Community Development
      oration*

Dr. Dianne Stewart
Emory University

Dr. Lewis T. Tait, Jr.
Imani Christian Center

Rev. Dr. Eugene Turner
Johnson C. Smith Theological Seminary

Rev. Lamont Anthony Wells
Lutheran Church of the Atonement

Min. Michael J. Wright

Gayraud S. Wilmore
Interdenominational Theological Center

Rev. Bridgette D. Young
Emory University

What do biblical scholars say about homosexuality and scripture?

The Whole Bible for the Whole Human Family ✛
Members of the Biblical Faculty of the Presbyterian
Seminaries Speak to the Issue of Ordination

June, 2001

Dear [General Assembly] Commissioner:

We, the undersigned, earnestly request that you will read the attached statement and consider it carefully. We are all professors of either Old Testament or New Testament. We represent over half of the faculty in Bible in our Presbyterian seminaries at the present.

We hope that the attached statement "The Whole Bible for the Whole Human Family" will assist you as you wrestle with some of the issues of this Assembly. We are greatly concerned that the Bible be heard, interpreted appropriately, and continue to guide us all in our quest for understanding, reconciliation, and justice.

As members of the church universal and as professors of Scripture in our Presbyterian seminaries, we affirm that the Bible is an indispensable means of God's communication, especially in a time when the church is urgently seeking to clarify its message and mission in the world. The question of whether gay or lesbian Christians should be ordained to the offices of deacon, elder, and minister of the Word and Sacrament arises at such a time.

We observe that this debate often revolves around six passages that refer to same-sex relationships. We would first of all caution the church against wresting these passages out of context and pressing them into service in our debate. On careful reading, these passages seem to be advocating values such as hospitality to strangers, ritual purity, or the sinfulness of all human beings before God. Before we can hear their meaning for our time, we must first understand their meaning in their own time.

Secondly, we would caution the church against any hasty conclusion that these passages present instructions for us on what we know as homosexuality today. In important sections of the Bible – the Ten Commandments, the prophets, the teaching of Jesus – this issue does not arise. Indeed the concept of homosexuality as now understood may not appear at all in the Bible. It is likely that the biblical authors never contemplated the phenomenon that we have been able to name and describe for only a little over a hundred years, a sexual orientation which is integral to the identity of a small minority of the human family.

Thirdly, we caution the church against an interpretation of the Bible that leads the church into pronouncing judgment upon a specific behavior of a whole category of persons in the human community. As the 1985 General Assembly observed in its Guidelines for the Interpretation of Scripture in Times of Controversy, "Let all interpretations be in accord with the rule of love, the twofold commandment to love God and to love our neighbor."

We would encourage the church at this time to interpret particular passages of the Bible in the light of the whole Bible, and in the recognition that Jesus Christ, the Redeemer, is the living Word of God. It is the gospel of Jesus that invites gay and lesbian brothers and sisters to full communion in the church; it is the Spirit of Jesus that calls and equips Christians for ministry; and it is the justice of Jesus that calls us to insure that those who are invited, called, and equipped are free to fulfill their ministries among us with the full recognition and support of the church.

Brian K. Blount
rinceton Seminary

Robert Brawley
McCormick Seminary

ianna W. H. Bos
uisville Seminary

Carson E. Brisson, Jr.
Union Seminary

es A. Brashler
ɔn Seminary (VA)

William P. Brown
Union Seminary (VA)

Walter Brueggemann
Columbia Seminary

John T. Carroll
Union Seminary (VA)

Marvin Chaney
San Francisco Seminary

Robert B. Coote
San Francisco Seminary

Charles B. Cousar
Columbia Seminary

Linda Day
Pittsburgh Seminary

Lewis R. Donelson
Austin Seminary

Susan R. Garrett
Louisville Seminary

Beverly Roberts Gaventa
Princeton Seminary

Frances Taylor Gench
Union Seminary (VA)

Theodore Hiebert
McCormick Seminary

Elizabeth Johnson
Columbia Seminary

Jacqueline E. Lapsley
Princeton Seminary

W. Eugene March
Louisville Seminary

Patrick D. Miller
Princeton Seminary

Cyris Hee-Suk Moon
San Francisco Seminary

Kathleen M. O'Connor
Columbia Seminary

Dennis T. Olson
Princeton Seminary

Eung Chun Park
San Francisco Seminary

Katharine Doob Sakenfeld
Princeton Seminary

Stanley P. Saunders
Columbia Seminary

Choon-Leong Seow
Princeton Seminary

Sibley Towner
Union Seminary (VA)

Patricia Kathleen Tull
Louisville Seminary

Paul W. Walaskay
Union Seminary (VA)

Antoinette Clark Wire
San Francisco Seminary

Christine Roy Yoder
Columbia Seminary

Index

"Lady Jayne, I have given my word I will not say anything about tonight. And I would never go back on my word. But you must see that I cannot just let the matter rest. You have said yourself you are not behaving as you ought."

She looked mutinous as she said, "And just what do you mean to do about it?"

He only wished he knew. For now, the best thing would be to make a strategic withdrawal so that he could regroup.

"I shall call upon you this afternoon, to take you for a drive in Hyde Park. That is when I shall tell you what action I plan to take." Once he'd decided what it would be.

"I shall be ready," she said, lifting her chin in a fashion that told him she was preparing to fight him every inch of the way. "This is it," she said, waving her hand at the frontage of an imposing mansion.

Having shown him where she lived, she ducked down a passage that led to the mews at the back. Then she turned around and stood quite still, staring up at him for a minute, with her head on one side as though trying to work him out.

"You have surprised me," she said at last. "I would never have imagined you could be so...decent."

* * *

An Escapade and an Engagement
Harlequin® Historical #1096—July 2012

Author Note

The Earl of Caxton has two granddaughters.

You may have read about Miss Aimée Peters in *Captain Corcoran's Hoyden Bride*. Having grown up in exile, Aimée was desperate to find security and put down roots. To that end, she travelled to Yorkshire to become a governess—only to find that her employer was not what she'd expected....

In *An Escapade and an Engagement* you will meet her cousin, Lady Jayne Chilcott. People think she is her grandfather's pampered darling. But she feels suffocated by the propriety of her lifestyle and longs for the kind of adventure she is sure Aimée must have had. The product of a bitterly unhappy arranged marriage, Lady Jayne vows she will only marry for love. But where is she ever going to find a man who will inspire anything more than mild contempt when her grandfather guards her so zealously that she never meets anyone new, let alone exciting?

That is until she clashes with the grim-faced Lord Ledbury, an ex-soldier who has come to London to find a suitable woman to become his bride. Lady Jayne has the right pedigree. But does he really want to get tangled up with a girl who is never happier than when up to her neck in mischief?

ANNIE BURROWS

An
Escapade
and an
Engagement

HARLEQUIN®
entertain, enrich, inspire™

Recycling programs
for this product may
not exist in your area.

ISBN-13: 978-0-373-29696-5

AN ESCAPADE AND AN ENGAGEMENT

Copyright © 2012 by Annie Burrows

Printed in U.S.A.

To Carol Townend, author of the "Wessex Weddings"—
whose hospitality is legendary, and whose insightful
and experienced advice has been of enormous help to me
in the completion of this book.

Chapter One

Lord Ledbury glared up at the ruched silk canopy of the bed he'd inherited from his brother, wide awake now, when not an hour since he'd felt so drained he was sure he could have slept for a week.

He hated this bed. He hated its soft feather mattress and the mounds of bedding that felt as though they were suffocating him. He hated the valet whom…no, that was going too far. He could not hate Jenkins for doing a job to the best of his limited ability. It was just that he was not Fred.

He could have talked to Fred as he'd undressed and prepared to go to bed. Probably managed to laugh off the more ludicrous aspects of the evening's sortie behind what felt like enemy lines—as they'd done time without number during the preceding six years of active service. No matter what deprivations they'd had to endure because of the damn fool orders some pompous ass higher up the chain of command had issued.

But he'd been obliged to leave Fred behind when he'd taken up residence in Lavenham House. And though he'd never experienced such luxury, never had so many servants in his life since coming to live here, he'd never felt so alone or so ill at ease. A spy must feel like this, he reflected bitterly, kicking off his covers and turning onto his side to glare at the fire glowing smugly in its ornate marble fireplace. Without benefit of his uniform to vouch for his identity. Cut off from his regiment, his comrades. Entrusted with orders that he alone could carry out.

Dammit, he was more likely to get some sleep outside on a park bench wrapped up in his old army greatcoat than he was in here, suffocated by all the trappings deemed necessary to coddle a lord. When he thought of all the times he'd slept out of doors, with conditions so harsh he would wake in the morning with his blanket frozen to the ground...

He sat bolt upright. At the end of this street there was a small park, with benches dotted about in it. And in spite of Jenkins' ill-concealed disgust, his army greatcoat still hung in the armoire....

He just had to get out of Mortimer's house for a while, and away from Mortimer's servants, even if there was no escaping the obligations Mortimer's sudden and unexpected death had foisted upon him.

Muttering imprecations under his breath, he got out of bed and pulled on a random selection of clothing by guesswork in the flickering shadows cast by the fire, making sure only of his army greatcoat. He sighed as he shrugged himself into it, feeling as though he was being taken into the arms of a friend. As though there was a part of him that was still Major Cathcart, even though everyone was suddenly calling him Lord Ledbury now.

He rubbed his hand briskly over the crown of his head to tidy his bed-rumpled light brown hair in the way that had become second nature to him on campaign as he left the bedroom, wishing it was as easy to smooth down his ragged temper.

His mouth flattened into a grim line as he limped down the stairs. He had not quite recovered from the interview with the Earl of Lavenham, that was half the trouble. He'd been braced to hear something unpleasant. Nothing less than a dire emergency would have induced his grandfather to summon him to Courtlands. And what he'd learned about his younger brother during that interview had certainly been a shock. But what still left him with a nasty taste in his mouth had been the confirmation that if only Charlie had been the sort who could have concealed his preference for men *he* might have returned to his regiment, been killed or maimed, and nobody would have given a damn.

The night porter leaped to his feet as he saw his master approach. He opened his mouth, as though about to say something, but one look was all it took to have the man hand him his cane, open the door for him and scuttle back to his chair without uttering whatever objection he had been about to raise.

Lord Ledbury heaved a sigh of relief as he stepped outside. He'd done all his grandfather had asked of him. Made all the sacrifices demanded. He'd resigned his commission, moved out of his lodgings and into Lavenham House. Bought the clothes, and begun to play the part, but...

He breathed in deeply as he made for the square. The night air was redolent of...soot, actually. And damp. With a hint of something indefinably green about it that could not be mistaken for anything other than the smell of springtime in England. It took him less time than he would have thought before he was pushing open the gate, considering the state of his leg. For which small mercy he was truly thankful. He might be able to find a measure of peace if he could only stretch out on one of the benches and look up at the night sky through a tracery of leaves.

Thanks to Mortimer's ignominious demise, he'd become a lord. And, as the last hope of the Cathcarts, he was going to have to find a bride. A bride worthy of becoming the next Countess of Lavenham. To that end, tonight he'd attended his first ball since he'd become Lord Ledbury.

He gave an involuntary shudder as his mind flashed back to the glittering ballroom, the eager faces of the matchmaking mamas who'd clustered round him, the horrible feeling of being under siege…

And, goddammit—but wouldn't you know it with the way his evening had been going—when he finally reached the bench on which he'd set his heart he found it already occupied.

By a strapping redcoat and a somewhat-reluctant female, to judge by the way she was beating at his broad shoulders with her clenched fists while he carried on kissing her.

He acted without thinking.

'Take your hands off her!' His voice, honed through years of bellowing orders across parade grounds, made them both jump.

The soldier turned to scowl at Lord Ledbury over his shoulder.

'This is none of your business,' he snarled.

'I am making it my business,' he retorted. 'This sort of behaviour is completely unacc—'

He broke off, stunned to silence when he caught sight of the female who was still struggling to disentangle herself from the redcoat's determined grasp. It was Lady Jayne Chilcott. He'd seen her earlier, at the ball he'd attended, and immediately asked his host who she was. For she was, without a doubt, the prettiest creature he'd ever clapped eyes on.

Berry, the former schoolfriend whose sister's come-out ball it was, had pulled a face.

'That,' he'd said scathingly, 'is Lady Jayne Chilcott—otherwise known as Chilblain Jayne. Lucy is in raptures to have her attend tonight, since she normally only goes to the most select gatherings. Her grandfather is the Earl of Caxton. Pretty high in the instep himself—and you will only have to observe her behaviour for half an hour to see why she's earned the soubriquet.'

He'd promptly changed his mind about asking for an introduction, taken a seat and Berry's advice. He'd watched her. It had not taken quite half an hour to agree that she *did* look as though she was regretting coming to a place that was frequented by people so far beneath her in station.

At least that was what he had assumed then. But now, as he studied the insignia that proclaimed the lowly rank of the soldier who'd been kissing her so passionately, he revised his opinion. He had thought, from her refusal to dance with any of the men who'd been falling over themselves to break through her icy reserve, that she was as cold and proud as Berry had warned him she was.

But she did not look proud now. She looked like a rather young girl torn between fright and embarrassment at the compromising nature of the situation he'd just interrupted.

It was in stark contrast to the anger blazing from her would-be seducer's eyes.

'I repeat,' said Lord Ledbury firmly, 'take your hands off Lady Jayne this instant.'

It was more than just his innate sense of chivalry that made him so determined to rescue Lady Jayne. In spite of what Berry had said, and the derisive way he'd said it, he hadn't been able to prevent that initial interest steadily growing into a sense of something resembling comradeship as the awful evening had dragged on.

As she had doggedly rebuffed all overtures with chilling finality, he'd found some comfort in knowing he wasn't the only person there battling under siege conditions. After a while he'd even begun to derive a perverse sort of amusement from the way her courtiers grovelled at her feet on one side of the dance floor, while he sat in state on the other, repelling all invaders with equal determination. Though at least the men who flocked around her had some excuse. He knew the matchmaking mamas who clamoured round *him* were interested only in his newly acquired wealth and title.

'The state of your face won't matter,' his grandfather had predicted, running his eyes over the furrow on his forehad that a stray bullet had ploughed across when he'd been only a lieutenant. 'Not now that you are such a catch. Wealthy in your own right and heir to an earldom. All you will have to do is turn up and sit on the sidelines and they will come to you. You mark my words.'

The mere thought of having to fend off flocks of avaricious harpies had made entering that ballroom one of the hardest things he'd ever done. Particularly with his grandfather's words still ringing in his ears. Knowing that none of them would have given him a second glance before Mortimer had died and catapulted him into the peerage tied him up into knots inside. Yes, he'd gone there to start looking for a wife. But did they have to make it so obvious they all wanted his rank, his position?

And not him?

But Lady Jayne would have attracted as many suitors were she a penniless nobody as she was so stunningly beautiful. He could not remember ever having seen a more perfect face. She had a flawless complexion, a little rosebud of a mouth and a profusion of golden ringlets that tumbled round her gently rounded shoulders. He had not been able to discern what colour her eyes were, but in a perfect world they would be cornflower-blue.

She'd shot him one cool, assessing look when he'd first come in and sat down. Later, when they'd both been surrounded by a crowd of toadeaters, their eyes had actually met, and for one instant he'd felt sure she was telling him she hated the attention, the flattery, the insincerity of it all, just as much as he did.

Not long after that, she'd risen to her feet and stalked from the room.

Once she'd gone, and he'd been the only prize catch left in the ballroom, he'd felt as though he had a target painted in the middle of his chest. Whilst she, too, had been repulsing unwelcome advances, he'd felt—no matter how erroneously—as if he had at least one ally in the place.

Once she'd gone, all the reasons why he didn't want to be there had become so overwhelming he had no longer been able to bear it. The heat of that stuffy room had made his head feel muzzy. The tension that hadn't left him since he'd taken the decision to do his duty by his family had become too great for a body so weakened by prolonged illness. He'd ached all over. He'd scarce known how to keep a civil tongue in his head. He'd had to leave, to get out of there and head home.

Only it hadn't been his home he had gone back to. It was still Mortimer's house. Another jarring reminder that he wasn't living his own life any more.

It would do him good, he suddenly realized, to knock somebody down. He had been spoiling for a fight ever since he'd walked away from his grandfather, bristling with the determination to prove once and for all that he was a better man than Mortimer and Charlie put together.

'Get up,' he snarled, advancing on the redcoat, who still had his arms round Lady Jayne. Mortimer and Charlie were both beyond his reach, one being dead and the other in Paris. And a man could not come to blows with his own grandfather, no matter what the provocation.

But this redcoat was just about his own height. And though he was younger, and probably fitter, the lad had not been tempered into fighting steel in the heat of battle.

The man got to his feet. Slowly.

'You are a disgrace to your uniform,' he said, angered still further by his slovenly posture when anyone under *his* command would have known to snap to full attention when he'd used that particular tone of voice. 'I would derive great personal satisfaction in seeing you brought up on a charge for this night's work. No officer should force his attentions upon an unwilling female.

If you were under my command you would be lucky to escape with a flogging.'

But before he had a chance to add that he would give the man a chance to settle the matter between them with their fists, Lady Jayne leaped to her feet and interposed her own body between him and the soldier, crying out, 'Oh, no! You could not be so cruel!'

'Cruel?' He was stunned by her reaction. 'You think it is cruel to rescue you from a situation that is plainly causing you distress?'

He steadfastly ignored the little voice that reminded him that he had been spoiling for a fight for ages. That this redcoat was just in the way when he happened to be in need of someone upon whom to vent his frustration. That if he had come across a young officer in the throes of a passionate clinch with a female as pretty as this one in Portugal he would have winked at the man, wished him luck and been on his way.

Ah, but this was no sloe-eyed señorita, nor the willing wife of a local grandee, he argued back. This was a young English lady, and she had not appeared willing. On the contrary, she'd been struggling with the lout. She'd looked frightened.

'I admit, I was a little taken aback by Harry's ardour,' said Lady Jayne. 'For he has never really kissed me like that before. But mostly I was afraid somebody might come by and discover us.'

'Do you really expect me to believe you were only trying to fight him off because you feared discovery?'

Though now he came to think of it she must have come here of her own free will, even if she *had* taken fright at the last minute.

'Yes!' she cried, lifting her chin to glare at him defiantly. 'Not that I expect a man like *you* to understand,' she said with contempt. 'But since my grandfather has forbidden Harry to approach me we *can* only meet in secret.'

He had not thought he could get any angrier. But her words were so inflammatory. What did she mean, *a man like you?* Why could she not just express her gratitude that he was here to rescue her? And, most of all, why wouldn't she get out of the way so he could just lay into this sneaking, slovenly excuse for a soldier?

'Did it never occur to you that your grandfather might have your best interests at heart? That it would be better to stay away from him?'

Lady Jayne was a great heiress. Her grandfather, so Berry had informed him, had no direct male heir, and it was common knowledge that he intended to bequeath to her the bulk of his fortune. Some penniless nobody was obviously not a suitable partner for a girl who would inherit so much. All this Harry had to recommend him, by the looks of it, was a handsome face, a pair of broad shoulders—and a ruthless streak.

'So you mean to betray us?' she said frostily.

Harry moved to stand beside her. He took her hand in his and raised it to his chest, where he pressed it to his heart.

'This is not the end. I shall not let it be. I swore that I would not let anything part us and I meant it. I still mean it.'

'Oh, Harry,' she said, turning to him with a woebegone face. 'I shall never forgive myself if he has you flogged.' She shot a glance of loathing in Lord Ledbury's direction. 'I knew I should never have agreed to this meeting.'

And as they stood there, gazing soulfully into each other's eyes, Lord Ledbury felt his irrational spurt of anger drain away.

If she was in love with this man, no matter what his own opinion of him was, no wonder she had behaved the way she had done in that ballroom earlier. Lord, he knew just how she must have felt. Had not his own grandfather ripped him from all that he knew, all that he loved, and set his feet on another path—one that he would never willingly have trod?

'Oh, for heaven's sake!' he snapped, annoyed that he was now obliged to continue in the role of upholder of propriety or he was going to look a complete fool. Even though half of him wished he could walk away and leave them to it. 'Stop acting like some heroine out of a bad melodrama and call your maid over. It is time you went home.'

She made no such move—only hung her head, looking shamefaced.

'Oh, Lord. Never say you came out without her?'

She could not even raise her eyes to meet his when she nodded.

This was getting worse and worse. He could not in all conscience leave her alone with a man who had no scruples about enticing a trusting young woman to meet him in secret, at dawn, without even the benefit of a maid to keep things within spitting distance of propriety.

'I suppose I shall be obliged to escort you home, then,' he snapped. 'And we'll have to hope nobody catches the pair of us—else *we* shall be the ones embroiled in scandal.' Which would completely ruin his plans.

He'd decided that since marrying was his inescapable destiny he would jolly well find a wife who would be such a superlative countess that generations to come would speak of her in awe. He wasn't necessarily going to find her in Almack's. He'd made a point of launching his campaign in the house of a man of little wealth, but sterling character, to demonstrate that attaching a woman of high rank was not his primary objective. He wanted the woman he married to have a certain...*something* that everyone would recognise.

Even him, when he came across it.

There was no way he was going to live down to his family's low expectations by tumbling into a match with a girl he scarcely knew in a way that reeked of suppressed scandal.

'Well, what are you waiting for, man?' He turned the full force of his frustration on the hapless young soldier. 'Get back to your barracks before I think better of covering for the pair of you. And pray that your absence has not been discovered.'

They both turned to him, faces alight with hope.

'You mean you have changed your mind?'

'I can still change it back if you don't remove yourself from the vicinity, double-quick,' he growled at the soldier. 'But first your name and rank.'

'Thank you, sir,' he said. 'Lieutenant Kendell, sir.' Then, pausing only to press one last kiss upon Lady Jayne's hand, Harry made a run for it.

Chapter Two

Lady Jayne gazed up at him, a perplexed frown creasing her brow.

'Why did you let him go?'

He looked steadily back at her, wondering why she wasn't asking a more pertinent question. Such as, how could Harry have just abandoned her without so much as asking his name? He could have been one of the most notorious seducers of womankind for all he knew.

'I can always report him later, if you like,' he replied scathingly. It was what he ought to do. He eyed the object of Lady Jayne's affection with disdain as he scuttled away into the shadows. It was hard to believe a man could behave so dishonourably towards a woman with whom he was genuinely in love.

'No, no! Please don't!' She seized his arm. 'It is all my fault. I know it was very wrong of us to meet in secret, but he loves me so very much…' Her little fingers kneaded at his sleeve as she plunged on. 'And I know I should not have come here without bringing my maid. But you see the doors are all locked tight at night, and

I could hardly expect Josie to climb out of a window,
could I?'

'You climbed out of a window?' A sudden foreboding gripped him. 'How do you plan to get back in?' If
he was going to have to knock upon her front door to
return her to her guardians at this hour in the morning,
the fat would be in the fire and no mistake.

'Oh, the same way, of course. But never mind that. It
is Josie that I am worried about. She did try to talk me
out of coming. I promise you she did. But she is only a
servant, after all. She has to do what I tell her.'

'And you took ruthless advantage of the fact?'

'I…I suppose I did, yes.' She caught her lower lip
between her teeth. 'And now, if you tell anyone I was
out here without her, when she is under such strict orders never to let me out of her sight, they will turn her
off without a character. Which would be grossly unfair.
Oh, no…' Her eyes shimmered. 'I could not bear it if she
was to lose her job and Harry was to be cashiered out of
the regiment just because I have not behaved as I ought.'

To his astonishment, one single, enormous tear
rolled down her cheek. And it struck him that everything about her behaviour at the ball earlier had been an
act. And that Berry would never have said what he had
about her if he'd seen this side of her. She might have
appeared cold and haughty on the outside but inside she
must have been counting the minutes until she could
escape. It put him in mind of the way he'd been at that
age, at stuffy dinners put on by the regiment to persuade
local dignitaries they had nothing to fear from having them quartered nearby. All the junior officers had
been under strict orders to be on their best behaviour.
And later they'd made up for it by running out into the

backstreets and behaving completely disgracefully as an antidote to all those hours of hypocritical posturing.

Lady Jayne might have come out here without a thought for anyone but herself, but now that he'd made her see that her misdemeanour could wreak havoc on the lives of others she was genuinely contrite. Just as sorry as *he'd* been the day after that banquet when the locals hadn't seen the funny side of finding that ugly statue in the middle of the river, bedecked in pondweed, but had regarded the desecration of their patron saint as an act of sacrilege.

'Never mind all that for the moment,' he said brusquely, to mask the fact that he was sorely tempted to promise her he would never breathe a word to anyone. And that wasn't just because of her contrition. Even if she hadn't cared a rap for the repercussions, he didn't have any right to castigate anyone for climbing out of a window to escape the crushing sense of family expectation. Not when he had done more or less the same thing himself. The only difference between them was that he'd had the liberty to walk out of his own front door when he'd felt the walls of his own personal prison closing in on him.

'What we have to do now is get you home without your escapade becoming common knowledge. Where do you live?'

'Oh, then you mean to help us?'

Her whole face lit up. She gave him such a dazzling smile that, in spite of that tear on her cheek, or perhaps because of it, he suddenly saw why her Harry had been unable to resist her. Any man with red blood flowing through his veins would risk the wrath of his commanding officer for a chance to hold such a divine creature in his arms. And for a kiss... What would he not risk for one kiss? The mere thought of bending to sip at that little rosebud of a mouth sent blood flowing hotly through his veins.

He inhaled slowly, savouring the feeling of being a healthy male responding to the possibilities inherent in being alone in a dark, secluded place with a pretty female in an entirely natural way.

To say that it was a relief was putting it mildly. He had assured his grandfather that medically there was nothing to prevent him from siring the next generation of Cathcarts. But the truth was he had not felt any interest in sex since he'd had his leg smashed at Orthez. All his energy had been spent on surviving—first the field hospital and then the foul transport back to England. And then one fever after another. And even though he'd been mobile enough to think about returning to active service some weeks ago, until his grandfather's shocking revelation had put a stop to it, he'd had no inclination to resume any kind of sex life. No matter how temptingly the offers he'd received had been presented.

He couldn't resist reaching out and gently, with one thumb, wiping away the tear that had reached the point of her chin. And as he felt the warmth of her skin against his own his body reacted as if he'd received a jolt of electricity.

Her own breath hitched, as though the current of lust that had seared through him had arced across to her, too.

It had been so long since he'd held a woman in his arms, so long since he'd wanted to, that for a moment he was tempted to tell her that if he might only kiss her...

He cleared his throat and forced his eyes away from

her mouth. What he ought to do was act the gentleman and take her straight home.

At once.

But the temptation to prolong this unexpectedly erotic encounter was too great to resist. He found himself saying the first thing—well, the first polite thing— that came into his head.

'Perhaps if you could explain exactly how such a great heiress comes to be tangled up with a man of his station…'

'You sound just like my grandfather!'

Her scorn doused his ardour as effectively as a bucket of cold water. Did he really look so much older than her that she bracketed him with her grandfather? No wonder she'd flinched when he touched her. It was just as well he had not voiced his crazy idea that she could purchase his silence on the whole matter with a kiss. She probably already thought he was a brute for merely breaking up her *tête-à-tête*.

'That is all he can think about,' she grumbled, impervious to the errant thoughts skirmishing through his brain. 'Rank and fortune. He never lets me meet anyone interesting or new! He was furious when he found out I had formed an attachment to Harry. As soon as he got wind of our friendship and learned that he has no title, no prospects at all, he forbade me to so much as speak to him. And banished me to London.'

'That sounds like an eminently sensible measure,' he said, loath though he was to take the side of anyone's grandfather in the suppression of youthful desires. 'You are far too trusting for your own good. A girl with more sense would know it really is not safe to meet men in the park, on her own, at daybreak.'

Particularly not when that lush mouth of hers could have such a startling effect on a man's libido.

'It certainly is not!' She looked furious. 'Because who knows *what* kind of person one might come across…prowling around the place, spying on people…?'

'I was not spying!'

'Then what were you doing? Something underhanded, I have no doubt.'

'Not a bit of it. I simply could not sleep, that's all.' At her look of scorn, he added, 'My leg hurt like the very devil, and the damn London servants will insist on banking up the fire and keeping all the windows shut. I had to get outside and get some fresh air. Though why the d…deuce I'm telling you all this I cannot think.'

She'd slipped under his guard, somehow. Taken him by surprise with her line of questioning.

Nettled, he snapped, 'That is all beside the point. I have no need to justify my actions…'

'No. You are a man,' she said bitterly. 'Men can do whatever they want, no matter who they hurt in the process, and nobody ever calls them to account.'

'You could not be more wrong. A man with any pride at all puts duty before his natural inclination. Duty to the Crown. Duty to his family…' He pulled himself up.

She'd done it again. Got him speaking his mind instead of saying what was appropriate to the occasion. Though God only knew *what* was appropriate to say on an occasion such as this. He would swear no etiquette book contained a chapter upon proper conversation in which to engage whilst escorting a woman home from a clandestine meeting with an ineligible suitor.

He eyed her with misgiving.

She clearly thought she was in love with her handsome young officer. But she could not really know much about him if they had only managed snatched moments together, like this. He wouldn't be a bit surprised to find her feelings had more to do with the uniform than the man inside it. He'd learned from experience that a scarlet jacket could have a powerful effect upon a susceptible female.

'And speaking of family,' he said, ruthlessly returning to the most pressing issue, 'your grandfather probably thought you would get over what he hoped was just a girlish infatuation if he offered you other distractions.'

Lady Jayne glowered at him before tossing her head and setting off briskly along a path that led in the opposite direction from the one he had used to enter the square. As he caught up with her, she said, 'It was more than that. I overheard him giving Lady Penrose strict instructions to get me safely married off before the end of the Season.' She laughed bitterly. 'Though how he expects her to accomplish that when he won't allow her to take me anywhere but *ton* parties, where I mix with people I have known all my life, I have no idea. *Ooh.*' She clenched her fists. 'You cannot begin to imagine what my time in Town has been like. Boring, boring, boring! I was beginning to think I knew just what a canary bird feels like, shut up in a gilded cage, by the time Harry arrived in Town. That first note he sent me, begging me to meet him...' Her fists uncurled as she trailed off.

'He kept on sending notes to me through Josie. To let me know which events he could gain entry to. And we began to meet in the gardens, or in a quiet room of the house, while the balls were going on downstairs, with Lady Penrose never suspecting a thing!'

He frowned down at her as they crossed the road and set off down Mount Street. He wished he had not already given his word not to tell anyone about this night's assignation. The more he learned about Harry, the more untrustworthy he sounded. And if anything happened to Lady Jayne because he'd kept quiet about this night's work he would feel responsible.

Although warning her guardians of what was going on would probably not do much good anyway. From what Lady Jayne had just said, her chaperone was clearly not up to the task of guarding such a highly spirited charge.

He rubbed his hand over the crown of his head. He couldn't report her to those who ought to protect her. Should he just warn her, then, of his mounting suspicions regarding Harry's motives? No. Given her reactions to him so far, she would probably assume he was yet another overbearing male attempting to oppress her. And he rather thought she would derive as much pleasure from flouting him as she did from outwitting her grandfather and chaperone.

But she really needed somebody who knew about Harry, and the lengths she would go to in order to get her own way, to watch over her. Somebody who wouldn't be fooled by the haughty, unapproachable facade she'd employed at the ball.

'Lady Jayne, I have given my word I will not say anything about tonight. And I would never go back on my word. But you must see that I cannot just let the matter rest. You have said yourself you are not behaving as you ought.'

She looked mutinous as she said, 'And just what do you mean to do about it?'

He only wished he knew. For now, the best thing would be to make a strategic withdrawal so that he could regroup.

'I shall call upon you this afternoon, to take you for a drive in Hyde Park. That is when I shall tell you what action I plan to take.' Once he'd decided what it would be.

'I shall be ready,' she said, lifting her chin in a fashion that told him she was preparing to fight him every inch of the way. 'This is it,' she said, waving her hand at the frontage of an imposing mansion.

Having shown him where she lived, she ducked down a passage that led to the mews at the back.

Then she turned round and stood quite still, staring up at him for a minute, with her head on one side as though trying to work him out.

'You have surprised me,' she said at last. 'I would never have imagined you could be so...decent,' she finished on a shrug.

'What did you think I would be like, then?' It shouldn't have made such an impact to hear that she'd had any expectations of him at all, considering they had only glanced at each other across a ballroom.

'Oh, I don't know... At the ball you looked so...hard. All those women who threw themselves at your feet had about as much impact on you as waves dashing themselves up against a cliff. And then, when you spoke of flogging Harry, I really thought for a minute that...'

She looked abashed. 'But you are really not cruel at all, are you?'

'I have sent men to their death without giving it a second thought,' he retaliated, lest she think his leniency with her on this one occasion meant he was a soft touch.

'Ah, but you don't take delight in it. That makes all the difference.'

He was about to defend himself from the charge of not being cruel when she stole all the breath from his lungs by hitching up her skirts and tucking them into a belt at her waist.

He knew he ought not to look. But how could he do her the disservice of not appreciating such a shapely pair of legs, covered in what looked like a junior footman's breeches, especially when not a day ago the sight would not have interested him in the slightest?

He was still swallowing too hard to ask if she needed any assistance in getting back into the house undetected when she scampered over to the horse trough and clambered up onto its rim. From there she swung herself up onto the stable roof.

Darting him an impish grin as she reached for the lower branches of a gnarled old apple tree, she said, 'I don't think you are such a cross old stick as you look.'

Having fired that Parthian shot, she clambered from one bough to another with the agility of a monkey, giving him one tantalizing glimpse of a perfectly formed bottom as she leaned over to push up a sash window which had been left open an inch, before vanishing into the house.

For some minutes all he could do was stand there, rock hard and breathing heavily, feeling as though he'd been hit by some kind of energising force.

He'd begun the night seething with resentment and frustration. But now he was savouring the delicious sensation of knowing everything was in working order.

And it had not been achieved through the determined wiles of some doxy. No, in spite of everything, it had been a natural response to a society female. He chuckled. It was good to know that there was one, at least, amongst them that it would be no hardship to take to bed. He eyed the window, half wondering what would happen if he were to climb up after her and...

The window slammed shut. He took a step back into the deeper shadows close to the stable. He'd come to London to contract a respectable alliance, not get embroiled in a scandal. It was no use standing here gazing up at the window through which she'd disappeared, wondering if the branches of that apple tree would bear his weight.

But the fact that he was thinking along those lines at all was immensely cheering.

He turned and walked away with a grin on his face. Lady Jayne was what was termed a handful. Continuing an association with her was going to bring him no end of trouble. He could feel it. And yet he was not dreading their next encounter. Not by a long shot.

In fact, he couldn't remember when he'd last felt so alive.

'Lor, miss, I been that worried about you,' exclaimed Josie, leaping to her feet, dashing across the room and hauling Lady Jayne in over the windowsill. 'Thank heavens you're back safe and sound and no harm done.'

'I am sorry you have been so worried,' said Lady Jayne. 'And I promise you,' she said vehemently, turning to shut the sash firmly behind her, 'that I shall never do anything so thoughtless and reckless and selfish ever again.'

Josie, who had been with her since she was twelve years old, and therefore knew her moods well, looked at her sharply.

'What happened? Something, I can tell. Have you fallen out with your young man?'

Lady Jayne shook her head. 'No, nothing like that.'

Although, in a way, she supposed she had. Even before Lord Ledbury had come along and put an end to their encounter she had wondered if it had been a mistake to leave the house to meet Harry. The darkened windows of the houses she'd snuck past had seemed to glare at her menacingly, so that she had already been feeling uneasy by the time she'd entered the square. It was not like sneaking out at dawn for an unsupervised ride or walk around Darvill Park, her grandfather's estate in Kent. She might run into *anyone* in a public park.

'We'd best get you into your night rail and into bed before that maid of Lady Penrose's comes in with your breakfast,' said Josie, turning her round and briskly unhooking the back of her gown while she undid her breeches.

She'd already been feeling distinctly uneasy when she'd found Harry. And then, instead of just taking her hand and murmuring the sort of endearments he generally employed during their snatched meetings, he had pulled her down onto the bench next to him and hauled her into his arms.

'I cannot bear to go on like this, my darling,' he'd said in accents of despair. 'There is nothing for it. We shall have to elope.'

Before she'd had a chance to say she would never do anything of the sort, he had kissed her full on the mouth. His moustache had scoured her upper lip in a most unpleasant way, and some of the bristles had gone up her nostrils. And what with his arms crushing her ribcage, half his moustache up her nose, and his mouth clamped over hers, she had felt as though she was suffocating. It had all been a far cry from what she had expected her first kiss to be like. When eventually she permitted some man to kiss her… And that was another thing, she reflected with resentment as she stepped out of her gown and breeches. She had not given him permission. He had just pounced. And he had been so very strong and unyielding that for a moment or two she had panicked.

It was not easy, even now, to keep perfectly still while Josie untied her stay laces and she relived those horrible moments in Harry's determined embrace. How relieved she had been when Lord Ledbury had come upon the scene, looking so ferocious. Not that she would ever admit *that* to a living soul. She ducked her head guiltily so that Josie could throw her night rail over her head.

She had not felt grateful for long, though. The way he'd looked at Harry, as though he wanted to tear him limb from limb, had caused her fear to come rushing back—although its focus had no longer been upon herself.

But then he'd dismissed Harry, wiped away the one tear she had not been able to hold back, and taken her home as though there was nothing the least bit untoward about walking through the streets at daybreak with a person he'd just caught in a compromising position.

She went to the dressing-table stool and sat down heavily.

Until the viscount had talked about getting Harry

brought up on a charge it had never occurred to her
that others might have to pay any penalty for her misdemeanours. She had cheerfully flouted the rules, safe
in the knowledge that any punishment meted out to
her would be relatively mild. Lady Penrose might have
forbidden her to attend any balls for a few nights, or
curtailed her shopping expeditions. Which would have
been no punishment at all.

At the very worst she had thought she might get
sent home to Kent. Which would have felt like a victory, of sorts.

It had taken the grim-faced viscount to make her see
that there would inevitably be repercussions for others
tangled up in her affairs, too. To wake her up to the
fact that she would never have forgiven herself if Josie
had lost her job, or Harry had been cashiered out of his
regiment, on her account. Thankfully he had listened
to her pleas for leniency for Harry and Josie, and had
given his word not to speak of what he knew about her
activities tonight.

She reached up and patted Josie on the hand as her
faithful maid began to brush out her hair, separating it
into strands so that she could put it in the plaits she always wore to bed. How could she not have considered
that others might have to pay for her misdemeanours?
How could she have been so selfish?

She raised her head and regarded her reflection in
the mirror with distaste.

People were always telling her how very much she
resembled her father. They were beginning to whisper
that she was as cold and heartless as him, too, because
of the wooden expression she had taken so many years
to perfect.

But you couldn't tell what a person was really like from just looking at their face. Only think of how wrong she'd been about Lord Ledbury. Earlier tonight, when she'd noticed him at Lucy Beresford's come-out ball, she'd thought him one of the most disagreeable men she'd ever seen. He had not smiled once, though people had been falling over themselves to try and amuse him.

She'd really disliked the way he'd behaved, as though he was doing Lucy's brother an immense favour by making his first public appearance as Lord Ledbury in his home. She'd thought Lucy a complete ninny for going into raptures about him for being some kind of war hero. He looked just the sort of man to *enjoy* hacking people to bits, and there was nothing heroic about such behaviour.

But he wasn't cruel at all. He could have ruined her reputation, and Harry's career, and left Josie destitute if he was the kind of man who revelled in inflicting pain on others. But he had chosen not to.

She looked at her cool expression again and felt a little comforted. She might look like her father, but she wasn't like him—not inside, where it mattered. Was she?

She gave an involuntary shiver.

'Not long now, miss. Then we'll get you all snug and warm in your bed,' said Josie, misinterpreting the reaction.

Lady Jayne did not bother to correct her mistake. She had no intention of adding to her maid's worries by telling her what had happened. Or confiding in anybody that Lord Ledbury's very forbearance, when she knew she deserved his contempt, had made her feel as though she had behaved in as selfish a fashion as her father had ever done.

She couldn't bear to look at herself any longer. Had she really encouraged Harry to fall so hopelessly in love with her that he'd acted recklessly enough to jeopardise his whole career? In just such a way had her womanising father destroyed the women who'd been foolish enough to fall for his handsome face and surface charm.

Not that Lord Ledbury would let that happen. Not now. He was bound to prevent her from seeing Harry again. He had made it clear he disapproved of a woman of her rank having a relationship with a man who had no fortune of his own. Or at the very least a title.

At last Josie had finished her hair, and she could get into bed and pull the coverlets up comfortingly to her chin as she wriggled down into the pillows.

Though she couldn't get comfortable. How likely was it that Lord Ledbury would be able to deter Harry from contacting her again? Not even her grandfather had managed that.

She chewed on her thumbnail. She did like Harry. Quite a lot. And she had been quite cut up when her grandfather had sent her to London to put an end to the association that had started when his regiment was stationed in Kent for training. And she had been pleased to see him again.

Until he had told her that the separation had almost broken his heart.

Oh, how she hoped Lord Ledbury could persuade him to abandon his pursuit of her! Because if he couldn't she was going to have to tell him herself that she had never really loved him. She had not seen it before tonight. But now that she was looking at her behaviour through Lord Ledbury's censorious eyes she had to face the fact that a very large part of Harry's attraction had derived from the satisfaction gained in knowing that to see him was to defy her grandfather.

Oh, heavens. Lord Ledbury would be quite entitled to write her off as a shallow, thoughtless, selfish creature.

She shut her eyes and turned onto her side as Josie slid from the room and shut the door softly behind her. Her stomach flipped over. She did not want to be the kind of girl who could casually break a man's heart in a spirit of defiance. Though she had never dreamed Harry's feelings were so deeply engaged. She tried to excuse herself. She had not done it deliberately! She had thought... She frowned, looking back on her behaviour with critical eyes. She had not thought at all, she realized on a spurt of shame that seared through her so sharply she had to draw up her legs to counteract it. Harry had just turned up when she was so frustrated with her life in Town that she'd been silently screaming at the weight of the restrictions imposed on her.

Though they were not all entirely the fault of her chaperone. She herself had made a stupid vow not to dance with anyone this Season, lest they take it as a sign she might welcome their suit.

Though, she comforted herself, even before Lord Ledbury had caught them she had begun to see that, in all conscience, she could not continue to encourage Harry. It had only been a moment before he'd come upon them. The moment when Harry had urged her to elope and she'd known she could never do anything of the sort. Even before he had kissed her, and it had become so very unpleasant, she had known she would have to break it off.

That was the moment when she'd known she was not in love with Harry. Not in that deep, all-consuming way which might induce a woman to give up everything—as her aunt Aurora, so her mother had told her, had done when she had eloped with an impecunious local boy.

'Oh, Harry.' She sighed. She hoped he would get over her quickly. He should, for she was not worth the risks he had taken. Anyway, he was certainly going to have more important things to think about than her in the near future. The newspapers were full of Bonaparte's escape from Elba. Every available regiment was being posted overseas in an attempt to halt his triumphal progress through France. And what with all the excitement of travelling to foreign climes and engaging in battles, he would soon, she hoped, be able to put her out of his mind altogether.

Though she would feel guilty for toying with a man's feelings for a considerable time to come.

Shutting her eyes, she uttered a swift prayer for him to meet a nice girl of his own class, who would love him back the way he deserved to be loved.

Chapter Three

'Lord Ledbury is coming to take you for a drive today? Are you quite sure?'

Lady Penrose regarded her over the top of her lorgnettes, which she was using to peruse the pile of correspondence that had arrived that morning.

'Yes,' said Lady Jayne, crossing her fingers behind her back. 'Did I not mention it last night?'

Lady Penrose looked pensive. 'I was aware he was at the Beresfords' last night, of course. But not that you had been formally introduced. Nor that an invitation had been given. Or accepted. In fact you should not have accepted at all.' She laid her glasses down with evident irritation. 'You know it was quite wrong of you to do such a thing. The young man ought to have applied to me for the permission which I alone am in a position to give.'

Though Lady Jayne hung her head, her spirits leaped at the possibility that Lord Ledbury was not going to have it all his own way after all. In any confrontation between the hard-faced viscount and her stern duenna regarding a breach of form she would lay odds on Lady

Penrose emerging victorious. Lady Penrose was such a stickler for etiquette. It was why her grandfather had appointed this distant relative to oversee her Season.

'She won't stand any nonsense from you,' he had warned her. 'And she is astute enough to spot a fortune-hunter a mile off. Yes, Lady Penrose will get you safely married before the Season's out…'

Lady Jayne felt the sting of his rejection afresh. He had been so keen to get her off his hands. His attitude had made her even more determined to take up with Harry when he had shown up. At least Harry *liked* her.

'Although,' mused Lady Penrose, 'since he is exactly the sort of man your grandfather would wish to encourage, I am inclined to permit the outing to go ahead.'

When Lady Jayne's eyes widened in shock, her duenna explained, 'I dare say he slid into bad habits during his years on active service. I have seen this kind of thing before with younger sons who never expected to inherit. It will take him a while to adjust to polite society, no doubt. We will have to make allowances for him.'

'Will we?'

'Of course,' said Lady Penrose, looking at her as though she was an imbecile. 'He is now a most eligible *parti*. It would be foolish beyond measure to make a to-do simply because he seems to have forgotten the way things ought to be done. I shall rearrange your engagements for today accordingly.'

Lady Jayne practically gaped at Lady Penrose. Up till now she had been scornful of just about all the young men who had attempted to fix their interest with her. Not that she'd had any objection to Lady Penrose frostily sending those men about their business. For she had no intention of marrying anyone—not this Season! If her grandfather thought he could marry her off just like that then he had another think coming.

She stayed angry for the rest of the day. By the time Lord Ledbury arrived to take her for the drive he had coerced her into taking with him she was almost ready to tell him to do his worst. Except for the fact that he might know Harry's commanding officer. It would only take one word in the right quarters to ensure he paid dearly for last night's foolishness. Which reflection only made her crosser than ever. It was so unfair that *he* could get away with behaving as badly as he wished and even a high stickler like Lady Penrose would forgive him because of his rank.

And then he had the gall to turn up at her front door in a *barouche*. If she had to be seen out and about with him, could it not at least have been in something a bit more dashing—like a phaeton? Did he not know that this was the very first time Lady Penrose had permitted her to go out driving with a man in the park?

No, she fumed, climbing in, he did not know. Or care. For he was not really her suitor.

At least there was some consolation in that. She twitched her furs up to her chin and glared at the groom's back as Lord Ledbury sat down next to her. She felt him giving her a hard look, but he said nothing. And continued to say nothing all the way to the park.

As they bowled along the streets she conceded that she supposed she could see why he had chosen such a stuffy, staid form of transport. With a groom to drive there was nothing to distract him from the lecture he looked as though he was itching to give her. He'd probably only held back last night because of that single tear remorse had wrung from her. Yes—she would warrant he'd feared she would cry in earnest if he shouted at her the way he'd shouted at Harry. That pensive expression as he'd wiped that teardrop from her chin had probably been due to him imagining how dreadful it would be to have to escort a weeping female home through the darkened streets.

It also accounted for the way he was darting her assessing glances now, as though she was an unexploded bomb that might go off in any direction should he make an unwise move.

Not that he would have succeeded in making her cry if he *had* shouted at her. She had learned almost from the cradle the knack of keeping her emotions well controlled. It had started with her determination never to let her father reduce her to tears. She'd refused to give him the satisfaction!

By the time they drove through the gates of the park she had managed to compose her features into the carefully blank mask behind which she always sheltered when on the receiving end of a dressing-down.

Though there was nothing Lord Ledbury could say to her that she had not heard a thousand times before— from someone whose opinion actually mattered to her.

'You are angry with me, Lady Jayne,' he observed dispassionately. 'It appears that since we parted you have decided to regard me as your enemy.'

'How can I be anything other than angry,' she retorted, 'when you *think* you have me at your mercy?'

He sighed. Her emphasis on that word *think* confirmed his belief that she was no docile creature to meekly reform after a stern talking-to.

'Even those who have been at war a long time can become allies against a common foe. Or act within agreed limits under a flag of truce.'

'I…I don't understand.' But she was intrigued. What could he possibly be thinking to make a remark like that?

'Perhaps we have more in common than you might think. For example, you told me that you were sent to London to contract a marriage, in spite of your preferences. Well, I too have been set upon a path I would rather not have trod. And before you rehash that argument about men only ever doing what they want, no matter who they tread down in the process,' he put in quickly, when she drew a breath to give him the benefit of her opinion, 'I would advise you not to judge us all by the conduct of the males to whom you are closely related. For I assume it is their conduct which has formed your opinion of my sex?'

'I… Well, um, yes.'

It had started with her father. He had made no secret of the fact that he resented her for being the only child of his to survive past infancy, when what he wanted from his wife was an heir. If she ever inadvertently crossed his path, the way he would look at her—his eyes so icy, his lips flattening in displeasure—would chill her to the marrow. It meant that she had spent most of her childhood roaming wild about their estate in an effort to keep well out of his way. There had been one groom who had taken it upon himself to teach her to ride, but apart from him she had never met a man who'd shown her the slightest bit of concern.

Until she'd gone to live with her grandfather. And his horror on discovering that she could barely read or write, let alone know the first thing about mixing in polite society, had resulted in him going to the other extreme. He had hired a succession of tutors and governesses who invariably gave up on her, telling him that she was impossible.

The real problem was that no matter how hard she had tried to absorb all the information they'd attempted to cram into her brain, there had always been more. So that no matter how hard she'd worked, she had never managed to measure up. It had felt as though not a single day passed without her being sent to her grandfather's study to hear how far she fell short of the standards he expected from a young lady living beneath his roof.

The set of her lips as she went into a brown study put him in mind of exactly the way he felt about his own brothers. Mortimer, his father's pride and joy, had gambled and whored his way through life, only to end up breaking his neck by falling from his horse dead drunk. And Charlie, his mother's precious baby, had been packed off to France, where he was living exactly as he pleased—no doubt at enormous expense—because the laws over there were far more lenient towards men of his stamp.

'I, too,' he said with a curl to his lip, 'have male relatives who care for nothing but their own pleasure. And they have left me with the unenviable task of cleaning up the mess they've created. Though it is far from being what I would wish to do at this juncture in my life, now that I have become a viscount I have had to resign my commission and embark on a hunt for a wife.'

'That's silly. I mean, there's absolutely no need to resign your commission just because your family is putting pressure on you to marry. Plenty of officers with titles marry, and even take their wives on campaign with them. And I should have thought that our country is in particular need of every experienced officer it can get if we are to keep Bonaparte from rampaging all over Europe again.'

'That was exactly what I said to my grandfather when he insisted I sold out!'

It was extraordinary to hear her voice his own objections with almost the same vehemence as he'd felt when his grandfather had banged his fist on the desk, his face turning purple with rage as he'd bawled, 'I want you married and setting up your nursery without delay. I let your father persuade me that Mortimer needed time to make his own choice. *Hah!* See where that got me! Chased every skirt in the neighbourhood and told me to my face he was enjoying himself too much to settle down. Well, I shan't make the same mistake with you! Either get yourself to Town and pick a bride, or I shall pick one for you.'

He shot Lady Jayne a wry smile. 'But after a lengthy…discussion…' the details of which he would never reveal to a living soul '…I realized that even though, as you correctly state, England does need experienced officers, Wellington himself would agree that the preservation of an old and distinguished family is of at least equal importance as trouncing the Corsican tyrant.'

He paused, gripping the handle of his cane so hard she wondered he did not snap the head clean off.

'My grandfather is old,' he said eventually, 'and, though he won't admit it, not in the best of health. Over the last year he has suffered a series of nasty shocks.

You probably know that both my father and then my older brother suffered fatal accidents within months of each other. He has become seriously concerned about the continuation of our family line. And, as he so pithily put it, anyone can lead troops into battle, but I am the last hope of the Cathcart family.'

His stomach swooped into the same knot as it had done that day, when he'd seen his entire life's achievements brushed aside as being of no consequence. For a moment the demons that had plagued his childhood had come swarming back. The demons that had insisted he was of no intrinsic worth. How could he be, when even his own parents did their best to ignore his very existence, whilst pampering and coddling his brothers?

But then he'd remembered that, in spite of what his grandfather had said about *anyone* being able to lead troops into battle, there was a damned sight more to being an officer than he knew. Earning the men's respect, for one thing, was no sinecure. The majority of them came from the gutters, and had a natural distrust of anyone who represented authority. But they'd learned to trust him with their lives. Depended on decisions he'd made for their very survival. And, more than that, he'd maintained their morale—even when times were at their toughest.

The demons had fled, whimpering, as he'd drawn on all the self-confidence he'd acquired during the eleven years he'd served in the army. Eleven years during which he'd grown from a diffident boy into a seasoned veteran.

His grandfather had implied that his only function in life was to father the next generation. But, by God, he was going to do more than that. If he could organize a regiment, then he could damn well learn to manage the estates that were now his responsibility.

And, what was more, he would make a better job of it than either of his self-indulgent brothers could have done.

'So… You are saying that you sympathise with my plight because you know what it feels like to be pushed into marrying when you don't really want to?'

'Something like that,' he said with a hard smile, continuing, 'I certainly admire the fact that you have not allowed your head to be turned by all the flattering attention you attract. From what I observed last night, one would expect you to be hanging out for a duke, or at the very least a marquess.' That was probably what Berry had assumed when she made it obvious she was not interested in any of the men who'd tried to get her to dance. 'You have half the male population of London at your feet, and yet you have set your heart on a man with no rank and few prospects.'

She was not cold and proud at all, or she couldn't have rushed headlong into such an inappropriate relationship.

He turned towards her to make his next point, to find her looking up at him, wide-eyed, and his breath caught in his throat. Cornflower-blue. The exact shade to round off the perfection of her features.

Damnation.

He'd half hoped that he would be able to detect some flaw upon seeing her in broad daylight. She had, after all, been on the far side of the ballroom the night before. And everyone knew candlelight was particularly flattering. And then in the park it had been so dark he might well have imagined her beauty was far beyond that which really existed. But here they were, their faces mere inches away, and her utter perfection had just literally taken his breath away.

'Your Harry…Lieutenant Kendell…must be so dazzled by you,' he eventually managed to grate, 'that he has completely lost his head.'

And perhaps that really *was* the truth. Perhaps he was no fortune-hunter at all. With those big blue eyes, that glorious mane of golden curls and that utterly kissable little mouth, she was capable of ensnaring just about any man she set her sights on. If she had given the lowly lieutenant the least bit of encouragement, she might easily have enslaved him.

But she wasn't going to enslave *him*. He whipped his gaze away from her mouth to glare at a hapless matron whose own barouche happened to be passing theirs. He was not going to allow this attraction, no matter how strong, to deflect him from his primary objective. Which was to marry a paragon of some kind.

He was not only going to learn how to manage his estates to the admiration of his peers, he was going to marry a woman who would excite envy and admiration. Not a girl whose very nature meant she was bound to teeter permanently on the brink of one scandal or another.

'Um… Actually…' She faltered on the verge of confessing the truth. He had just said he admired the way she was not hanging out for a man with a grand title. It was so rarely she heard any praise for anything she did that she was loath to admit she didn't deserve even that.

Not that she *did* think people should attempt to marry for social advancement.

'I believe that people should only marry for love,' she declared.

'I might have guessed,' he said, so scathingly her temper flared up all over again.

Her own family had been quite needlessly torn apart when her aunt Aurora had eloped with a man the Earl of Caxton had decided was beneath her, socially. Her grandfather would still not permit anyone to mention her name. Which had, according to Josie, wounded her mother deeply. Yet the man with whom she had eloped had been the son of a gentleman. There had been no need to banish them both and forbid any communication between the sisters, surely?

There had always been a sort of gaping hole in the family where Aunt Aurora and her husband ought to have been round which they all had to tiptoe. And she had long since come to the conclusion that her grandfather had behaved in a perfectly ridiculous fashion. Just because his daughter had fallen in love with a man of whom he did not approve.

'If two people love each other—really love each other—then nothing should be allowed to stand in their way,' she said vehemently.

His heart sank. For he'd hoped that in the light of day she'd somehow wake up and see that Harry was not worth the risks she was taking. And then he could forget about this detour and return his full attention to the important business of scouring London Society for his bride.

But the tone of her voice revealed a determination that no amount of arguing was going to be able to shake. She left him with no alternative. He was going to have to employ a little subterfuge so that he could limit her ex-

posure to potential danger, whilst keeping close enough
to protect her should it become necessary.

'Then who am I to stand in the way of true love?'
he said, with such sarcasm she just knew she wasn't
going to like whatever he was going to say next. 'Not
that I condone your behaviour, young lady. Nor his.
Especially not his.'

Ah, that was more like it. She knew how to deal with
a man who spoke to her with just that tone of disapproval in his voice.

She lifted her chin and looked him straight in the eye.

'You have no right to criticise my behaviour.'

He quite liked it when she squared up to him, he realized, leaning back against the squabs to study her mutinous expression. When she dropped the frigid mask she
employed to deceive the rest of Society and revealed her
true self. It made him feel privileged to get a glimpse of
a facet of her nature she permitted nobody else to see.

He'd felt like this last night, too, when she'd been
pleading with him to spare her maid. She'd completely
forgotten all about acting as though she didn't care
about anything. Her eyes had glowed with a similar
fervour, and those petal-soft lips had trembled with
emotion....

It was only with a great effort that he tore his eyes
from those tantalizingly tempting lips. It made his voice
quite gruff when he said, 'Catching you in the arms of
your lover last night gives me *every* right to speak my
mind. I know what you are capable of. I know what
you are really like.'

He raised one gloved hand to silence her when she
drew breath to object.

'And I cannot, in all conscience, just allow you to

carry on as you have been doing. Dammit, if anyone else had caught the pair of you together there would have been hell to pay. I have no confidence that if I do not, personally, put a curb on your behaviour you will not carry on sneaking out to meet him in secret. And it must stop. Do you hear me?'

She nodded, her lips pressed hard together on the reflection that there was nothing so infuriating as being ordered to do something she had already decided on doing.

'Now, it will not be as bad as all that. If you do me one favour I am willing to arrange for you to see your young man, in circumstances which will compromise neither him nor you.'

'You will do *what?*' How could the man be so exasperating? She had been relying on him insisting she give Harry up completely.

'I will arrange for you two to meet. But only when I, myself, will be your chaperon.' He half turned towards her again. 'Now, look. Everyone knows I have only very recently sold out. What could be more natural than for me to be seen about with other military men? Lieutenant Kendell will be accepted into certain situations if he is with me. And I seem to be exactly the sort of man your family would encourage you to mix with. The fact that we are here, riding out together, with only my own servants to chaperon us, is proof of that. It will be quite easy for me to ensure that you may see each other whenever his duties permit. In a properly managed, decorous fashion. Not in this sneaking way in which you have so far engaged.'

She felt ready to explode. The last thing she could do was tell him he had got completely the wrong idea about her and Harry. He had already made her feel stupid and selfish. If she admitted that she had fallen into the relationship in a fit of pique with her grandfather, and was now quite keen to wriggle out of it again, she would never live it down!

She was going to have to appear to agree to his terms. Oh, Lord, and that meant that she would have to meet Harry again and tell him to his face that she did not love him. Could never marry him.

It would be painful. Very painful. But in a way would it not be a fitting punishment for the way she had led Harry on these past months?

Though she still could not understand why on earth Lord Ledbury was so keen to act as a go-between. Just when she had been relying on him to put an end to what was becoming an increasingly untenable situation, he was coming to their aid—as though he had every sympathy for what he assumed was a pair of star-crossed lovers.

'Why are you doing this?'

He took a deep breath. 'I am going to ask you to do something for me that means I shall have to take you into my confidence. I am going to trust you to keep what I am about to tell you to yourself. Just as you are trusting me to keep my mouth shut about your continuing relationship with Lieutenant Kendell.'

He was going to trust her with a secret? A great deal of her irritation with him ebbed away. Even if his words did contain that thinly veiled threat about *him* keeping quiet so long as *she* kept quiet, nobody had ever reposed any confidence in her upon any matter whatsoever. On the contrary—all her life her male relatives had been drumming it into her that she was completely useless.

'I want you to help a…a friend of mine.' He frowned. 'Perhaps it is best I go back to the beginning. You know I was wounded at Orthez last February?'

'No.' But hadn't he said something about not being able to sleep because his leg troubled him? She looked down at it. Then her eyes flicked to the cane she recalled he'd made use of when he'd limped into Lucy's ballroom the previous night.

She caught her lower lip between her teeth, feeling really ashamed of all the nasty things she'd thought about him just because he'd looked so grim-faced.

'Stupidest thing, really,' he admitted, looking a bit uncomfortable. 'My horse got shot out from under me, and instead of jumping clear I let the damn thing roll on me. Clumsy. I was pretty well out of it for a while. And then I came to in the field hospital, with Milly defending me like a tigress from surgeons whose sole idea of a cure is to amputate anything that looks the least bit untidy. So, you see, she saved my leg.'

He held up one finger as though keeping score.

'Then, eventually, I got sent back to England on a transport, while the rest of my regiment pushed across the border into France. Milly's father, who was the regimental quartermaster, gave his permission for her to come with me as my nurse, thank God, else the fever I contracted would most probably have carried me off.'

He held up another finger.

'I was weak as a kitten all through last summer. And desperately hard up. But thanks to Milly's ingenuity and Fred's skill at foraging—perhaps I should mention Fred is, or was, my batman—I slowly began to recover. And then winter came, and I took an inflammation of the lungs. It looked as though I was done for, but they both stuck with me even though by this time I could not even pay their wages…'

'But you are a wealthy man!'

'I am a wealthy man *now,*' he corrected her. 'Before Mortimer died I had to live on my pay. And what with doctors' bills and so forth…'

'But surely if you had applied to your family, they would have…?'

'I have already told you that you are not alone in being disappointed in your male relatives, Lady Jayne. I wrote on several occasions, but never received any reply.'

'How can that be? Did they not receive your letters? Do you suppose they went astray?'

'Oh, no,' he said, looking particularly grim. 'The minute my brother died the family's man of business came to inform me that I was now Viscount Ledbury— proving that they had known exactly where I was, and how I was circumstanced, all along.'

And they'd left him? Hovering between life and death? Oh, how could they?

'Would it surprise you to learn that my first reaction on hearing of my older brother's death was gratitude— for at last I had the means to reward the only two people who had shown any loyalty towards me?'

'Not one bit.'

She was only surprised that he was so determined to do his duty by a family that had neglected him so woefully. A family that, by the sound of it, cared as little for him as hers did for her. She found herself wanting to lay her hand upon his sleeve and tell him she understood all about that particular kind of pain. But that would be the very last thing he would want. She knew that for certain because the last thing *she* wanted was for anyone to discover that she was constantly repressing a keening wail of her own. *Why does nobody love me? Or even like me?*

'When I learned that I would have to move into Lavenham House and actively start looking for a wife, I set Milly up in a snug little house in Bedford Place and gave her a generous allowance. I told Fred to stay with her, though I would have preferred to have kept him on as my valet. But, you see, she has no acquaintance in London. I could not just abandon her, after all she has done for me. It is no exaggeration to say I owe her my life. And, no matter how bleak things looked, she always looked on the bright side. She kept our spirits up. It could not have been easy for her, coming to what was to her a foreign country and having to adapt to its ways. And its climate.'

And then there was the fact that when he'd told her he was going to have to leave the army, get married and take up his position in Society, she had burst into tears and told him she was in love with him. Not that he was altogether sure he believed her, but still… He hated the thought that everything he did now must be hurting the only person who had ever said they loved him.

'I worry about her,' he admitted. 'Only last week I went round to see them both and she came running down to the kitchen dressed in an outfit that made her look…tawdry. When she told me how much she'd laid out for the gown I could not believe she'd spent so much and ended up looking so cheap. To be frank, she desperately needs guidance. From a woman of good taste.'

His eyes skimmed her outfit. She was wearing a carriage dress of deep blue, a jaunty little bonnet that framed the natural beauty of her face and chinchilla furs about her shoulders to shield her from the breeze, which was quite brisk that day.

'I know it will involve a great personal sacrifice for you to spend time with a woman of Milly's class, but I cannot think of anyone else I would rather she emulate. I cannot imagine you ever choosing anything that did not become you.'

He thought she was a woman of good taste? That was two compliments he had paid her within the space of a few minutes. Two more than she'd ever had in her life, apart from on her looks—which did not count since she hated the fact she resembled her father so closely.

'I promised her father I would take good care of her, but I find it is not enough to just give her a house and an allowance. I am afraid if I do not find some way to restrain her she will end up becoming…easy prey to men who have no scruples. It was while my valet was shaving me this morning that I thought of you.'

It had suddenly struck him that setting Lady Jayne a task would make her feel as though he was making her pay for allowing her to see Harry—rather than let her suspect he felt compelled to keep an eye on her. Or, more specifically, Kendell.

And she had complained of feeling bored. She would enjoy the sensation of having a little adventure. And this time he could ensure the adventure was harmless.

'I realized that you would be the perfect person to teach Milly a little about genteel behaviour and style. For you are not so high in the instep that you would look down your nose at Milly and make her feel uncomfortable.'

She'd given her heart to a low-ranking, impoverished

soldier, hadn't she? And she had no qualms about engaging in a spot of deception when it suited her purposes.

'And I cannot do the thing myself, much as I would wish it, because—well, you must see how it is. Were I still just Major Cathcart nobody would pay any attention. But now I am Lord Ledbury. If I were to escort her to a modiste everyone would think she is my mistress.'

Worst of all, if he relaxed the stance he had taken towards her Milly herself might start to think she was making some headway with him. And he could not encourage her to think she meant any more to him than—well, than Fred did. They had all become very close, living as they had done this past year. They'd become more like friends than master and servants. But you couldn't be just friends with a woman. Not, at any rate, a woman who said she was in love with you.

'She…she isn't your mistress?'

'If she was, I would be the one to take her shopping, wouldn't I?'

'Oh,' she replied, a little perplexed. It sounded so very odd for a man to go to such lengths to see to a woman's welfare. Not to let anyone think she *was* his mistress, which was the natural conclusion to draw. Unless… Suddenly his reference to them having more in common than she might guess, his interrogation of her opinion of marriages between persons of unequal rank, and the way he'd sung Milly's praises all began to make sense.

Lord Ledbury was in love! With a girl of lowly station. No wonder he had looked so kindly on her own situation. No wonder he had jumped to all the wrong conclusions, too. His head must be so full of doomed love affairs between persons of different ranks that he could see them everywhere.

'Say no more,' she said, gently laying her hand upon his arm. Her heart went out to him. No wonder he looked rather cross most of the time. He was the living image of all the tortured, romantic heroes she had ever read about in the books Josie had smuggled in to her.

'Not surprising you can't take to reading,' she had said, 'if all you have is that rubbishy stuff meant for little children. This is what young ladies of your age enjoy.'

'Life can be so unfair,' Lady Jayne said to Lord Ledbury softly, completely forgiving him for every harsh word he had uttered, every criticism he had levelled at her. When a man was in the throes of a painful, thwarted love affair, it was bound to make him a little short-tempered.

'Of course you do not want anyone to say unpleasant things about your…friend. I shall be only too pleased to meet her, and help her in any way I can.'

In fact it would be quite wonderful to be the one giving advice to someone else, instead of constantly being on the receiving end of it. Even if it was only on matters of fashion and etiquette.

'Somehow,' he said with a smile, 'I never doubted it.'

Was that a third compliment? She positively glowed with pleasure.

But then his expression turned hard and business-like once more.

'I have already told you that I am in Town primarily to find a bride,' he said. 'And, since our families would definitely approve of a match between *us,* I propose to make it seem as though I am trying to fix my interest with you. And you would do well to make it appear as though you reciprocate that interest,' he said quite sternly, 'if you want to continue seeing Lieutenant Kendell. Though I warn you, I will not allow this covert operation to interfere with my primary objective. Which is to find a woman who is worthy of holding the title of Countess of Lavenham. Is that clear?'

She turned to look out of the carriage as though somebody she knew had caught her eye. As though Lord Ledbury had not just cut her to the quick with one throwaway remark. After all those compliments, genuine compliments, she had begun to think that he quite liked her. But now he'd made it plain that he would rather not have to spend any time with her at all.

'Abundantly,' she replied coldly. 'Though,' she observed after a moment or two, 'I cannot help but remark that I think you are carrying your sense of duty too far.'

'By which I assume you mean you think I ought to marry for love.'

Yes! If he was in love with Milly then he ought to marry her, and that was that. Why, earls married widows with shady reputations, or even actresses upon occasion. It caused a bit of a scandal—but when had what others thought ever stopped a man of rank from doing just as he pleased?

'It is the *only* reason one should marry...'

'Well, there we will have to agree to differ.'

Oh, the man was impossible. But there was no point in trying to make him see how foolish he was being. Apart from the fact he was a man, and men always thought they knew best, they were only—as he'd put it—working together under a flag of truce.

And yet she couldn't help feeling rather sorry for

him. The poor man must be in hell, being in love with
one woman whilst feeling duty-bound to marry another.
True, she had been packed off to London to be married
off, but at least her affections had not really been engaged elsewhere. He could not even elope, as her aunt
had done—not when he had so many responsibilities.
He was not that kind of man. She had only met him the
night before, but already she could tell he was determined always to do the right thing. No matter what the
personal cost. Why, he wouldn't even take Milly shopping in case it gave rise to the suspicion that the woman
he loved was his mistress. Even though most men of
his class would have made her his mistress in reality,
without batting an eyelid.

Well, she would not say any more upon that topic.
Not only would it be like prodding at a decaying tooth,
but they did not know each other well enough to share
those kind of confidences.

Though she would do whatever she could to help his
lady-friend. Apart from any other consideration, she rel-
ished the chance to be really, truly useful to someone
for the very first time in her life.

'Oh!' she said, clapping her hands in glee. 'I have just
had a brilliant idea. I shall be in Conduit Street tomorrow. I have to purchase some new gloves. If you could
arrange for Milly to loiter outside the front of Madame
Pichot's at about ten o'clock I could pretend to recognise
her, and introduce her to Lady Penrose as an old friend.'

He looked at her with approval, making her swell
with pleasure when he said, 'Yes, I think that could
work.'

Not for long. She sighed. The first thing Lady Penrose would do, upon her introducing a new friend,

would be to write to her grandfather and enquire if Milly was proper company for her to keep. And as soon as he wrote back, disclaiming all knowledge of any such person amongst her acquaintance, the game would be up. But there was no saying how long it might take for a letter to reach him if he were not at Darvill Park for any reason. So they might have a few days before their ruse was discovered.

And in that time she would do all she could to help the pair who, for reasons of stupid custom—because he was all bound up with doing his duty rather than following his heart—could not be together even though they plainly should be.

'Tell me how I might recognise her,' she said. 'What does she look like?'

'Milly? Oh, she is…' He looked at her, a puzzled frown on his brow. 'She is quite a bit taller than you. Dark hair and eyes. Strong. Plain of face,' he said, his eyes wandering over her features individually and softening. 'Nothing much to look at at all, really.'

And yet he loved her. She was plain, and poor, and yet the eyes that could look as hard as chips of granite turned all soft and smoky when he thought about her.

Because they had shared all those hardships and she'd come through them all with flying colours.

Jayne knew she would never have been able to nurse a man through such a difficult time. She had no skills, no experience. And would never be allowed anywhere near a sick room in any case.

She turned her head away abruptly while she grappled with a fierce stab of jealousy for the girl who, despite all her disadvantages, had managed to capture the heart of a man like this. A man unlike anyone she'd ever met before. Now that she wasn't quite so cross with him she could admit that she found his rough-hewn face ruggedly attractive. Even that terrible scar, which at first sight had made him look a bit scary, now only served as a reminder that he was a battle-hardened soldier, a man to be admired for his bravery.

She heaved a deep sigh. If any man in London deserved to find happiness with the woman he loved, then it was this man.

It was such a pity he couldn't see it for himself.

Chapter Four

The next evening, Lady Jayne had barely arrived at the Cardingtons' before Lord Ledbury came over.

He bowed to Lady Penrose. 'May I claim the hand of Lady Jayne during the next waltz? Not to dance, but to take the air on the terrace?'

'Oh, may I, Lady Penrose?' Lady Jayne put in hastily, before Lady Penrose could object. 'Lord Ledbury was terribly wounded at Orthez. He does not dance.'

She hoped that putting those two statements together might make Lady Penrose soften towards him. Not that she believed he *could* not dance if he wanted to. After all, he was fit enough to go prowling around public parks at dawn. But he clearly wanted to talk to her—and not many men, she had noted, were capable of carrying on sensible conversations while executing the complex figures of any dance, let alone the waltz.

'It is rather warm in here,' said Lady Penrose, after a visible struggle with herself. Having been given the information that Lord Ledbury did not dance, she had little choice but to relax her rigid rules just a little, or risk losing the first suitor in whom her charge had shown any interest. 'Perhaps you might go and sit on that bench, just there.' She indicated a spot just through the open doors, which would be clearly visible from where she sat. 'It is a little unorthodox, but in *your* case,' she said with a slight smile, 'I think there would be no harm in it. I shall have a footman send you out some lemonade.'

Lady Jayne could barely stifle a giggle at the implication that nobody could get up to anything improper whilst drinking lemonade.

'Phew!' she said as they made their way to the open doors. 'It is a good thing you are such a catch, or you would never have got away with that.'

Lord Ledbury flinched. It was just typical that the first woman to rouse his interest should dismiss him so airily. But what else could he expect? She was determined to marry for love. And he'd learned from the cradle that there was nothing in him to inspire affection. His own parents, who'd had no trouble at all doting on his other brothers, had seemed barely able to recall they had a third son. True, his father had only had time for Mortimer, while his mother had practically smothered Charlie, but that had done nothing to soothe the sting of their joint rejection of him. Or to lessen the impact of Lady Jayne's indifference to him now.

He took himself to task as he took his place next to her on the designated bench. He had rank and wealth to offer a woman now. And there were plenty who would be perfectly satisfied with that. He only had to recall how they'd flocked round him at Lucy Beresford's ball.

He had no need of love—not in the kind of marriage he intended to contract.

Particularly not from a flighty little piece like this.

'You are looking very pleased with yourself this evening,' he observed dryly. 'I suppose I should have expected it. You are never happier than when you are up to your neck in mischief, are you?'

She turned to stare at him, wide-eyed, at the unfairness of that remark, and saw that he looked as though he was really annoyed with her about something. Though, cudgel her brains as she might, she could not think what.

That morning she had driven up to the front of Madame Pichot's at the prearranged hour, in Lady Penrose's town carriage, and, seeing a tall, dark-haired girl loitering on the pavement, gazing wistfully at the window display, had sat forward and said artlessly, 'My goodness. Can that be Milly? Whatever can she be doing in Town?'

And then she had leaped out nimbly and darted up to the girl to make sure she was the right person. By the time Lady Penrose had exited the carriage with rather more decorum she'd thought enough time had passed for her to have extracted the news from her supposed friend that she had recently come into some money, quite unexpectedly, and had come up to Town to purchase a fashionable wardrobe.

Having imparted that information to Lady Penrose, she had then swept Milly into the shop, chattering about the newest fashions in that month's *La Belle Assemblée,* and naturally the modiste, seeing the two on such good terms, had assumed Milly must be a somebody, and treated her accordingly.

'Now you are looking at me,' Lord Ledbury was saying, 'as though you expect me to congratulate you for this morning's work. Did you come here expecting me to thank you?'

'Well, yes,' she replied, growing more mystified at his ill humour by the minute.

Milly had certainly been thrilled at the way the morning had turned out. She had admitted that she would never have dared set foot in an establishment like Madame Pichot's. But now she would be able to return whenever she wanted, after an introduction like that. Even if Lady Jayne was not able to go with her, Madame Pichot would never let one of her customers leave her shop looking anything less than elegant. Which was surely what Lord Ledbury wanted?

'Well, I cannot thank you for issuing her with a false name. Milly informs me that she is now to be known as Miss Amelia Brigstock!'

Oh, so that was it. 'That is entirely your fault,' she retorted, stung by his determination to find fault with her in spite of all she had achieved on his behalf. 'You omitted to tell me her full name.' And she had not criticised him for his lack of foresight, had she? She had just plugged up the leak as best she could, to make sure the whole campaign did not sink before it even got underway. 'Since she was supposed to be a long-lost friend, newly come to Town, I could hardly ask her what it was, could I? When Lady Penrose asked me to introduce her I had to come up with something.'

His hands tightened on the head of his cane. A muscle twitched in his jaw.

She reminded herself that he was not in the best of health, and that being in pain could make anyone short-tempered.

Whilst arranging her skirts into decorous folds, making sure the train was well out of the way of his feet, she resolutely stifled the pang of hurt his lack of gratitude had inflicted. Only when she was confident she could do so in a calm, even tone, did she point out, 'And I assumed Milly must be short for something. Amelia is a good, safe kind of name for a girl who is supposed to be completely respectable, though not from the top drawer. And the name Brigstock just popped into my head.'

'Her name is Milly,' he grated. 'Just Milly. And there is nothing wrong with that.'

'There is if I am to invite her to go about with me and pretend that we are bosom friends.'

He looked aghast. 'I have not asked you to do that! Surely you only need to take her shopping a few times to teach her the difference between taste and tawdriness?'

She mellowed a little. How could she not, when he was demonstrating such faith in her fashion sense?

But still… 'You have not thought this through at all, have you? I have not gone shopping with a *friend* once since coming to Town. If I am to suddenly wish to do so with Milly, then Lady Penrose has got to believe she is someone exceptional. A special friend. Or she will become suspicious.'

Lady Jayne never went shopping with friends? He'd thought that was how all fashionable young ladies spent their days.

They were both obliged to suspend any effort at conversation when a footman approached with the drinks that had given them the excuse to go out onto the terrace. But once Lady Jayne had taken just one sip, she pointed out rather tartly, 'You wished me to exercise some influence on her. Which I have promised to do. But you did not give me enough information to see me through any social awkwardness which presenting her to Lady Penrose would entail. I did my best to smooth over that awkwardness. I thought it was what you military types called thinking on your feet.'

He eyed her with misgiving. All he'd wanted was some pretext for making her think they were doing each other a favour—something to distract her from questioning his real motives behind monitoring her and Lieutenant Kendell's meetings so closely.

He could never have guessed just how little freedom she had—not even to go shopping. He'd assumed she'd been exaggerating when she'd said she felt caged, but now he understood what she had meant. It must be intolerable. No wonder she resorted to telling lies and climbing out of windows. Though he couldn't very well encourage her propensity for getting into mischief by admitting that. So, instead, he observed, 'All you have done is make everything twice as complicated as it need be by adding yet another layer to the deception you are practising upon Lady Penrose.'

Guilt made her stomach twinge. She did not want to practise any deception upon Lady Penrose at all. After living under her aegis for only a few weeks she had discovered that, though reserved and inclined to be strict, basically she was a kind woman. So kind, in fact, that after observing the two girls together in the shop she had invited Milly back to Mount Street. Immediately catching on to what a marvellous opportunity this would be to spend some time together in private and concoct a suitable background story, Milly had accepted the invitation with alacrity.

'I am sure you wish to catch up with each other,' Lady Penrose had said once they arrived, and then had retired to her own room leaving them entirely unsupervised.

Lady Jayne did not think she had ever laughed so much since… No, she had *never* laughed so much as she had done that afternoon, closeted in her room with Milly and her lively sense of humour. She had wondered if this was what it would be like to have a close female friend. She had no idea. She had never had *any* friends she had chosen for herself. Her grandfather vetted everyone she came into contact with so closely that by the time they measured up to his impossibly high standards she had lost interest in them.

Milly was like a breath of fresh air. Even though Jayne had been a little jealous of the esteem in which Lord Ledbury held her to begin with, once they had retired to the privacy of Lady Jayne's room and got talking—well! Milly had seen so much, had had so many exciting adventures growing up in the tail of the army, and recounted them so amusingly that Lady Jayne forgot to be anything but completely enthralled. How she wished she might have had but a tithe of Milly's experiences. Once her parents had died, and she had gone to live with her grandfather, Lady Jayne had not set foot outside Kent. While there, she had scarcely been allowed off the estate except for church on Sunday, or to visit the few neighbouring families of whom her grandfather approved. She felt so green and naive and ignorant beside Milly.

After she had gone, Lady Penrose had summoned her to her room.

'That girl appears to have acted upon you like a tonic,' she'd said, the moment Lady Jayne had taken a seat. 'I had thought just at first she looked a little…common…' Lady Penrose had arched an enquiring brow.

'That is one thing I hope to help her with while she

is in Town,' she had said, seizing her opportunity. 'I had hoped, if I might supervise her purchase of a new wardrobe and just give her a nudge—you know, about what is truly stylish...'

Lady Penrose had continued to look at her in silence, that eyebrow raised, until Lady Jayne had admitted, 'Well, no, she is not from a terribly good family. But I do like her.' And by that time it had been the truth.

'There is nothing wrong with having a few friends from lower levels of Society, provided one does not let them become too encroaching,' Lady Penrose had said with a pointed look.

Lady Jayne had nodded her understanding. Any friendship with a person of Milly's class would be allowed to go so far, but no further.

'I have not been able to help noticing,' she had then said, with a troubled air, 'that you have not been very happy while you have been staying with me. It was one of the reasons why I decided we should accept Miss Beresford's invitation to attend her come-out, even though she is not from one of the families your grandfather approved. I had wondered, when you expressed an interest in attending, if you and *she* had struck up a friendship?'

Lady Jayne had only gone to that wretched ball because Harry had let her know he could be there, and they had arranged an assignation in the library, but she couldn't very well admit that.

When Lady Penrose saw that she had no intention of making any response to her tentative enquiry, she continued, 'I have rarely seen you smile, and certainly never heard you laugh, until Miss Brigstock came upon the scene.' She smiled. 'For that alone I am inclined to like her.'

'I hate having to deceive Lady Penrose,' Lady Jayne said now to Lord Ledbury with feeling. 'I wish it was not necessary.'

'Yet Milly tells me you have invited her to go shopping again tomorrow?'

'And then to Gunter's for ices.' Her face brightened considerably. 'She will enjoy that, will she not?'

'She will,' he said, wondering what was making her look so cheerful. He would not have thought that a sheltered Society beauty like her could have anything in common with an army brat. Was she really so lonely that she could look forward to going shopping and having ices with a girl like Milly? If what she said about disliking deceiving Lady Penrose was true, then he could only believe she was so lonely that even Milly's company seemed appealing, or...

Hang it. How could he have forgotten the reason she'd agreed to meet Milly in the first place? Lieutenant Kendell. He'd promised that if she took Milly shopping he would reward her with a sight of her lovelorn lieutenant.

His mood, which had not been all that good to begin with, plummeted still further as he saw that, in spite of knowing Lady Jayne was not at all the kind of girl he could ever seriously consider marrying, it was still galling to know her face would never light up at the prospect of spending time with him.

Even if she hadn't already been in love with someone else, she'd already let him know, in no uncertain terms, that he held no appeal for her whatsoever. That he was, in short, a *cross old stick.*

He turned from her abruptly, using the excuse of placing his empty glass down on the stone coping to conceal any of the feelings that, heaven forbid, might be revealed in his expression. Nor did he particularly want to watch her light up when he told her what steps he had already taken in accordance with the promise he'd made her.

'I have taken a box at Drury Lane. I shall be inviting you to join a party I shall get up next Tuesday. Be sure to attend.'

Lady Jayne glowered at him. The ingrate! After all she had done, the lengths she was prepared to go to be of help to him and Milly, all he could do was bark further orders at her.

He got to his feet.

'The waltz has finished and we must make our way back to Lady Penrose,' he said.

It was so insulting for him to attempt to escape her presence the moment the last strains of music died away that she remained right where she was. And it struck her that this was another reason why she'd always agreed to see Harry. He actually *wanted* to be with her. She wasn't a responsibility who'd been thrust on him. And whenever the time came for them to part he always pleaded for just a few more moments.

'Have you not forgotten something?'

'No.'

'Well, then, may I make a suggestion that if the need should arise,' she said, getting to her feet in her own good time, 'you may send a note via Josie, my maid. You can rely on her discretion.'

'Smuggled letters?' He looked at her, aghast. 'I am

beginning to feel as if I have walked into some kind of badly written play.'

The entire situation was getting out of hand. He'd correctly deduced that Lady Jayne could be a bit of a handful, but she was far more than that. She was like a force of nature. He had only asked her to give Milly a few hints about what a truly elegant lady would wear, and all of a sudden they were best friends—going out and buying ices at Gunters, and now this!

'Not such a great strategist, are you, if even *I* can see that we might need to contact one another before Tuesday? I can foresee any number of circumstances arising which might require *me* to contact *you*. And there will be no way for me to do so openly. Lady Penrose would never let me have private communication with a young man.' She shot his scarred face one scathing glance. 'A relatively young man,' she corrected herself, 'without close supervision. Do not be deceived by the fact she allowed us to sit outdoors for the duration of this dance. Normally she guards me far more closely.'

'I am not a bit surprised,' he snapped, stung by the way she'd once again pointed out that he was far too old and battered for a fresh young beauty like her to give him a second glance. 'If I were in charge of you I would post guards on your door at night.'

'It would not do you a bit of good if you did,' she replied waspishly, 'since I always go out by the window when I do not wish anyone to know where I am going.'

She could not believe he had goaded her into saying that when it was completely untrue. She had only crept out that way once since coming to London, and the outcome had been so appalling she had vowed never to do so again. She could not believe, either, the power he had to wound her when she scarcely knew him. Or that he could make her so cross that she could not stop herself from lashing out in a completely irrational manner.

His shocked gasp did, at least, give her a moment's satisfaction. But only until she took her seat beside Lady Penrose and watched him walk stiffly away—when she realized she would have much rather heard him praise her for her resourcefulness and thank her for being so helpful.

And how likely was that?

Lady Jayne had never looked forward to a trip to the theatre so much. She couldn't wait to see Lord Ledbury's face when he saw she'd prevailed upon Lady Penrose to take Milly along as one of their party. Lady Penrose had not minded in the least. It was not as if she'd begged to have Milly admitted to a *ton* event. Why, anyone could go to the theatre.

And one morning in Milly's company had convinced her that Lord Ledbury was being as ridiculous as her own grandfather had been. There was no sensible reason why he should not marry Milly. She was just as bright and far more pleasant than any well-born lady he was ever likely to meet.

Besides, the way he'd criticised her at the Cardingtons' still rankled. She was determined to show him that not only could she teach Milly how to dress well, but she could turn her into the kind of woman he could take anywhere.

Lord Ledbury was waiting for them in the doorway to the box he'd acquired. He greeted Lady Penrose before turning to her.

'This is Miss Amelia Brigstock,' she said, the second

he noticed who was standing beside her. 'I do hope you don't mind me bringing her along? Only she is such a very good friend of mine.'

The smile of welcome stayed on his lips, but to her surprise it died from his eyes and the muscles in his jaw twitched as though he was grinding his teeth.

She watched in mounting bewilderment at the total lack of any perceptible sign of softening from Lord Ledbury as Milly curtsied, and offered her hand, and blushed prettily, exactly as any young lady just presented to such an imposing aristocrat might have done.

Having been as short with Milly as politeness would allow, he then turned his attention back to her.

'Permit me to introduce you to the other members of my party,' he said.

She felt very uncomfortable as she took his arm and allowed him to lead her into the box. She couldn't understand what she had done wrong. Why had he not seemed pleased to see how well Milly could behave in polite company after only a few lessons in etiquette? There had been a kind of suppressed excitement about her, but she did not think anyone who did not know the whole story would have been able to detect anything untoward in her demeanour. Why was he not bursting with pride at her accomplishment?

And then she wondered if she had been terribly insensitive. He looked as though he was just barely keeping the lid on a seething cauldron of various hurts and resentments at a time when he was still, to judge by the pallor of his complexion, very far from well. The poor man had no idea that she was trying to prove to him, and the world, that Milly could easily take her place at his side, given a little instruction. Having her thrust under his nose like this, when he clearly still believed he could never marry her, looked very much as though she had twisted the knife in the wound, which was the very last thing she'd wished to do.

'You already know Beresford and his sister,' he said as they acknowledged her.

Lucy was not behaving half so well as Milly. She was so excited to be one of such a select party that it looked as though her brother was only just preventing her from prostrating herself at Lord Ledbury's feet.

'And now I must introduce you to one of the few military men still fortunate enough to be stationed in London,' he said, ignoring the adoring way Lucy was gazing at him. 'Lieutenant Kendell.'

Then Harry, who had been hovering in the shadows cast by the pillars holding up the tiers of boxes, stepped forward, bowed smartly, and said, 'Honoured to make your acquaintance.'

Her stomach lurched. She found herself hoping, as she curtsied and held out her own hand, that she was managing to conceal her reactions half so well as Milly had just done, when Harry took her hand, tucked it into the crook of his arm, and tugged her away from Lord Ledbury.

'Allow me to help you to your seat,' he said aloud. In her ear, he murmured, 'This is intolerable. He pursued me to the barracks. Now the devil has me on such a short leash there is no way I can escape him. He will ruin me if I step out of line.'

Lord Ledbury clenched his fists as he saw Kendell bend down to whisper in Lady Jayne's ear. The system that sent good men off to die while no-goods like this Kendell remained behind to prey on vulnerable heiresses was monstrously unfair. Not that the boy would be much good on the battlefield, he sneered. He wouldn't want that handsome face bashed about, or his uniform sullied.

He indulged himself with a vision of striding across the box and planting Kendell a facer to stop the man taking the chair next to Lady Jayne's. The fool! Could he not see that not only was he drawing attention to them by behaving in such an obvious manner, but he was also making her uncomfortable?

Well, he couldn't rearrange the man's face, but he could spare Lady Jayne's blushes by distracting his other guests from what was going on.

Turning his back on them, he devoted himself to doing just that.

'My darling,' Harry murmured, 'we cannot go on like this. It is such torment.'

'Oh, Harry,' she said, gazing mournfully into his ardent face.

She dreaded having to tell him it was all over. But it was wrong to keep him dangling like this, in a mix of agony and hope. The longer she put off the moment of parting, the worse it would be for him.

'Come to me where we met before,' he begged her. 'This time I shall have a carriage waiting, so that we can escape from them all. Forever.'

'No!' Oh, this was dreadful. He was still thinking in terms of making a runaway match, while she was looking for an opportunity to sever the connection entirely.

'You need not be afraid,' he said cajolingly. 'I understand how badly Lord Ledbury frightened you, coming upon us like that and uttering all those threats, but I swear I shall never let him hurt you. Once we are married I can protect you from him, and all those like him. My treasure…'

'It is not that,' she snapped. There were so many things wrong with that statement she did not know where to start. She was not afraid of Lord Ledbury. And she did not need Harry to protect her from him or anyone. And how dare he accuse her of being too timid to run away with him? If he thought her so lacking in nerve then he did not know her at all! If she had really loved him nothing would have made her hesitate. Nothing!

She glanced round at the other occupants of the box. Lord Ledbury was standing next to Milly, including her in a conversation that also encompassed his other guests. Whilst also managing to distract Lady Penrose from the fact that she and Harry were standing far too close, and whispering…

'Then what is it?'

She would scarcely get a better chance than this, whilst everyone else was busy exchanging greetings and deciding which chair to take. Now was the time to tell Harry it was over.

Time to stop making excuses for herself. Time to grow up and shoulder responsibility for her actions, not feebly hope somebody else would sort out the mess she'd made. She should never have taken up with Harry when he came to London searching for her, no matter how wonderful it had felt to have him persist in his pursuit of her in the face of her grandfather's objections.

She took a deep breath, looked him straight in the eye…and pictured the aftermath. Harry would be devastated when she told him it was over. Nor would he be able to disguise his hurt, or the fact that she had caused it. He was not made of such stern stuff as Lord Ledbury. Nobody, to look at *him,* would ever be able to guess he was experiencing such deep emotional as well as physical pain.

In fact at that moment she *did* look at him, and it struck her that now she had owned up to not being even slightly in love with Harry that Lord Ledbury cast him completely in the shade. The very perfection of Harry's features, when compared with Lord Ledbury's battle-scarred visage, made him look…well, like a pretty youth play-acting at being a soldier. While Lord Ledbury was the real thing.

'Oh, Harry.' She sighed again, shaking her head. She could not do it. Not here. It would be downright cruel of her to dash all his hopes in front of these theatre-goers. 'I…I just want to talk to you, that is all. Alone.'

She needed to tell him it was over in a private place, where his grief would not expose him to any loss of dignity. And if that meant breaking her pact with Lord Ledbury, to see him only where he could watch over them, then so be it. She owed Harry that much.

'I don't suppose…' She caught her lower lip between her teeth as a plan began to take shape in her mind. 'Can you get an invitation to Lord Lambourne's masquerade ball next week?'

'I dare say I could. And everyone will be in costume anyway, so the hosts won't know if I'm someone they've invited or not if I tag on to another party. It will be perfect. You are a clever girl…'

Lady Jayne cringed. Harry was the only man who had ever given her such unstinting praise. How she wished she could return his regard.

Seeing her pained look, he became all solicitude. 'It

will be difficult for you, though, escaping from your dragon of a chaperone, will it not?'

Actually, she did not think it would be as hard as all that. They had already discussed the event at some length. They both knew that her grandfather would never approve of her attending such an event. But Lady Penrose had admitted that she thought it was a pity, since it was just the sort of thing for a girl of her age.

'I shall contrive something,' she said, biting back her impulse to defend Lady Penrose from the slur on her character. 'Don't I always?' To her shame. She really had to stop going behind her chaperone's back.

And she would!

Once she had freed herself from Harry.

'Yes!' Harry hissed in triumph, seizing her hand and giving it a squeeze. 'I shall count the hours until we can be together again. Truly together...'

Lord Ledbury saw the proprietorial way Lieutenant Kendell grasped Lady Jayne's hand and wanted to knock the bounder's teeth down his throat.

He broke off the conversation in which he'd been engaged quite rudely and strode across the box. He had no idea what the young man had been saying, but he could see he was making Lady Jayne uncomfortable. And, even though he knew she would resent his interference, he could not stand by one second longer, doing nothing.

'Have a care,' he growled at Harry. 'You ought not to be standing so close. Are you trying to draw attention to yourselves? Do you want Lady Penrose to suspect you might be the very man Lady Jayne was sent to London to avoid?'

Harry flushed, and let go of her hand.

'Miss Brigstock,' he said, beckoning Milly over. 'The

performance is about to begin. Do take this seat next to your friend.'

Harry glared at him, but could hardly object to his host ordering the seating arrangements—particularly not when he was only just supposed to have been introduced to Lady Jayne. With bad grace, he took a seat behind the girls. And Lady Penrose herself sat beside him.

It was a good seating arrangement from Lord Ledbury's point of view. Milly soon took Lady Jayne's mind off her own woes by mercilessly making fun of the actors on the stage, who were very far from being the most talented he'd ever watched. Before long, Lady Jayne was giggling behind her fan.

He had never seen her looking so carefree.

That was when he understood why Lady Jayne had taken to Milly so quickly. Her parentage was irrelevant. They were both about the same age. And Milly had brought sunshine into her life.

He was just congratulating himself for being indirectly responsible for chasing away the shadows that her entanglement with Kendell had cast over her, when Milly did something that made his blood run cold.

Chapter Five

She laughed. That was all. But Milly had the most infectious laugh he'd ever heard. It was what had drawn him to her in the first place. What had drawn many of the younger officers to her father's billet.

Anyone who'd ever heard that laugh would never forget it. They would take a second look at the shapely and assured young woman at Lady Jayne's side and perceive beneath the Town bronze the ragged girl with the dirty face who'd been the regiment's darling.

A shiver of foreboding went down his spine. Even though most of the men who might have recognised Milly had already been deployed, she could still pose a threat to Lady Jayne's reputation. It would only take one of the more curious amongst the idlers loafing around the gentlemen's clubs to investigate his background and discover that he'd been living under the same roof as Milly for over a year. That once he'd moved into Lavenham House he'd had set her up in her own dwelling and given her a generous allowance.

And assume she was his mistress.

People were already casting speculative looks towards the occupants of their box. There would be no end of conjecture about each of his guests, and why he had invited them to form such a small, select group.

What conclusions would they draw about how his 'mistress' had come to be on terms of intimacy with Lady Jayne?

He cursed himself roundly. He'd been annoyed with Lady Jayne when she'd criticised his strategy, since he'd proved himself a skilled tactician time and time again on the battlefields of the Peninsula. But perhaps she'd had a point. He wasn't used to manoeuvring through the morass that was polite society, or considering the fragility of a woman's reputation.

At that moment Lieutenant Kendell leaned forward and said something in Lady Jayne's ear. She forced her lips into the semblance of a smile, but it was a far cry from the natural gaiety she'd been expressing before. She was so good at masking her feelings that everyone else would probably conclude that she was freezing out an importunate young man who was trying on his charm with her, the same way she always did. But he detested the effect her lover was having on her.

If he ever found any evidence to prove the fellow did not really love Lady Jayne, he would make damn sure he never got near her again.

He glowered across the box and Kendell sat back, leaving Lady Jayne in peace for the present. It was the best he could do for now with regard to Kendell, but he could definitely deal with the potential for disaster he'd created by introducing her to Milly.

When it came to the first interval he made his way to Lady Jayne's side and with a jerk of his head dismissed Kendell.

She was so glad he'd come to her rescue. She did not think she could take much more of Harry's endearments. They made her squirm with guilt.

And, from the way Lord Ledbury had been glaring at them, Harry had been far too obvious in spite of the earlier warning. She lifted her chin, bracing herself for the scold she was sure he was about to give her, though for the life of her she could not think how she could have prevented Harry from making a spectacle of himself. Surely it was Harry to whom he should be addressing his concerns?

'This association with Milly is getting out of hand,' he said the moment Harry had moved out of earshot. 'I never imagined, when I asked you to give her a touch of style, that you would take her up this way.'

'What?' It was the very last thing she had expected him to say.

'She is not, and never has been, a proper person for you to know...'

That sounded so very like the kind of criticism her grandfather would have levelled at her that her surprise turned to anger.

'Well, you introduced me to her. You asked me for my help, and—'

'Yes, I know,' he said more gently. 'But I had no notion then, what a warm-hearted person you are. Or how lonely.'

She blinked. She would never have thought such a hard-faced man could be so perceptive. He'd seen right to the heart of her. And put his finger on who she wanted to be but was never allowed to be.

'I thought you would spare her a few hours to take

her shopping, discreetly, not…fling yourself headlong into such an inappropriate friendship.'

'Oh.' His unexpected compliment had touched her so deeply that the warm glow it created melted her anger away. 'But… Milly is a perfectly lovely person. I do not consider a friendship with her inappropriate at all. In fact—'

'That's enough,' he said, the flinty look returning to his eyes. 'In the long run, this association can only be bad for you both.'

'Bad for both of us? Are you suggesting that I am a bad influence on Milly?'

'Not intentionally. And so far you have done her a great deal of good. She has taken advice from you regarding her dress and manners that she would never have taken from me. But was it wise to bring her here, tonight, for example? Is it really kind of you to introduce her to a world in which she can never have so much as a toehold?'

She firmed her mouth mutinously. Milly could have very much more than a toehold if he would only relinquish his absurd belief that he ought to be making a splendid dynastic marriage. If she became his countess people might talk for a while, but the novelty would soon wear off. There would be some other scandal brewing, somewhere, to make them lose interest— particularly if she behaved well.

'You must have noticed how many looks have been directed at our box tonight,' he persisted. 'Everyone wants to know who my guests are. And if they don't know, they will make it their business to find out. You know what nasty minds people have. How long do you think it will be before somebody jumps to the conclusion that I have foisted my mistress on you? You would become a laughing stock.'

'Much I care for that,' she said, militantly lifting her chin.

'Your loyalty is commendable, but in this instance it is not very wise.'

She supposed she could see his point. People would want to know who Milly was now that she had been seen in public in such elevated company. And people *were* always prepared to think the worst. They would never credit any man behaving with such generosity towards a woman of lowly birth unless she was his mistress. And he had gone to such pains to shield Milly from precisely this sort of conjecture.

'Oh…' No wonder he'd been so cross with her for bringing Milly along tonight. All that talk about not wanting *her* to become a laughing stock was so fustian. It was Milly's reputation he was trying to protect.

'This ruse has gone far enough. I cannot permit the association between you two girls to continue.'

'What?' She had been on the verge of apologising for exposing Milly to public scrutiny, and promising she would carry on the friendship with more discretion in future. But now he expected her to drop Milly altogether? Just when she was going to be most in need of a real friend?

Breaking off with Harry was going to be the hardest thing she'd ever done. But at least she'd thought she would have Milly to turn to for consolation in the aftermath.

But if Lord Ledbury had his way her life would descend into that same dreary round that had pitched her into Harry's arms in the first place. Only now it would be far harder to bear because for a short while she'd discovered what it felt like to have a friend, a girl of her own age, who had given her a glimpse into a world she'd only ever been able to dream of.

For years she had yearned for some kind of adventure. She had sometimes wondered, wistfully, what it would have been like to have been the Earl of Caxton's other granddaughter. The one who had got away from England and its stuffy rules and restrictions altogether. Lady Jayne might not actually be having an adventure now, but hearing Milly talk about hers was almost as good.

And then again, once Harry was out of the picture, Lord Ledbury would no longer need to pretend any interest in her, either. He would openly court other women whilst cutting her dead. Not that she wanted to marry him, or anyone else—not this Season. That was not the point.

The point was… Well, she couldn't think what the point was when he made her so cross. She was sure she didn't know why being set at a distance from him should bother her in the least, when he was so overbearing and critical…and…and he had no right to tell her with whom she might be friends! She had defied her own grandfather when he'd tried to dictate to her on just such a matter. Should she meekly fall in with Lord Ledbury's orders?

Absolutely not!

She was not going to give Milly up, and that was that.

Oh, how glad she was that she'd already arranged to meet Harry behind his back.

She would show him that she was quite capable of running her own life *and* choosing her own friends.

With a toss of her head she turned away, without vouchsafing him a single word, and took a seat next to Lady Penrose.

Just as she had predicted, it was not very hard to persuade Lady Penrose to allow her to attend the Lambournes' masquerade ball. The very day after the theatre trip, when they had been discussing how much they had enjoyed it, and how much Milly had added to their enjoyment with her witty remarks, all she'd had to do was sigh wistfully and say what a shame it was she would never be able to take her to a ball. Then she'd picked up the invitation, and said, 'This is the only sort of thing where we might get away with it, since everyone would be masked and nobody quite sure of anyone's identity.'

Lady Penrose had looked at her through narrowed eyes. 'You really wish to attend this masked ball, do you not?'

Lady Jayne had nodded.

Lady Penrose had frowned thoughtfully.

'I suppose I ought not to be surprised. It is exactly the sort of thing to appeal to you young things rather than the staid parties which suit me. And do you know,' she had said, her lips pressing together in an expression of annoyance, 'I think you *ought* to be allowed to enjoy your first London Season. You have not uttered one word of complaint about the limited events to which I have taken you, though I can tell they have not always been to your taste. You are such a good girl, Jayne, that I cannot think why your grandfather feels he needs to be so strict with you. This is exactly the way he treated your aunt Aurora, you know. No wonder she ran off in the end. It would have been much better if he'd allowed her an outlet for her high spirits, rather than trying to crush her. Not that you are anything like her. Dear me, no. Whilst you have lived under my roof you have always behaved exactly as you should. If you really wish to attend this ball, then I... Yes, I do believe I shall allow you to go. You deserve a treat.'

Lady Jayne had been ready to curl up with shame. She had not behaved as she should—not at all! She had sneaked away to meet Harry in libraries, or out on chilly terraces, and had even climbed out of her window to meet him in the park.

Well, she'd make it up to Lady Penrose by *really* being a model of decorum once the masquerade was over. Aside from the matter of defying Lord Ledbury's decree with regard to Milly, which did not count. If Lady Penrose did not object to Milly, then that was all that mattered.

But she soon discovered that though it was all very well tempting to put right all the wrongs she had done with regard to Harry, in order to reach the moral high ground she had to scramble through some very treacherous territory. She even turned Lady Penrose into an accomplice!

'You will need a disguise, not a costume,' Lady Penrose declared. 'A mask will not be enough. If you wear a dress that is too memorable somebody might look too closely at you and recognise you, which would never do. Wear something plain. The plainer the better. Something you have never worn before and will never wear again. And you must definitely cover your hair,' she said, eyeing Lady Jayne's golden ringlets with a frown. 'It is so distinctive.'

She'd ordered Josie to scrape it away from her face, fix it in tight braids and, as an added precaution, cover it with a white sort of bonnet thing, so that even if the hood of her pale blue domino should slip nobody would catch so much as a glimpse of a golden ringlet.

But the most daring part of her disguise would be Lady Penrose's absence.

'Nobody will believe I would ever let you out of my sight, so strictly have I adhered to your grandfather's terms up until now,' she said with a gleam in her eye. 'And they also know that if I were to go I would never, absolutely never, do anything so vulgar as dress up as a shepherdess or a Greek nymph.' She shuddered at the very thought. 'No, if I were to chaperone you I would do so in a proper evening gown, with perhaps a loo mask as a concession to the theme of the event. So even if somebody should suspect you look a bit like Lady Jayne Chilcott, the fact that I am not there will persuade them they are mistaken.'

She raised a hand to her throat and gave a nervous laugh. 'My goodness, I am become quite a rebel! I do not know whether to congratulate myself for finally showing Lord Caxton that he has no right to dictate to me about which venues I consider suitable for you to attend, whilst I have the charge of you, or whether to give myself a stern talking-to for allowing you out of my sight. Though I cannot be sorry,' she declared, 'that *someone* from our family is attending, even if nobody knows who you are. As you know, I had wanted to support Lord Lambourne's return to Society. He made mistakes, but I hope we all know our Christian duty well enough to extend a spirit of forgiveness now that he is reconciled with his wife.'

But, in spite of the delight they took in planning their rebellion against Lord Caxton, by the time it came to Tuesday night both ladies were in quite a state. Lady Jayne gave up waiting decorously on the sofa and stood at the window, watching out for Milly's arrival.

Lady Penrose simply paced the floor.

'Oh, dear,' she said, for the umpteenth time. 'I should not be doing this. If anything were to happen to you, your grandfather would never forgive me.'

'What could possibly happen to me? I shall only be at a masquerade ball. In a private house.'

'These events sometimes degenerate into sad romps. It is why your grandfather would disapprove.'

'Miss Brigstock and I will have a male escort, Lady Penrose.'

'Yes, but we hardly know this Lieutenant Kendell.'

'Surely he must be perfectly respectable,' Lady Jayne replied mischievously, 'since Lord Ledbury introduced us to him.'

She had taken great delight in getting her seal of approval for the male escort in question by emphasising his connection to Lord Ledbury. The mere mention of his name always soothed Lady Penrose's ruffled feathers. And Lady Jayne hadn't been able to help enjoying using him to enable her to go through with an enterprise he would roundly condemn, should he ever find out about it. It was a fitting revenge for the way he'd tried to dictate with whom she could be friends.

At last the long-awaited carriage drew up outside. They had decided to hire a hack, since travelling in Lady Penrose's town carriage would betray their identity at once.

She saw Milly getting out and so, before Lady Penrose had time to think better of letting her go out without her, she flew across the room, gave her a swift hug, promised that she would be very, very careful, and ran from the room.

'This is so exciting,' said Milly as Lady Jayne bundled her back into the hired cab and climbed in after her.

Exciting was not the word Lady Jayne would have chosen to describe the emotions churning round her stomach. She was riddled with guilt at not only deceiving Lady Penrose, but making her an accomplice. She was dreading giving Harry the news that would break his heart. This evening was going to be quite an ordeal.

A bit like lancing a boil. Quite painful, and messy, but once it was done she would be able to return to a more healthy state of mind. Eventually.

'You look adorable,' said Harry, who had been sitting in one corner, hidden from the inquisitive eyes of the footman who had opened the carriage door for her. He had gone to pick up Milly first, thinking it would be best for them all to arrive together, rather than waste time trying to locate each other whilst heavily disguised if they made their way to the ball separately.

As he ran his eyes over her with smouldering intensity her discomfort increased all the more. For one thing, it was hard to accept compliments and admiring looks when she was about to break things off with him.

For another, she knew she did not look in the least adorable. She looked like a nun in a wimple.

'What do you think of my costume, Lieutenant Kendell?' Milly twitched aside the heavy cloak she wore, drawing Harry's eyes away from Lady Jayne.

'My word,' he said, his mouth spreading into an appreciative grin. 'That is quite something.'

Indeed it was, thought Lady Jayne with a spurt of feminine jealousy. Milly had told her that she had once seen a Spanish woman wearing a dress of red satin, with hundreds of ruffles round the skirts, which had looked so incredibly opulent that she had vowed if ever she had any money she would buy such a dress for herself. She knew, of course, that such a style would normally be quite unsuitable for everyday, but it would be perfect for a masquerade ball. Red satin she had promised herself, if ever she had the means, so red satin she would have.

Her own plain white muslin gown, and the blue silk domino that covered it, were positively insipid in comparison with Milly's flamboyant costume. Particularly since it moulded to Milly's figure as though it had been painted on. She even had a red mask—Lady Jayne sighed enviously—studded with tiny red beads to resemble jewelled eyebrows.

She had to remind herself quite sternly that it was ridiculous to feel jealous when the whole point of her nondescript outfit was to deflect attention, not to attract it.

Their host and hostess were waiting, arm in arm, at the head of the stairs to greet their guests as they arrived. Lord Lambourne was dressed in some kind of military uniform, while his wife was dressed in a costume very similar to Milly's. Spanish ladies were obviously in vogue for masquerade balls this Season.

Their party passed on into a ballroom where dancing was already underway. No sooner had they got there than a rather portly man in black silk, sporting a pair of red devil's horns, lurched up to them.

'Do I know either of you fair maidens?' He peered at Lady Jayne and Milly in turn. 'My, but I am going to enjoy endeavouring to penetrate your disguises.'

The lascivious tone of his voice made Lady Jayne pull her domino tight to her throat and shrink closer to Harry.

But Milly gave a sultry gurgle and replied, 'And I shall enjoy fielding your efforts to do so.'

He couldn't tear his eyes from the front of Milly's very tight and daringly low-cut bodice when he asked her to dance.

Had Lady Jayne been on the receiving end of such a lascivious look she would have slapped the portly devil's face, but Milly did not appear to feel in the least bit insulted. On the contrary, she laughed with apparent delight and went off to dance with a perfect stranger...

Leaving her alone with Harry.

Chapter Six

While Lady Jayne was trying to think of some way to rescue Milly, even though she did not look as though she wanted rescuing, Harry swept her onto the dance floor.

As he twirled her round and round she remembered exactly why she had begun to look out for him whenever she had attended any of the assemblies that the locals had put on to welcome his regiment to their part of Kent. He was such a good dancer.

It was sad to think this would be the last time they ever danced together. She was going to miss dancing with him. Well, the truth was she was already missing dancing altogether. She bitterly regretted the fact that she had been so adamant in rejecting all offers to dance with anyone when she had first come to Town. It would make it very awkward to accept anyone now. Though she could not think of anyone she was likely to enjoy dancing with anyway—except perhaps Lord Ledbury, who would not read more into it than was really there. Only he never danced, either. She was not sure why. He scarcely limped at all. Though he did sometimes look very fatigued. And it was at those times that he became particularly crotchety with her.

According to Milly, he got crotchety with her, too. Apparently, during the year she'd acted as his nurse, they had frequently bickered. Though Lady Jayne found that hard to believe. Milly was such a sunny, good-natured person that it was hard to imagine her bickering with anyone. Even Lord Ledbury. Although admittedly she was never in his vicinity for long before something he said or did annoyed her.

'You feel it, too, don't you, my darling?' Harry murmured into her ear, bringing her back to the present with a jolt. 'Being forced to meet only in secret is breaking your heart, is it not?'

'Oh, er...' Far from worrying about Harry, she had just spent the entire dance thinking about another man.

Lord Ledbury was invading her thoughts far too often. She would be glad when this evening was over and she would be free of him, as well as Harry. She *would,* she told herself sternly as her spirits inexplicably plunged at the prospect of seeing him heave a sigh of relief as he realized that he could bow out of her life for good.

Harry slid his arm round her waist and towed her from the dance floor. 'Enough of this. Though it is delightful to hold you in my arms, I need to talk to you.'

He took her along a short corridor and into a conservatory. Seeing that it was already occupied by a couple of pairs of lovers, tussling on most uncomfortable-looking benches, he led her past them and out through French windows onto the terrace beyond. Then he turned and shut the doors behind them, so that she could scarcely hear the music from the ballroom any more.

She clasped her hands at her bosom, her heart pounding as she prepared to give him the little speech she had prepared in which she planned to tell him that she had mistaken her feelings, beg his forgiveness and urge him to forget her.

But then he seized her hands and said, 'I cannot bear sneaking around like this. Give me the right to call you mine. Marry me. I know it will mean eloping, but…'

'Harry, no…'

'Darling, yes. We could just walk out of this ballroom, get into a cab and run away together.'

'No, we could not…'

'Ah!' He smiled at her fondly. 'You are thinking of the practicalities. You are right to do so, my clever darling. We must have the money to pay for a licence and so forth. You will have to go home first, and get hold of whatever you can…'

She could not help it. She snorted.

'Well, my pin money is not going to get us very far.'

'But surely your grandfather does not keep you short? You dress so well. And your jewels alone must be worth a fortune.'

'I dress well because I have accounts all over Town and the bills are all sent to his man of business to settle. I have very little actual money to spend. But let us not talk about money. Harry, I have something I need to tell you…'

'It will be different once we are married, though, will it not? There must be some kind of settlement which will mean that your husband will have charge of your fortune?'

'What fortune?' she scoffed. 'If I marry a man of whom my grandfather disapproves I shall be cut off without a penny.'

'I am sure he would not be so harsh…'

'That's because you don't know him. He has already cut off his own daughter without showing a single sign of remorse. How much easier will it be to do the same to me?'

'Daughter? What daughter?'

'Oh. Well, it is not known outside the family. And even within it we only speak of my aunt Aurora in whispers. But she ran off with a penniless local youth, and Grandpapa not only banished her from the country but forbade anyone to speak her name in his presence.'

A look of confusion flashed across his face. 'But surely your *father* must have settled something upon you. You cannot be entirely dependent upon your grandfather?'

'I suppose we could live on the pittance that he set aside for me. But the bulk of his fortune, along with all the land, went to the new holder of his title.'

'You mean you have *nothing*?'

That was not strictly true. The lawyers had drawn up what they considered a reasonable settlement when her mother had married the Marquis of Tunstall, to provide for any female offspring of the union. But in comparison with what a son would have had Lady Jayne considered her inheritance from him to be a paltry sum.

His face distorted with fury, Harry thrust her roughly away from him.

'You bitch!'

She was not sure what hurt most. Her hip, where it had caught on the corner of the balustrade, or her feelings at being called by such a vile word. Or the expression of complete loathing on Harry's face.

'All this time you have been leading me on when you knew full well there was never any chance I could marry you!'

This was terrible. She had known he would be hurt when he learned it must end, but she'd never expected him to think she'd deliberately deceived him. No wonder he was furious.

'I did not mean to lead you on,' she said, stretching out her hand as she begged for his understanding. 'I simply did not think.'

He seized her by the upper arms, his fingers digging into her flesh.

'Well, if you think,' he snarled, thrusting his face into hers, 'that I am going to keep hanging around on the off-chance your grandfather might change his mind about me, then you are very much mistaken. This is farewell, my lady.'

Then his mouth came crashing down on hers. And it was horrible. Far worse than the last time he'd kissed her. It was as though he was trying to punish her. She could taste his anger in the metallic tang of blood when his teeth ground against her lips. Though she did not try to fight him off, as she had the last time he had pounced on her and taken liberties. She just stood there, rigid in his embrace, accepting the punishment she felt she fully deserved.

'My God,' he said, abruptly letting her go. 'What a narrow escape I've had. You don't even have what it takes to keep a man warm at night.'

She groped behind her for the balustrade. Her legs

were shaking so much it was all that kept her from slumping to the ground.

'They call you Chilblain Jayne—did you know that? Because though you look delectable enough to heat a man's blood to boiling point, the minute he tries to put his hands on you the frost you exude will freeze *all* his extremities.' He laughed mockingly as she flinched. 'Frankly, I don't have the patience to try and thaw you out. Nobody would even attempt to without the lure of the Earl of Caxton's fortune. You are just not worth the effort.'

And then he turned on his heel and stalked off into the house, leaving the French doors swinging wide behind him.

She pressed her hand to her bruised lips, feeling sick.

It had all been a sham. He had been pretending. Deceiving her because he wanted her money. Not her. Never her.

But then, when had anyone ever wanted her?

She felt like curling up into a ball and keening with pain. But she could not. She just could not bear to think someone might witness her humiliation.

She had to find Milly and get home.

She blundered her way back to the ballroom, half blinded by the tears she could not even wipe from her eyes because of the mask she dared not remove lest anyone recognise her.

But before she'd made it through the door a pair of arms shot out and grabbed her. A man, a very large and very strong man, whirled her right off her feet and carried her, kicking and struggling, back into the conservatory.

* * *

Lord Ledbury's spirits had been steadily sinking since the night of the theatre trip. But they had hit rock bottom the night before, when he'd seen the bet written down for all to see. Two so-called gentlemen had staked a tidy sum on the precise amount of time it would take Morty's successor to thaw out 'Chilblain Jayne.' His insistence that she appeared to welcome his suit had blown up in his face. Spectacularly.

He had only taken her for a drive once in Hyde Park—but she had never gone driving with any other man. Whenever he approached her in a ballroom he got a polite smile, and the pleasure of her company for a stroll about the room—whereas she sent every other petitioner about his business.

And then she'd accepted a seat in his private box at the theatre. He should have known from the amount of interest each of them had garnered individually at Lucy Beresford's come-out ball that speculation would rise to fever pitch when they were seen together.

He had wanted to hit somebody. Thrash them. Only he was not quite sure upon whom to focus his anger. The men who'd made the repulsive wager, himself for making her the subject of vulgar speculation or Lieutenant Kendell for being the man with whom Lady Jayne was secretly already in love.

Ever since that night he'd stood beneath her window, savouring the miraculous effect she'd had on his manhood, he'd been having the most disturbingly explicit dreams about her. Dreams from which he woke in a tangle of sheets, covered in sweat and rock-hard. And every time they'd met since then his physical response to her had grown stronger.

But it wasn't merely lust. The more he got to know her, the more he liked her as a person, too. Even when her behaviour irritated him he could see that she was acting from motives he couldn't help admiring.

Worst of all was the fact that every other woman paled into insignificance in comparison with her. He'd hoped that since she'd resurrected his interest in sex he might be able to divert it to some other suitable female.

No such luck. She was the only woman he wanted to haul into his arms and kiss into submission.

And, to his annoyance, just lately he'd begun to daydream about the various ways a man could permanently dispose of a rival in a crowded city like London. Kendell would not pose much of a challenge. He might wear a uniform, but he'd never got it dirty. And he wouldn't be expecting a physical attack...

Though his murderous daydreams always ended the same way. With Lady Jayne finding out what he'd done—for she was so bright she was bound to—and cheering as he was led to the gallows.

And she would. She didn't like him. He'd thought she had begun to soften towards him a little, but since the theatre trip there had been a definite withdrawal. The few times he'd managed to insist they spend some moments together her smiles had been forced, rather than natural. And, no matter how much he'd goaded her, he hadn't been able to rouse her from her abstraction.

Why should it feel so important to try, anyway? He'd come to Town to find a wife. Surely amongst the gaggle of girls on the catch for a husband there must be *one* who could oust Lady Jayne from the forefront of his mind?

But he could not face another night of searching in

vain for some elusive quality that would raise one of this Season's debutantes above the average. He could not stomach one more stuffy *ton* event, where everyone was on their best behaviour and nobody said or did anything *real*.

For just one night he needed to behave disgracefully. To get more than a little drunk and dance with a dozen women of the kind who would not take his interest in their charms as a prelude to a marriage proposal. Maybe even kiss one or two of them if he felt like it and they showed willing. And hopefully break the incomprehensible hold Lady Jayne had over him.

The Lambournes' masquerade promised exactly the kind of mild debauchery he was seeking.

Almost immediately upon his arrival he'd begun to pursue a shepherdess whose main attraction had been a gown that was so low-cut he could actually see the outer edges of her nipples. He'd just persuaded her onto the dance floor and into his arms when he'd heard Milly laugh.

Since he hadn't expected her to gain entry to an event like this he'd turned round, in some surprise, to see who had escorted her here.

He'd frozen when he'd seen the woman standing on the edge of the dance floor beside her.

Lady Jayne. With Kendell.

Well, if she held him in such disdain she thought she could flout their agreement, then to hell with her!

He'd pulled the shepherdess hard against his loins and resumed dancing in a way that paid no heed to the proprieties. But in spite of the gratifying response the shepherdess gave him he was painfully aware of Lady

Jayne, swirling round the dance floor with Kendell, a look of dreamy absorption on her face.

When they left the ballroom, arm in arm, they took with them any last remnant of desire he'd fleetingly felt for the wanton little shepherdess. The thought of Kendell holding Lady Jayne in his arms, kissing the lips that *he* dreamed of nightly not fifty feet from where he was standing, made him feel physically sick.

He broke out in a cold sweat. Suddenly it all made sense. When some of his fellow officers had talked about falling in love they'd described the same symptoms from which he was suffering. They'd said it made them blind to the attractions of all other women. To think he'd scoffed at them, insisting all cats were grey in the dark.

Well, he knew better now. He hadn't seen it sneaking up on him, but he'd been well and truly ambushed by the one emotion he'd never thought would come into his life.

He'd gone and fallen in love with the most unsuitable, unattainable woman in London.

He rather thought he must have groaned, because the shepherdess looked up at him with concern.

'You ain't gonna cast up your accounts, are yer?'

He managed a strained smile. 'I hope not. But just in case…' He pried her arms from about his neck. She readily took the hint, patting him on the shoulder sympathetically before skipping off in search of a fresh partner.

Goddammit. In spite of just saying Lady Jayne could go to hell as far as he was concerned, he'd been lying to himself. He was the one in hell. He turned to glare at the door through which she'd wafted with Kendell—

only to see the man himself come storming back into
the ballroom with an ugly look on his face.

But without Lady Jayne.

He waited for her to appear in his wake, and when
she did not he just knew something dreadful must have
happened.

He pushed his way through the swirling crowd of
dancers. He had to find her. She was alone out there
somewhere, and unprotected, at the kind of event she
should never have come to in the first place.

He'd barely got through the door when she ran full
tilt into him and, before he'd had a chance to identify
himself, began lashing out at him in a panic.

There was only one thing to be done. He picked her
up, placing one hand over her mouth to stifle her protests, and carried her into the conservatory.

'Hush,' he said once he'd set her on her feet. 'You're
safe now. I'm here.'

She looked up at him then, but if anything her eyes
grew even more panicked.

'Don't you recognise me?' he said softly, when it
looked as though she was desperately thinking of some
way to dart past him.

Lady Jayne looked up at the face of the masked man
who'd just picked her up and hauled her into this darkened alcove with such ruthless determination. When
she'd tried to scream for help he'd put his hand over her
mouth. He hadn't appeared even to notice when she'd
kicked out at him with her flimsy evening slippers.
It had felt like trying to wrestle with a walking...oak
tree. What kind of a party was this? No wonder Lady
Penrose had had second thoughts about allowing her to

come here. She must have known the kind of disgraceful things that went on.

The oak tree had put her down eventually, but with her back to the wall. And his shoulders were so broad they blocked her view of the rest of the room. Though she already knew that the other occupants of the conservatory were so intent on their own pleasure that they had not even noticed a struggling nun being carried into the room by a…corsair! For that was what he looked like. She could see now that he'd set her down. He wore a mask, and a red bandana over his hair. He had a cutlass tucked into the belt that spanned narrow hips clad in indecently tight breeches. His ruffled silk shirt was open to the waist, and a pair of thigh-length sea boots completed the outfit. He took his hand from her mouth the moment she stopped struggling. Not that she would yield to the rogue! But he was so big and powerful she would never be able to escape him—except perhaps by persuading him to let her go.

'Lady Jayne…'

The gentleness of the voice saying her name pierced right through her mounting panic. She looked properly into the eyes that were regarding her through the slits in his black mask. They were grey. And full of concern.

As they had been that night he'd wiped the tear from her face.

'L-Lord Ledbury?' The rapid pounding of her heart steadied and slowed when he nodded and took his arm from her waist. But thankfully he remained exactly where he was. Shielding her from view.

Protecting her from possible exposure.

It was not some lecherous stranger, intent on making sport of her. It was Lord Ledbury come to…to tell her off for behaving so badly, no doubt. But, even so, she had never been so glad to see anyone in her life.

'I was so careful with my disguise,' she began to excuse herself. 'How on earth did you recognise me?'

'How did I recognise you?' He shook his head ruefully. Her image was imprinted on his brain. Though she was covered in the most unflattering garment ever devised, she could not hide her height, or the shape of her figure.

And her mask did not cover her mouth.

He dreamed about those lips. What they would taste like. How they would feel pressed on various parts of his body.

'Your mouth,' he grated and, because he couldn't help himself, he reached out, meaning to trace the outline of those lush lips with the tips of his fingers.

And that was when he saw the smear of blood, the cut, the puffiness that spoke of a bruise already forming below the tender skin.

'What the hell did he do to you?' He had a pretty good idea. He'd witnessed the fool trying to force himself on Lady Jayne in the park. And it looked as if her reaction tonight must have been the same as then. It was one thing for a girl of her age and sheltered background to indulge in romantic dreams, but Kendell ought to have learnt that she wasn't ready for unleashed passion. 'This is why I did not want you meeting him without me around. I would never have let something like this happen to you.'

'Y-yes, I know. It was all my own fault.'

She'd brought it on herself. And now Lord Ledbury was angry with her, too. That he was also angry with Harry was of scant comfort. She could not endure a lecture—not now. Not after Harry had turned into a stranger in the blink of an eye. A frightening stranger who had torn down the romantic fantasies she'd been weaving round herself, leaving her naked, bereft and bleeding.

'B-but, please, d-don't...'

'Lady Jayne,' he said, gently brushing something from her cheek. 'Don't cry.'

'I'm not crying. I n-never cry.' She hiccupped.

'Then he must have really hurt you,' he said fiercely, 'because you most certainly are crying.' Very gently he lifted her chin and examined her lower lip, which was swelling rapidly round a jagged tear.

'He w-wanted me to...' She shook her head.

His blood ran cold. Had it been worse than ardour getting out of hand?

'But when I said I would not, he...' Her face crumpled. 'He was just...it was...and now it is over...'

Then she flung her arms round his waist, and hid from the questions in his eyes by burying her face in the solid warmth of his chest.

'Just take me home,' she sobbed. 'Please take me home!'

It was over! He put his arms round her and rocked her while she wept. Or were they rocking together? He hardly knew. He was sure of only two things.

Kendell was out of the running.

And she was in his arms.

He felt as though he was being torn in two. Until now there hadn't been any choice. But now his body was pulling him one way, demanding he abandon all aspirations to find a *suitable* wife and commit to this woman, the only woman it wanted to possess. And to hell with all his carefully laid plans. And the future he'd envisaged, with his glorious countess at his side, helping him improve his estates and leaving such a legacy that generations to come would speak in awe of the seventh Earl of Lavenham and his redoubtable wife.

It was all he could do to prevent himself from blurting out that she was better off without a no-hoper like Kendell. That he was ready to take the fool's place like a shot...

And then he was no longer in a dilemma. He simply couldn't imagine her looking up at him in dawning wonder and then them kissing and it all ending happily ever after. His life had never resembled any kind of fairy story. His reality was that she was only clinging to him because he happened to be there, and she'd learned enough about him in their short acquaintance to know she could trust him.

She only wanted one thing from him. She wanted him to take her home.

Well, he could do that much for her.

It would mean letting her go, that was the trouble...

No, dammit, it wouldn't! Keeping one arm round her shoulders, he guided her into the hall, snagged a cloak from a footman who happened to be passing with guests' discarded outerwear and, wrapping it round her to shield her from view, got her outside and into the first available hack he could hail.

She did not object to any of it. On the contrary, she clung to him throughout as though her life depended on it, weeping as though her heart was broken.

It probably was. His mouth flattened into a grim line. Thank heaven he hadn't made a complete fool of himself by blurting out all that nonsense about taking Kendell's place. He'd had enough of standing in for some other man since he'd come back to England. Besides, what good would it do her for him to make a declaration he had no intention of following through? He might be dazzled by Lady Jayne. He might want her so much he felt sick to think of her in another man's arms. But that didn't mean he had any right to burden her with the news.

Especially not when he hadn't come to terms with it fully himself.

No, what she needed right now was somebody she could just lean on.

So when she slumped onto the seat of the hired hack, looking utterly forlorn, he took the risk of putting his arms round her again. Far from rebuking him, she burrowed into him again, clinging like a limpet while the storm of sobs continued unabated.

He held her tight. Inhaled the scent of her hair. She smelled like roses and honeysuckle. Every time he smelled a rose from this day forward he would remember this moment and savour the memory of holding her delicious curves against his body. He knew his dreams would grow even more vivid now that he had reality to mingle with his fantasies. But he was willing to pay that price. For who knew when he would ever get another opportunity like this? It was not as if he was taking advantage of her moment of weakness. She was drawing comfort from his embrace. And he was taking damn good care to make sure that source of comfort did not become distasteful to her by not letting her suspect exactly how her proximity affected him.

It was quite some time before she unwound her arms

from his waist, looked up, sniffed and asked, 'Where is Milly?'

He cupped her cheek with the palm of his hand, marvelling at her ability to think of another when she was in such distress.

'Do not worry about Milly,' he said gruffly. He could cheerfully wring Milly's neck. What had she been thinking, to aid and abet Lady Jayne in meeting Kendell behind his back? But, since he wanted to soothe her fears, he explained, 'Milly is a daughter of the regiment. She is well used to looking out for herself.'

Lady Jayne's self-esteem shrivelled even further. She'd thought Harry's confession that he would not have bothered with her were she not rich had been bad enough, but now Lord Ledbury was treating her as though she was as fragile as porcelain, while having complete confidence in Milly's ability to look after herself.

In spite of being plain and poor, Milly had managed to capture the heart of the man who was holding her in his arms—much against his inclination, if the stiffness of his posture was anything to go by. She cringed to think of how proud she had been to have influenced Milly's dress sense. As if that mattered. Lord Ledbury loved her just for being herself. Because Milly had something about her that far outweighed her own rank and wealth.

But then, had not Harry just explained that there was *nothing* about her that could attract a man apart from her money? She did not even know how to kiss properly!

She swiped at the tears dripping from her chin with the backs of her hands. Why had she believed his lies in the first place? She'd always known she was worthless.

Her father had never let her forget that she had disappointed him by not being a boy. He'd regarded her very existence as her mother's unforgivable crime. And then her grandfather had confirmed her worst fears by taking one look at her, reeling in horror, and paying legions of professionals to change her into something he would not find quite so obnoxious.

The last thing anyone had ever wanted her to be was herself.

And yet when Harry had told her all those lies about how much he adored her she'd believed him. Why had she been so stupid?

Because she'd wanted *somebody* to love her. Anybody. Even somebody whose regard she could not return.

And that was when she remembered that the whole point of meeting Harry tonight had been to tell him that very fact. She didn't love him. She'd never loved him.

And then she realized that the only reason the things he'd said had hurt her so badly was because they had struck directly at wounds she already bore. She didn't care what *he* thought of her. Not one bit! Not now she knew what a lying, deceitful...*toad* he was. Fancy taking such ruthless advantage of an insecure girl. Just to get his hands on her money.

And to think that for the last few weeks she'd been racked with guilt over the prospect of hurting his feelings.

Well, she wasn't going to waste one more moment feeling any guilt whatsoever in regard to Harry Kendell. She was just glad she'd never fallen completely under his spell, and that now she'd broken free.

She reached into her reticule, got out a handkerchief and blew her nose with some force.

Her mother had warned her never to let any man crush her spirit. Days after her father's funeral. She'd been too weak to rise from her bed for several months, and though she'd never been robust enough to let a boisterous child invade her rooms, she'd suddenly summoned Jayne to her side.

'I outlived him,' she'd whispered hoarsely. 'It was the only victory I could gain, but I did it. Before I go, I want your promise that you will never let a man crush you, either. Remember you are a Vickery. We always rise above whatever adversities life thrusts upon us.'

Mama had certainly risen to the challenge of being married to the odious Marquis of Tunstall. She had gone down fighting him to her last breath. His only wish, for years, had been that his invalid wife would die, so that he could remarry and get the heir she had failed to give him.

She shuddered. Did relations between men and women always have to be a battle?

Lord Ledbury, feeling her convulsive movement, put his arms round her again.

And brought her back to her senses.

What must he think of her? And, oh, Lord, how many times had he made the driver go round in circles while she wept into what little there was of his shirt-front?

It had been kind of him not to take her straight home, but still… She sat up straight, making it clear she no longer needed his support.

'I beg your pardon,' she said. 'I have finished crying now.'

For a moment he considered telling her that he would not care how long she cried if it meant she would stay in his arms. Except that it tore him up inside to see her so wretched.

Reluctantly, he released her and let her sit up.

Hating the physical distance she put between them as she inched along the seat, he reached for her free hand and held it between both of his own.

'Lady Jayne, I shall not pry. But if it would help you to talk about what happened I swear I would never betray your confidence. And if there is any way I may be of further service, you have only to ask.'

She wiped her nose. She had no intention of admitting what an idiot she'd been to fall for Harry's glib lies. But on the other hand he was being so kind...

And, in a way, she did owe him something of an explanation for dragging him away from the ball where, by the looks of that costume, he'd gone to have the kind of fun nobody ever got at the events where she usually met him.

Strange... She'd never thought of him as anything but a creature of duty. But seeing him in that outfit showed her there was more to him than met the eye.

What a pity she'd not gone to the masquerade with him. He looked as though he would have been a much more entertaining escort than Harry. And he wouldn't have crossed the line, either....

She shook herself and lowered her eyes to where he was holding her hand between his own.

'Harry had been trying to persuade me to elope with him for some time. Tonight, when he saw that nothing he could say or do would ever persuade me to take such a reprehensible step, he became very angry. He... Well, let us say he left me in no doubt that he never cared for anything about me but my fortune.'

'I knew it!' He'd known a man who was truly in love could never have enticed a lady into a series of such scandalous escapades. It was disrespectful. If Harry had really loved her, wouldn't he have begged her to wait for him, rather than urged her to elope? If *he'd* gained a place in her affections, when he'd been a mere lieutenant living on his pay, he would have waited forever. Done whatever necessary to prove his worth to her family by his conduct within his regiment, if nothing else. Lady Jayne was the sort who would stand by her word, once given. She would never have married anyone else.

But to find out that the man for whom she had taken such risks had only been toying with her… He frowned down into her bleak little face. And his heart turned over in his chest. She did not deserve to have her trust shattered like this.

By God, if he ever got his hands on Kendell…

Lady Jayne flinched at the murderous expression that came over him. Though how it was possible to hurt any more, after hearing him say he'd always known no man could really be in love with her, she wasn't sure. But there was definitely a pain in her chest. It was so sharp it hurt to draw air in past it. She had to get away from him before she broke down all over again.

'You may set me down at Lady Penrose's house now.'

He saw her face close up and bitterly regretted the fact that she was turning back into the lifeless little puppet he'd first encountered at Lucy Beresford's come-out ball.

'Not yet,' he said. 'Your eyes will still be red. And your nose…'

'Lady Penrose is hardly going to miss this, is she?' She indicated her torn lip. 'I shall have to give her an explanation. And,' she said, drawing herself upright, 'I am now ready to give it.'

He almost gasped with admiration. She must have an inner core of steel.

'Do you wish me to come in with you? Would it help at all?'

She shook her head. 'I have taken up far too much of your time as it is.'

The polite tone of her voice as she tugged her hand free of his was worse than anything that had gone before.

Do not withdraw from me, he wanted to beg her. *Do not shut me out.*

In the event, what he said was, 'As you wish.'

She clearly wanted to be on her own. He could understand that. Her pride made her reluctant to reveal her weaknesses. People who had not glimpsed her real self looked at her frozen expression, the one she was wearing now, and assumed she was cold all the way through. But it was as much a mask as the little scrap of satin she'd donned to attend tonight's masquerade. Only she put it on to conceal the depth of her hurt, not merely her identity.

Nobody, apart from himself and Lady Penrose, would ever know anything about this night's work. And he would hazard a guess that she would tell her duenna as little as she possibly could. He would be the only person to know that tonight she'd had her heart broken.

And all he could do about it was take her home and hope that Lady Penrose was kinder than she looked.

Chapter Seven

'I had not expected you back quite so early,' said Lady Penrose, looking up from the book she was reading. Her eyes narrowed upon Lady Jayne's lower lip, and her hand flew to her own mouth. 'I knew I should not have let you go to such an improper sort of party! They always get too boisterous. And there is always some man who gets out of hand.'

She braced herself for a scold when Lady Penrose shut her book with a snap.

'My dear, I am so sorry. You have led such a sheltered life. Nothing can have prepared you for the vile behaviour in which some men indulge when in their cups. But how did it come about? I thought you would stick close to Miss Brigstock all evening.'

'Oh, I…er…slipped away from her for a moment or two…'

'That is all it takes,' said Lady Penrose acidly. 'Men need no encouragement at the best of times, and when they are masked, and think they can get away with taking liberties without anyone knowing quite who they are… But what of the gentleman who escorted you there? I trust he came to your rescue?'

'No, he…he turned out to be a very great disappointment. In fact,' she said bitterly, 'he abandoned me not long after we got there.' Which was as much of the truth as she felt able to confess.

'But then however did you get home? I heard a carriage. Is Miss Brigstock with you?'

When Lady Jayne shook her head, Lady Penrose turned pale.

'Never say you had to get *yourself* a cab?'

'Oh, no. Fortunately Lord Ledbury…er…recognised me, saw that I'd had to extricate myself from a…predicament, and…um…escorted me home.'

Lady Penrose sagged with relief. But after only a minute's reflection, she sat up straight again. 'Lord Ledbury? He was there? And brought you home? The two of you were quite alone in a hired hack? I am not sure that this is not worse… Can we rely on his discretion, do you think?'

'You need have no worries on that score. Lord Ledbury will not tell anyone.' The last thing he'd want would be for anyone to know they'd spent the last half an hour locked in each other's arms.

Lady Penrose looked at her sharply. 'You trust him that much?'

'Yes. I do.' She was being unfair to accuse him of wanting to hush everything up for his own sake. He had shielded her from scandal once already. And he'd had nothing to gain that time.

He was innately chivalrous. She could never, not for one instant, imagine *him* trying to inveigle his way into an heiress's affections, then urging her to elope with him. Not that he needed an heiress. He was wealthy enough in his own right.

Nor was he the sort of man to humiliate a woman by telling her what vile nicknames people called her. Though he would probably know they called her Chilblain Jayne. Of course he would.

Oh, God. Had *he* ever referred to her by that name? A shaft of pain seared through her.

'Well, then, we must hope no real harm has been done. You have already paid dearly enough for learning about the true nature of men.' Lady Penrose looked at her lip. 'My advice to you is that you look upon this evening in the light of an educational experience. And we need say no more about it.'

It had definitely been educational. Harry had taught her a lesson she was not about to forget in a hurry. A lesson she should have learned years ago. She was unlovable. Completely worthless.

'May I go to bed?' she asked in a small, chastened voice.

'Of course,' Lady Penrose replied kindly. 'And do not repine too much. Just try to remember what you have learned so that you will not repeat the same mistake again.'

'Yes, that is what I shall do,' she said.

She would certainly never let another man fool her into believing he was interested in anything but her fortune.

She climbed the stairs slowly, trailing her hand along the banister. How could she have been so stupid? And she wasn't just thinking about falling for Harry's lies now, but her whole attitude since coming to London. She'd been so hurt and angry at the way her grandfa-

ther had treated her that she had rebuffed all the overtures of friendship made. Not that she liked any of this
year's crop of debutantes all that much anyway. They
were all so keen to get husbands, and their conversation revolved so exclusively around that topic, that five
minutes alone with any of them would have made her
boiling mad. But if she only had a circle of friends...

But there was no way back from the stance she'd
taken. Not now. She would just have to carry on as
though nothing had changed. When she got to her room
she would be able to remove the mask and domino she'd
worn tonight, but she could never let down her guard
with the people among whom she moved in Town. Or
they would start to wonder what had happened to wreak
such a change. And ask questions she had no intention
of ever answering.

She paused on the landing, head bowed. She was
trapped in a disguise she'd made for herself. And
the only people who would persist in trying to break
through it would be the truly desperate fortune-hunt-
ers. The ones who wanted access to her money badly
enough to put up with the chilblains they'd get from the
frost they said she exuded.

And she had nobody to blame but herself.

Over the next few days she found that she was glad
Harry had bruised her face. For each day Lady Penrose
would take a long hard look at her and decide that it
would be better to stay in her room and inform callers
that she was indisposed. It gave her a legitimate excuse
for staying out of circulation while she came to terms
with what an idiot she'd been. Though it might be a long
time before she felt ready to face anyone.

The first posy of flowers from Lord Ledbury arrived the very morning after the masquerade. And every day he sent her another.

Lady Penrose became so excited about the daily delivery from the florists that Jayne wondered whether she ought to explain that Lord Ledbury was just being kind. She didn't want her to get her hopes up for nothing. For, though flowers usually signified romantic interest, she knew he couldn't possibly have any romantic feelings towards her, having seen her at her worst. Though she would always treasure the memory of receiving flowers from Lord Ledbury, she was sure his concern was a transitory thing. It would wane just as surely as the flowers he sent withered and died.

One afternoon, Lady Penrose came to her room, took a chair, and gave her a stern look.

'Now, I know you have not come down to receive any callers, and I agree that that has been the best policy up till now. But today there is a visitor I think you would like to receive...'

Her heart leaped. Had Lord Ledbury done more than just send flowers via his footman today? Had he come in person? He had already seen the bruise on her mouth, so Lady Penrose would not feel she had to hide it from him.

'She has always acted like a tonic upon you,' said Lady Penrose, quashing her hope even before it had fully formed, 'and so I have said I will ask if you would receive her up here, in your room. Otherwise, you know, she might think you have fallen out with her over the masquerade. And, although you were both rather silly that night, I do not think what happened there was her fault, was it?'

Lady Penrose's gentle reproof struck her to the core. She had been so wrapped up in her own misery that she'd not spared a thought as to how Milly had got home. Lord Ledbury had said she could look after herself, and she'd been so jealous of the complete confidence he placed in her that she hadn't questioned that assumption.

'Of course I will see her,' she said.

Lady Penrose smiled approvingly, and went away to let Milly know she could come up.

'Richard,' said Milly, the moment she came through the door, 'was that mad at me for going to the masquerade with you. Rang a peal over me as if whatever it was that happened to you there was all my fault!' She sat down on the bed, untying the ribbons of a very fetching bonnet as she did so.

'Oh, no. I am so sorry…'

Milly shrugged her shoulders. 'It's not your fault he's got so stuffy since he come—I mean *came* into that title. And, anyway, he was there, too, wasn't he? Looking much more like his old self. He used to be such a great one for dancing and kicking up larks. You should have seen him doing the fandango when he was just a captain. Not many of the British officers ever mastered the steps properly, but he kept on and on at it, practising with the Portuguese women until he was as good as any of the muleteers.'

Somehow, Jayne could see it. Well, she could now she'd seen him in that corsair outfit, anyway. Putting on that costume had given him the liberty to be that dashing young officer Milly had just described once more. She'd got used to seeing the grim expression he wore in Society settings—but who wouldn't look grim if he had to go about looking for a suitable wife when deep down he didn't want any Society lady at all?

'So, why have you come today? Has something happened? I know Lord Ledbury does not want us to meet again, so...'

Milly made a rude noise, flapping her hands in a dismissive gesture. 'You weren't going to pay any attention to that silly notion of his, were you? That wasn't the impression I got when we planned getting into the masquerade, anyhow.'

Lady Jayne sat down on her dressing-table stool. When Lord Ledbury had first told her she was not to meet Milly again she had been incensed, and vowed he had no right to dictate with whom she might be friends. But in the aftermath of Harry's defection she'd begun to question her own judgement. Maybe she ought not to be so ready to flout authority. Or at least perhaps she ought to try and cultivate the habit of sitting down and thinking before reacting rebelliously to a stricture she found perfectly ridiculous.

Tentatively, she suggested, 'I expect he is only trying to protect you...'

'Protect me?' Milly gave her a searching look. Then, with a conspiratorial grin, she said, 'You don't really believe that, do you? It's been my experience that the stupid notions men have about how they want their women to behave only end up making everybody miserable.'

'Well, I can't argue with you there,' said Lady Jayne, thinking of how miserable all the men in her own life had made her.

'They're all self-serving bastards.'

'Not Lord Ledbury! You don't mean him, Milly.'

Milly pouted. 'Yes, I do. I know I can't ever marry

him. Not now he's come into that title. But he's got so starchy nowadays that he won't even make me his mistress.'

Lady Jayne was not used to such forthright speaking. Her cheeks a little warm, she said, 'It is not the thing to *want* to be a man's mistress. It isn't at all proper.'

But if she were in Milly's shoes how would she feel? If she knew she could never marry him, she rather thought she might be prepared to take whatever small crumbs Lord Ledbury scattered her way. After having been held in those strong arms, she knew she wouldn't feel the least bit revolted if *he* wanted to kiss her. If she'd been meeting him in the park, rather than Harry, she would definitely have wanted to kiss him back. And if *he'd* suggested eloping...

She pulled herself up sharply. It was *Milly's* relationship with Lord Ledbury they were discussing.

It was funny, but when she'd put herself in the theoretical position of being Lord Ledbury's forbidden love she'd seen herself getting swept away. But as soon as she tried to imagine Milly on the park bench kissing him she felt most uncomfortable. And her mind shied away from thinking about them going to bed altogether.

'Oh, let us not get into a quarrel about that. I have been so wretched since the night of the masquerade. And I am really glad you've come to see me.'

'In spite of what Richard might say if he found out?'

'Even then.'

Lord Ledbury clearly had his reasons for wanting this friendship to cease, but neither she nor Milly agreed with him. It was two to one.

Milly grinned. 'So come on, then, tell me all about it. I've been dying to find out what really happened between you and that handsome soldier of yours, and Richard just closes up like a clam whenever I ask him for details.'

The hour flew past, and by the time Milly left Lady Jayne's the mood had lifted considerably. Her bruise had almost disappeared, and her spirit, too, was reviving. It would not be much longer before Lady Penrose decreed she was fit to return to Society. And she would be ready.

She was a Vickery, after all. And Vickerys were never crushed by adverse circumstances. She was not, most definitely not, going to appear as though there was the slightest thing troubling her.

She took extra care over her appearance on the night of her first ball after the break with Harry, choosing a gown that had never had an outing before. When she'd had her last fitting she had adored the spangles on the overdress, and thought the white embroidery on the satin underskirt raised the outfit above the ordinary. But as she stood in front of the mirror she was appalled to see a glittering ice maiden looking back at her.

'Not the diamonds, Josie,' she said with a shiver. 'The sapphires tonight.'

'Yes. They will bring out the colour of your eyes.'

She didn't care about that. But at least they did not add to the impression of coldness that made everyone mock her.

Not that she cared. She lifted her chin as she walked into the ballroom later, telling herself she was ready to face them all down.

But in the event she did not notice who else might have been there. Because she saw Lord Ledbury, and for a moment all she could think about was how good it had felt to fling herself into his arms and let him hold her while she wept. Nobody in her whole life had held her like that. Nobody.

She tore her eyes away from him and made a great production of finding a chair, settling herself and Lady Penrose, arranging her skirts and flicking open her fan. She needed to cool her heated cheeks. How could she have considered running across the crowded room and flinging herself at him? He would be appalled. He had not minded coming to her assistance in a moment of need. When he was masked and nobody knew who he was. But he set such store by appearances that he wouldn't even let anyone see him take Milly to a modiste. He would detest being made a spectacle of at a *ton* event.

From across the room Lord Ledbury watched her surreptitiously as she pulled her dignity around her like a suit of armour. It set her apart from the frivolous gaiety of the rest of the guests. She might as well have been holding up a placard saying Keep Away.

To her right, he observed Miss Beresford look at Lady Jayne and giggle at something her friend Lady Susan Pettiffer whispered behind her gloved hand. Rage roiled up inside him. Yes, tonight she might look as though she deserved the nickname that some wit had coined for her, but they had no idea how bravely she was dealing with Lieutenant Kendell's perfidy. He would like to see Miss Beresford's reaction to such a betrayal. She would not get up and go about as though nothing had occurred. She would, no doubt, make a grand drama out of it, involving maids and her mama, recourse to the vinaigrette, and probably a doctor or two, and then a retreat to some seaside town for a rest cure.

He'd had no intention of drawing attention to how he felt about her by singling her out tonight. And he'd taken great care, while she had been absent from Society, to try and deal with it by searching even harder for a woman who would actually want to become his wife.

The trouble was, he was beginning to wonder why he'd ever thought it so important to prove himself to what remained of his family by marrying a woman who would impress them. He couldn't stop thinking about how it had felt to hold *her* in his arms.

And then the moment she'd walked in the door all the merits of the other girls he'd been…interviewing over the past week had faded away to nothing.

She was the only woman he really wanted.

Then almost at once his own needs were swept aside by the conviction that what *she* needed at this moment, more than anything else, was a friend.

He strode across the room, and bowed over her hand.

'I am pleased to see you have recovered from your indisposition,' he said, conscious that others would be listening.

'Thank you,' she said politely. 'I am completely re-covered now.' It was the only way she could think of to tell him that she had learned her lesson where Harry was concerned. That she would never be so stupid again.

He glanced at her mouth, concern briefly flaring in those smoky grey eyes.

'Would you care to take a walk with me, Lady Jayne? Outside on the terrace? The gardens of this house look particularly enchanting by moonlight, and the air is mild tonight.'

Her heart stuttered in her chest. She had thought he would distance himself from her, since he no longer

had to seek her out to inform her when the next meeting with Harry could take place. And, since he would
also assume her association with Milly was at an end,
they would have very little to discuss. She'd braced herself for the conjecture that would arise. She'd imagined
people whispering that he had not the stamina to *thaw*
her. The only thing they might wonder at was that he
had persisted for this long. Yet he'd marched right over,
the moment she'd set foot in the ballroom, exactly as
he'd always used to.

She wondered what he wanted to talk about tonight.
Not that she had any intention of refusing his request.
She had never done so before, and to do so now would
only create speculation about what might have changed
between them.

'May I, Lady Penrose?'

'Of course, my dear.'

Rising gracefully to her feet, she threaded her hand
through his extended arm and strolled outside with him.

'How are you, truly?' he said, the moment they were
out of earshot of anyone else.

'Completely recovered, as I told you before. Well,'
she said with a brittle smile, 'to *you* I will confess that
occasionally I still feel a little sorry for myself. But now
the bruise has healed I have no excuse not to go about
in Society again. And let me tell you I have no intention of sitting at home and repining over a man who
proved himself to be completely unworthy of my regard. I would rather die,' she admitted, with some vehemence, 'than let anyone know what a fool I have been.'

Her voice was hard. Her face a mask of hauteur. He
did not think he had ever seen a more tragic little figure in all his life.

'Fortunately Harry will not dare to breathe a word of what he was up to, lest he gain a reputation that would hamper future enterprises of the same sort,' she said, with a perspicacity that amazed him.

He wished he knew the right thing to do, or say. He could not stand to see her in such pain, yet walling herself off from it with this show of not caring. But the very worst thing he could do would be to offer her sympathy. She would hate him if he were to cause that wall of ice to crack and make all her grief come pouring out in such a public place. But he was still compelled to let her know that, in him, she had a friend who would always remain tactfully silent, yet stolidly faithful.

'You know, I hope, that you can trust me not to reveal what went on?'

'Of course I trust you,' she said, looking up into his stern face. She would trust this man with her whole future. He would never let her down.

And just like that she understood *exactly* what it was that had made her aunt Aurora defy convention to run off with the man she loved. If she ever won the heart of a man like this she would follow him to the ends of the earth if he should ask it of her. She gasped at the audacity of even *thinking* such a thing, tore her eyes away from him and fanned her heated cheeks briskly.

He took a step back. Dammit, he had been standing too close to her. Just because she'd let him hold her in his arms when she'd been distressed, it did not mean she was ready to repeat the experience.

A friend. That was all she wanted him to be.

'May I take you for a drive tomorrow?'

'Are you sure? I mean, there is no need.'

'There is every need. You have more need of me now than at any time since we first met.'

'I do not *need* anyone,' she retorted. Then hung her head. 'But, yes, I would enjoy going for a drive tomorrow.'

No, she did not need anyone. He'd watched her pulling herself together after Kendell had betrayed her trust, marvelling at her inner strength.

He would be a fool to think he might be able to make her fall in love with him, even if he knew how to begin courting her.

But then... He hadn't expected *whichever* woman he eventually decided to propose to to love him, either.

His heart began to beat very fast.

Was there a chance for him after all?

He certainly had one advantage over every single other man she knew, and that was his knowledge of the affair with Harry. He knew she was unhappy, and why, and he could at least offer her an escape. He could take her away from Town, and all its unpleasant associations, and give her the opportunity to recover.

And, as an added benefit, he could offer her the freedom she craved.

The freedom to be herself. That had to be worth something, didn't it?

Ye gods. He was seriously thinking about proposing to Lady Jayne Chilcott.

'Then I shall see you tomorrow,' he said curtly, and led her back to her seat beside Lady Penrose.

For the rest of the evening Lady Jayne surreptitiously followed Lord Ledbury's movements. He sat out the quadrille in the company of a plain, plump girl she didn't know. He took a walk round the perimeter of the ballroom with Lady Susan Pettiffer during the first half of a set of country dances. And he escorted Lucy Beresford into supper. At least, Lucy would have liked to think so. The truth was closer to being that they were in the same party, which included her brother and the plain plump girl.

It appeared that his search for a suitable bride had been continuing apace while she had been out of circulation. Well, what had she expected? He was the kind of man who, when set a task, did it to the best of his ability. She only had to think of Milly's description of how determined he had been to learn the fandango.

It was as if he regarded his whole life as a contest which he was determined to win. She'd noticed his belligerence the very first night they'd met, though she hadn't understood its cause. He'd walked into that ballroom and glared round as though defying anyone to question his right to be there. She smiled ruefully. Now she knew him better she wouldn't be a bit surprised to learn that part of what drove him was the need to prove to his family that he was a better man than they took him for.

Her smile faded away. That made it especially kind of him to continue with the pretence on which they'd agreed—that he was interested in her and she was responding to his suit. If he wouldn't even marry Milly, the woman he loved, he most certainly wasn't really going to consider a silly chit who'd almost been seduced by a man with nothing to recommend him but a handsome face. Who was a harum scarum creature that he'd watched getting into one disgraceful scrape after another.

Not that she wanted to get married anyway. She'd promised herself she wouldn't.

So why did she suddenly feel so depressed?

'I am growing quite tired, Lady Penrose,' she said morosely, plying her fan to stir the stuffy air of the ballroom. 'May we leave soon?'

'Of course, my dear,' said Lady Penrose. 'You need to recoup your strength so that you look your best for your outing tomorrow.'

Lady Jayne's heart sank still further. Her chaperone was convinced Lord Ledbury was developing a tendre for her. She was going to be so disappointed when it all came to nothing.

Chapter Eight

'What you need,' Lord Ledbury said, the moment his groom had set the carriage in motion, 'is a change of scenery.'

'Yes. Thank you. It was a lovely idea of yours to take the air in the park this afternoon.'

'No, no, I didn't mean that.' He turned his upper body to face her. 'You were drawn tight as a bowstring last night at that wretched ball, trying to preserve a calm facade so that nobody could tell how badly you are suffering. It would do you good to get out of Town altogether for a space. Spend some time recovering in the countryside.'

For a moment she was quite worried. She had thought she had done such a good job of concealing her lowness of spirits. She darted a glance at Lord Ledbury, who was gazing at her with one of his searching frowns. She relaxed, remembering she had confided as much to him last night. And was touched to see he'd been thinking about what she'd said, and was offering his advice.

'It is kind of you to be concerned for my welfare. And, to be honest, I should dearly love to return to

Kent, in some ways. Only...' She pulled at the fingers of her gloves. 'I really, really don't want to let this business with Harry defeat me. Going home *would* feel like a defeat. Besides,' she continued with a wry smile, 'I cannot think of anything that would induce my grandfather to have me back.'

'I did not mean to imply I thought you should go home. Far from it.'

He took a deep breath and took the gamble of his life. He knew she was the wrong woman in so many ways, and yet if he wrote her out of his life irrevocably, without even trying... Well, he would always regret it.

'I would like you to attend a house party I mean to get up at Courtlands, the family seat in Buckinghamshire.'

While she was maintaining her defences so rigidly, to conceal the depth of her hurt, he stood no chance of ascertaining what her feelings towards him had the potential to become. But in the less formal atmosphere of a country house party there would be plenty of opportunities for breaching the rigid etiquette Society enforced. Rides in the woods, strolls through the shrubbery, picnics by the lake...

'A house party? So early in the Season?' People did not normally start deserting the capital until the weather started to grow uncomfortably hot.

Unless they wanted to introduce a prospective bride to the head of a family, and give them a glimpse of the property of which they might one day become mistress.

Was he that close to making a decision? A shaft of pain went through her. How on earth could he think it would *do her good* to watch him make his selection from whichever other girls he invited down there, whilst discounting her from the running altogether?

She averted her head sharply while she grappled with her emotions. He wasn't being deliberately cruel. Not Lord Ledbury. It sounded as though he really just wanted to offer her some respite from the nightmare that her Season had become. He could have no idea that he was catapulting her into an altogether different kind of nightmare, since she'd taken great care not to let him know how very much she was beginning to... admire him.

'The grounds of Courtlands are quite lovely at this time of year,' he said. 'But, to tell you the truth, I need an excuse to get out of Town, too. You are the one person to whom I can confess this, but I feel almost like a traitor, doing nothing but going to balls, or performances at the theatre, when it looks as though the whole of Europe is about to be plunged into yet another war.'

She could have kicked herself. Why did she always only look at things from her own point of view? Every day the papers reported more regiments sailing for the Low Countries, and poor Lord Ledbury was stuck in England, obliged to find himself a suitable bride—whilst his heart belonged to Milly.

'It must be terribly frustrating for you,' she said. 'Everyone who has any military experience at all seems to be scrambling to get across to the continent and join up. If I were a man, and I had been used to being in the army, having to kick my heels in London whilst others went off to trounce Bonaparte would make me want to scream with frustration.'

That surprised a wry laugh from him. 'I would never scream, no matter what the provocation. But I admit that sometimes it is all I can do to keep a civil tongue in my head when people who have never been involved make stupid remarks about…oh, how shocking it is that Bonaparte's former marshals won't arrest him, for instance.'

'As if they would! On fat Louis Bourbon's orders!'

'That is a remarkably perceptive thing for such a… I mean, you follow the news? The political news?'

She supposed she should be glad he'd swallowed back whatever derogatory remark he'd been on the verge of making. 'Why should I not read the newspapers?'

'Not many ladies would. I'm pretty certain that most would not consider it a fit topic of conversation, either.'

She wondered whether that was a rebuke, as well. Except he didn't look the least bit cross with her. And that encouraged her to admit, 'Well, I don't say that I always understand everything I read, especially when a report seems to contradict the one that went before it, but…'

'War can be a confusing business. Nobody can ever really know the truth of any battle unless he was there,' he said grimly. 'And as for what gets printed in the papers…' He drew a deep breath, as though deliberately distancing himself from whatever thoughts had put such a grim expression on his face.

'Let us not speak of such matters on such a lovely day.' She laid her hand tentatively upon his sleeve, the only way she could think of to express her sympathy.

He felt the pressure of her hand, and the rather sad little smile that accompanied it, like a benediction. Sometimes it was as though Lady Jayne could see into his very soul. Nobody had ever intuitively understood him the way she did.

He wished he could snatch up her hand, carry it to

his mouth and press his lips upon it in homage. His fingers flexed as he willed himself not to behave in such a rash manner. She wasn't ready to think of him in those terms. Besides, they were in a public park. He must not do anything to add to the speculation that had resulted in that bet being written down. He wanted to protect her from that kind of nastiness, not make her situation more uncomfortable than it already was.

Besides, he needed to persuade her to come down to Courtlands—not frighten her into refusing the invitation.

'Come, Lady Jayne. You have admitted that you would rather be in the countryside than in Town. And Kent is not an option. I am offering you Courtlands.' Perhaps in more ways than one. 'Please say you will come.'

His expression turned exceptionally earnest. As though it really mattered to him that she should be there. Though she could not imagine why. Except... She was the only person who understood how hard it was for him to pick a bride of whom his family would approve when his heart really belonged to Milly. Did he want her there to lend him moral support?

'I...I don't know,' she prevaricated. Was she up to putting aside her own hurt and supporting him this way? Nobody else had ever asked for her support. It was a huge compliment. To avoid having to make a definite answer either way, she asked, 'Who else will be going?'

'Berry, with whom I was at school. He renewed our acquaintance when I first moved into Lavenham House. And his sister Lucy. We first met at her coming-out ball, if you remember?'

Lady Jayne's mind flew back to that night. How she

had thought him grim and unapproachable as she'd watched him fending off the advances of ambitious matchmaking mothers. And then how later he'd come so magnificently to her rescue. Still looking grim, to be sure, but not in the least bit unapproachable. She'd somehow poured out her whole life story, telling him things she'd never shared with another living soul.

He was looking at her as though he was remembering that night, too. Little shifts in his expression told her that he was reliving it all just as she was. The shock of coming across her in the park, his anger with her for behaving so disgracefully, his sympathy for all the people she'd dragged down into the mire with her...

She tore her eyes from his and said, 'Yes—and who else, pray?'

'Another young lady who happens to be a friend of hers, Lady Susan Pettiffer, and a couple you may not know: Tom Waring—Lord Halstead, as he is now—and Miss Julia Twining. But does it really matter? Courtlands is a vast building. You need not even speak to any of them, should you not wish to. Please, think about it seriously.'

Serious? Could there be anything more serious than to hear that *these* were the women from whom he meant to make his choice?

Admittedly Lucy Beresford must *seem* as though she would make a good countess, in that she had a zeal for charitable works. Oh, yes, she could just picture her swanning into the houses of the *deserving poor* on his estates, distributing largesse with a self-satisfied smile.

And, yes, admittedly Lady Susan had a brilliant mind. She read extensively, attended lectures at all sorts of obscure scientific societies and could talk at great length upon just about any topic under the sun. He could probably see her presiding over fabulous dinners...where she would cut the less brilliant among them down to size with her rapier wit.

And, in spite of what he thought, she did know who Miss Julia Twining was. She'd found out last night on the way home, when she'd asked for the name of the plump girl with whom he'd sat out the quadrille, attempting to draw her into conversation. A lot of men found her voluptuous curves very attractive, Lady Penrose had informed her. And the fact that she was shy was no drawback. Men often liked a woman to have a meek and biddable disposition.

Some men, yes. But surely not a man of Lord Ledbury's temperament? He would walk all over her. And grow bored with her. And make her dreadfully unhappy. For how could the poor girl do anything but fall in love with him if she married him?

He wouldn't grow bored with Lady Susan, she admitted. She was so clever there would never be any lack of things to discuss. But they could never be in total harmony, for Lord Ledbury was basically kind and Lady Susan was...not.

Lucy was beginning to look less unappealing in comparison with those two. She did at least appear to have a kind nature. Grudgingly she conceded that Lucy Beresford might not make too bad a fist as Countess of Lavenham when the time came. She would see to the welfare of the tenants—albeit in such a way that they would all feel crushed by her condescension. But what kind of wife would she be? Not a loving one.

And Lord Ledbury ought to have a wife who loved him. When she thought of how hurt he must have been when his family ignored his sufferings after his injury at Orthez... And how he had more or less expected it...

No. She couldn't bear to think of the rest of his life being as grim and cheerless as his youth must have been. She must warn him what these three girls were really like. There was plenty of time to find someone else—someone with whom he stood a chance of finding some measure of happiness.

She turned to him, intending to warn him that if he married any one of these three girls he would regret it for the rest of his life. She even drew a breath to form the words.

But she never spoke them aloud. For she could not believe he would heed any warning *she* might give him. Not the girl he'd caught making a total fool of herself over a man like Harry. She'd demonstrated she was an exceptionally poor judge of character by being so completely taken in.

Oh, this was awful. Her own unhappiness seemed so small and petty in comparison with the misery upon which he was about to embark.

What on earth was she to do?

She wasn't sure she could bear to go to Courtlands and witness him proposing to one of those girls, knowing it would lead to a lifetime of misery for him.

But if she didn't go she would feel as if she'd abandoned the one person who'd selflessly come to her aid not once, but several times in the few weeks since they'd met.

'I will think about it,' she said, her throat feeling as though she had swallowed broken glass.

'Then I suppose I shall have to be content with that,' he said, looking anything but.

* * *

The formal invitation arrived four days later. Lady Penrose took one look at it and let out a little cry of delight.

'Oh, my dear! Just think what this means! Nobody who has witnessed the very close attention he has been paying you could possibly mistake Lord Ledbury's intention.'

Well, clearly they could, thought Lady Jayne bitterly. The fact that she was on the guest list did *not* mean that he wanted to marry her. He was just killing two birds with one stone. Forging ahead with his campaign to make a brilliant match, whilst doing his chivalrous best to offer a friend for whom he felt sorry some respite from the nightmare her Season had become.

'Naturally you will not be the only young lady who has been invited,' Lady Penrose continued. 'That would look too obvious. But I am sure you are the one he intends to offer for. Only think of the gallant way he came to your rescue after that masquerade. The posies he sent you every day...'

'I do not think I wish to attend.' She had thought long and hard about it, and come to the conclusion that there was nothing she could do to sway a man of Lord Ledbury's determined nature. All she would achieve by attending his wretched house party would be to make herself more miserable than she already was.

Lady Penrose's mouth gaped. 'You cannot mean that!' She looked intently into her face. 'Or perhaps you do.' She laid her hand briefly over Lady Jayne's. 'It was your grandfather's idea you should find a husband this Season. Not yours at all. And if you do not wish to marry Lord Ledbury then you are quite right.

We ought to refuse this invitation. It would not do to raise false hope in his breast. That would be unkind.'

'It is not that...' There was no hope in his breast at all. But how to explain her certainty without confessing the nature of their entanglement?

Lady Penrose clucked her tongue and shook her head. 'I see. You enjoy his company but you are not ready to make such a momentous decision. Well, I never did think you were old enough for a London Season. I told your grandfather that it would have been better to take you to Bath, or Harrogate, or perhaps a seaside resort this year—just to try your wings in public, without all this pressure to settle down—but there. What could I do?'

Lady Penrose laid the invitation aside with evident regret.

'Now, while we are on the subject of your grandfather, I think I had better tell you at once that I have received a rather...unsettling letter from him.'

Her heart sank. He must have finally announced that she had fabricated prior knowledge of Milly, and Lady Penrose was going to take her to task for the deception.

'I am sorry if he is angry with you about Milly. But you see, I...'

'Milly? How can he possibly be angry about Milly when he knows nothing about...' Lady Penrose trailed off, looking a little uncomfortable.

'You did not mention my friendship with her?' Lady Jayne was astounded.

'No.' She flushed. 'I knew full well that your grandfather would disapprove of her. But he left you here under my care. And in my judgement the fact that she is of lowly birth is outweighed by the fact you enjoy her company so much. I have noticed that you do not make friends easily. That, of course, is because your grandfather would not allow you to mix with anyone except long-standing connections to the family.' She pulled a disapproving face. 'Only when you are with Miss Brigstock do you unbend and become the carefree girl you ought to be at your age. She makes you laugh. For that alone I would defy a hundred cross old earls. But that has nothing to do with the case. Here,' she said, thrusting the page towards Lady Jayne. 'You might as well read it for yourself.'

Lady Jayne's astonishment increased. Lady Penrose had never permitted her to look at any of the letters her grandfather had written before, even though they referred to her. But then she was clearly still a bit flustered after her admission that she'd deliberately defied Lord Caxton by omitting to mention Milly to him.

Well, well. It seemed Lady Jayne was not the only one who instinctively rebelled against her grandfather's high-handed attitude.

With a little smile upon her face, she bent her head to peruse his letter. But after she had scanned only the first few lines she felt as though her world had been turned upside down.

He had received confirmation that her scandalous aunt, Lady Aurora, had died some years previously. But her daughter had recently returned to England and, due to what Grandfather referred to as a stroke of good luck, had been made known to him. Her breathing grew faster, and more shallow, as she read with increasing resentment how this girl, Aimée, had spent her childhood jaunting all over Europe, having—just as she had imagined—all kinds of adventures, before marrying the Earl of Bowdon and making her home in Staffordshire.

But what hurt her beyond anything else was the list of instructions he gave Lady Penrose regarding Jayne's reception of this Aimée when she came to Town.

As if she was not quite capable of knowing how to behave!

And to think of this cousin, experiencing the delights of Rome and Paris and Naples, whilst she had been immured in Kent, hedged about with draconian governesses! Or occasionally escorted to the houses of families she had known from birth, where she was not even permitted to walk down a corridor without a maid to dog her footsteps. And now he *admonished*—yes, that was the word he had used—*admonished* Lady Penrose to ensure her compliance with his plans to reinstate cousin Aimée into Society. The family had to stand together in this, he had insisted, underlining the word *together* twice. The girl was not to be held accountable for the sins of her parents.

Suddenly she knew exactly how the stay-at-home brother had felt when his father killed the fatted calf to welcome the prodigal home. She had always thought him a rather mean-spirited sort of fellow when hearing the parable expounded before, but here was her grandfather, expecting her to drop everything and—and *perform* for him like some kind of trained poodle, with Lady Penrose flicking the whip to guarantee the quality of her performance. Well, she would not have it!

'This is rather inconvenient, is it not?' she said coldly, handing the letter back to Lady Penrose. Inside she was seething with resentment and hurt. But nobody would ever have guessed. She did not know it, but she had never resembled her father so much in her life.

'Inconvenient?'

'Well, yes. Because, having given it careful thought, I have decided I ought to accept the invitation to Lord Ledbury's house party. So I will not be in Town when this long-lost cousin arrives, will I?'

Lady Penrose looked at the letter, then to Lady Jayne's face, and to the writing table by the window on which all the invitations lay scattered.

'You have changed your mind about the house party…?'

'*Made up* my mind, Lady Penrose. Don't you think it is positively my *duty* to go? After all, Grandfather sent me to London for the express purpose of finding me a husband.' *Get the chit married off,* had been his exact words, she recalled bitterly. 'And I do seem to have captured the interest of a man of whom he would thoroughly approve. If I do not attend this house party,' she said airily, 'Lord Ledbury might slip right through my fingers.'

A smile of comprehension spread slowly across Lady Penrose's face. 'Oh, indeed, yes. It *is* your duty to do all you can to attach the kind of husband of whom your grandfather would approve. And I,' she said, taking up her pen with an air of unholy glee, 'am going to take great pleasure in writing to inform him that his plans to come to Town and make us all dance to his tune will just have to wait a week or two.'

Chapter Nine

Lady Jayne twisted her hands together in her lap. She couldn't believe she'd done it again. Had she learned nothing from the scrapes she'd got into in London?

Making Lady Penrose her accomplice to get her into the Lambournes' masquerade was as nothing compared to this. It made not a scrap of difference that her chaperone was thoroughly enjoying flouting her grandfather's wishes. She had let her temper get the better of her, and not only was she going to Lord Ledbury's house party but...

She darted a glance at the other occupants of the carriage, who were chattering away as though neither of them had a care in the world.

She should never have dragged Milly into it. And yet at the time, with her temper raging so hot, it had seemed like the perfect solution. Well, that was because she hadn't stopped to calm down and think rationally. She had just told Lady Penrose that she would enjoy the house party much more if she had her dear friend with her, and her chaperone had made all the arrangements.

With the result that here they all were, travelling down to Courtlands together.

She turned her head sharply and looked out of the window, lest the other two should attempt to include her in their conversation. She didn't know what to say to them. How to deal with the guilt she felt at the disaster that was looming. Lord Ledbury was going to be so... angry. Confused. Hurt.

Why hadn't she taken his reaction that night she'd taken Milly to the theatre into consideration? When she had thought it would be a lovely surprise for him to see how beautifully Milly could cope with polite society. But it had been no such thing. She might as well have taken a dagger and plunged it into his heart. And this... this sneaking of her into Courtlands would be ten times worse. For he was actually steeling himself to propose to someone. Only of course she hadn't thought of that in the moments immediately after reading her grandfather's letter. She had just thought that men were so *stupid,* and so *tyrannical* that what could any woman with an ounce of spirit do but thwart them at every turn?

It wasn't even as if she had been angry with Lord Ledbury, either. But somehow her determination to thwart male stupidity had spilled over into her muddled thoughts about his house party and before she knew it she'd decided to get Milly down there to stop him proposing to any of those women who were bound to make him miserable. She knew he wouldn't listen to any arguments she might put forth. But he surely couldn't withstand the appeal of Milly herself? Surely he couldn't do anything so cruel as to propose to another woman whilst Milly was under his roof?

And before she knew it not only was Lady Penrose

up to her neck in schemes to defy their menfolk, but Milly, too, was gleefully anticipating seeing the look on Lord Ledbury's face when she walked into Court-lands through the front door.

So even when she'd begun to have second thoughts she hadn't been able to back down. Milly would have been so disappointed if she'd tried to put her off. But it hadn't been until they'd actually climbed into the coach this morning that she'd begun to consider there would be even further-reaching consequences. For that poor cousin of hers.

It was not going to be easy for Aimée to carve out a place for herself in Society, even if she had now married an earl. And, had Grandpapa not ordered her about in his usual overbearing, not to say insulting manner, she would have been thrilled to be meeting her and hear-ing all about her adventures.

Oh, bother her temper! Well, she would make it up to her cousin once this house party was over. She would most definitely not stand for anyone turning their noses up at her just because she was unfortunate enough to be the product of a runaway marriage. Really, the rules that governed Society were ridiculous! If not for those rules her aunt Aurora would never have had to elope in the first place. And Lord Ledbury could just marry Milly, and then there would have been no need for her to have resorted to such underhanded tactics.

Though it was no use trying to lay the blame else-where. She held herself entirely responsible for the di-saster that was about to unfold. Lord Ledbury was going to be so angry with her for meddling. He had been most tolerant of her behaviour up to now, but this latest es-capade was completely unforgivable…

And then it was too late, for the carriage was slowing for the turn between the two gateposts guarding the entrance to Courtlands.

Milly fell silent. Both girls pressed their noses to the window, straining for their first glimpse of Lord Ledbury's ancestral home.

It didn't disappoint. Not that it was anywhere near as imposing as Darvill Park, her grandfather's mansion in Kent, for it was a scrambling mixture of styles, as though it had been added to by successive generations in accordance with the architectural style of the day. But it did look welcoming.

Even the immense grey-stone *porte-cochère,* under which their carriage drew up, looked as though it had been added for the comfort and convenience of guests, rather than to blend in with the ivy-clad redbrick frontage of the house.

She was glad of its shelter, for it had been raining steadily all day. But her knees were trembling as she climbed out of the coach, dreading Lord Ledbury's reaction.

She grasped Milly's hand as they climbed the four shallow steps to the front door. Her guilt redoubled. Milly had far more to risk from this venture than she did. What had she done?

She went quite faint with relief when she saw a housekeeper standing in the open door, rather than their host. It only delayed the inevitable confrontation, but once Mrs Hargreaves had shown them up to their suite of rooms at least she no longer had to fear the prospect of being turned away altogether.

'This is lovely,' said Milly, wandering over to look

out of Lady Jayne's window, which was right over the *porte-cochère,* at the front of the house.

'What is your room like?' Lady Jayne crossed their shared sitting room and opened a door on the far side. 'It is a bit small.'

'I've slept in far worse,' said Milly with a grin. 'And at least we've got this—' she indicated the sitting room '—to escape to if things get a bit uncomfortable down-stairs.'

'Oh, Milly, I'm beginning to think I should not have brought you here. Lord Ledbury is bound to be angry. What if I've ruined everything for you?'

'I wanted to come here,' said Milly, and turned away with a pained expression on her face. 'At least I can see what it would be like to live as a fine lady, if only for a few days.'

Lady Jayne recalled Lord Ledbury's words on the night of the theatre, that it wasn't kind to show Milly a world in which she could never have so much as a toe-hold. And she felt more ashamed of herself than ever.

They had both washed and changed out of their trav-elling clothes by the time Lady Penrose came to their room. She had her own suite of rooms, she told them, on the same corridor, but with quite a different view. And not nearly so large.

'But then, I have it all to myself,' she said, with a smile for both girls. 'Are you ready?' She ran her eyes over their outfits, though Lady Jayne knew she would find nothing about Milly's appearance with which to find fault. Only Lord Ledbury would know she was not a perfectly respectable young lady, brought along to act as her companion. What was more, it was not only her appearance that Lady Jayne had changed. She had spent hours drilling her, so that she now knew as much about how to behave during a country house party as any young lady who'd been bred to it.

Lady Penrose gave her nod of approval and rang for a footman to escort them all downstairs to the rose salon, where Mrs Hargreaves had told them guests assembled before going in to dinner.

Lady Jayne's heart was pounding erratically by the time their footman opened a door, bowed and withdrew, to indicate they had arrived. She peeped anxiously past Lady Penrose's shoulder. Lord Ledbury was standing just inside the door.

When he saw Milly, the bland smile of welcome died from his lips. His hand clenched convulsively on the back of the chair on which he'd been leaning, his knuckles turning white. While he said all the correct things to Lady Penrose, Milly sidled past him and scuttled into the room. Lady Jayne could not blame her for running for cover. He was quite fearsome when his eyes turned all wintry like that.

When he'd finished greeting Lady Penrose, he turned the full force of his disapproval upon her.

Out of long habit of enduring blistering scolds from her grandfather, she composed her features and looked straight back at him. Though she fully accepted she was the one Lord Ledbury would blame for leading Milly astray, she had no intention of cringing or making excuses. Not here, in the doorway, with all those beady eyes watching avidly from behind their languidly waving fans.

'Lady Jayne,' he said, through gritted teeth that from a distance might have passed for a polite smile. 'I had no idea you would be bringing Mi…Miss Brigstock.'

He leaned in closer and whispered right into her ear, in a furious undertone, 'What on earth possessed you to do such a thing? Are you mad?'

She smiled up at him, and playfully tapped his shoulder with her fan, as though he had made some flirtatious remark. 'Determined,' she replied.

'Determined to do what?'

She shook her head and wagged her finger reprovingly. 'You will thank me later. I know you will. So don't pretend to be cross.'

'I am not pretending, da...dash it all. Oh, this is intolerable,' he hissed, darting a glance over his shoulder to see exactly how many of his guests were watching their interplay. Leaning in close again, he growled threateningly, 'We will have to speak privately about this. Later.'

She smiled up at him enigmatically, hoping he would take the look as acquiescence. For she had no intention of getting into a tête-à-tête with him.

'I shall get a message to your maid. My God,' he said, closing his eyes briefly and shuddering. 'To think I once said I would *never* sink to the level of smuggling notes to you via your maid. And now you have got me saying I shall do exactly that. The minute you set foot in my house, you have...' He opened his eyes and stared down at her. 'You are just like one of Congreve's rockets. So small and innocuous-looking, but if a man takes his eyes off you there is no telling what direction you will veer, or where the next explosion will go off.'

Since she'd spent the entire journey bewailing her lack of control over her temper, she could hardly argue with that assessment. So why did it hurt so much to hear Lord Ledbury say it out loud?

'One day you will apologise for speaking to me like

that,' she said vehemently. And, raising her chin, she stalked past him and made straight for the sofa on which Lady Penrose was sitting.

She sank onto the cushions with more necessity than grace. And it took her some time to stop trembling. The confrontation with Lord Ledbury had taken more out of her than she'd expected.

If she weren't so well-trained she would fling herself back amongst the cushions, cover her face with her hands, and wail with misery. For there were still five days of this to get through.

Instead, she consoled herself by observing that the other young ladies already down, Miss Twining and Miss Beresford, were also sitting beside their own chaperones, looking just as edgy as she felt.

The gentlemen of the party were all standing by a window which, to judge from the snatches of conversation she could overhear, overlooked the stables. Amongst them was a tall, bulky, elderly gentleman who was telling them about the various rides to be had in the vicinity. She assumed he must be Lord Ledbury's grandfather, Lord Lavenham.

Lord Ledbury was welcoming a latecomer to the room when she eventually gave herself permission to look his way again. Lady Susan Pettiffer was smiling up at him. And he was smiling right back, as though he didn't mind *her* flirting with him. He wasn't telling *her* she was like an unexploded bomb he dared not take his eyes off, or castigating *her* for polluting his orderly house with her unruly presence. Her fingers curled into claws. *I shan't let you have him,* she vowed under her breath.

And began to feel much better. All the people who'd

come here were playing their own game. And hers was no worse than anyone else's. That cat Lady Susan did not love Lord Ledbury in the least. She just wanted to be a countess.

At least she was not plotting anything for selfish reasons. She resolutely ignored the little voice that whispered how she always said it was for a good cause when she was about to embark on some course of action she knew was questionable. It had been her temper that had led her into this, not duplicity! She'd gone and committed herself to this house party, and when she'd known there was no way out of it she'd wished she could find some way to prevent him from becoming a sacrifice on the altar of family duty. She couldn't have borne to watch him pledge himself to anyone but the woman she knew he loved. Knowing she'd secured his happiness was the *only* thing that would console her for knowing *she* did not even make the running. The one comfort she would take with her into the future she saw unfolding before her. The future where she dwindled to an old maid, living the life of an eccentric recluse, since *nobody* would ever want to marry Chilblain Jayne.

She managed to eat a respectable amount at dinner, considering the tension that had her strung tight as a bow. Milly helped by behaving impeccably. She conversed in turn with each of her dining partners, making Lady Jayne want to nudge Lord Ledbury, and say, *See?*

Only he was not seated near enough for her to do any such thing. And whenever she looked his way he studiously ignored her. Though from the way he chewed his food and threw his wine into his mouth he was barely keeping a lid on his own temper.

It was only after dinner, when all the ladies withdrew, that Lady Jayne perceived Milly was not entirely at ease at all. It was when she came straight to her side, clutching her fan, white-knuckled, that she appreciated just how much of an ordeal this must be for her. She had warned Milly that after dinner the ladies would all be expected to perform for the gentlemen. And Milly had confessed that she had never learned to play a musical instrument.

It had taken some planning and hours of practise to surmount this obstacle. Fortunately Milly had a good strong singing voice. After putting their heads together, they'd come up with several ballads with which they were both familiar. Lady Jayne would play the music as she sang, with Milly accompanying her and, with the help of subtle prompts, turning the pages so that it looked as though she knew how to read music. They had only gone through the pieces a couple of times before Milly began to improvise a very pleasing harmony to the melody Lady Jayne was to be singing. To her delight, although Milly lacked formal training, she had certainly heard far worse from girls who'd had the benefit of years of expensive tuition.

The only thing that might let them down was Milly's nerves.

Lady Jayne need not have worried. After a slightly wobbly start, which only served to make Milly look appropriately bashful, their performance went without a hitch. And, judging from Miss Beresford's look of acute annoyance when the gentlemen of the party applauded their duet with what she thought sounded like genuine appreciation, they really had done themselves proud.

Lord Ledbury alone did not applaud. He kept his

arms folded, glowering at them both tight-lipped. He'd clearly realized that to perform so well together they must have put in hours of practise. Which meant they had both flouted his orders not to meet each other. She returned to her seat in a subdued frame of mind. Yet another crime for him to lay at her door. Although, from what Milly had told her, Milly herself had never been all that biddable to start with. She thought nothing of going behind Lord Ledbury's back, or *acting on her own initiative,* as she phrased it, when she disagreed with him.

But justifying her actions by mentally accusing Milly of being as intractable as she was did not make Lady Jayne feel any less uncomfortable.

Nor did the look of malicious triumph Lady Susan shot her. Nobody could possibly guess what had provoked Lord Ledbury's simmering fury, but it was enough to encourage her pretensions. Because he had applauded everyone else's performance.

The evening only grew more uncomfortable after that. The other prospective brides were trying too hard to impress Lord Ledbury. And since he was in a foul mood, due to her bringing Milly along, their efforts to please him were only making them look increasingly desperate.

Eventually the arrival of the tea tray heralded the imminent cessation of hostilities. She went to fetch a cup of tea for Lady Penrose, since she had become deeply engrossed in conversation with Miss Twining's duenna. She was not all that surprised when, the moment she reached the table where Mrs Hargreaves presided over the teacups, Lord Ledbury materialised at her side.

Before he had the chance to lay into her, she smiled

up at him brightly and said, 'Yes, thank you, I am having a lovely time. *Such* congenial company.'

'Sarcasm does not become you.'

'I am not being sarcastic. Well, not wholly. I like the look of your grandfather.' She regarded the rotund old gentleman wistfully. He was laughing heartily at something Lady Susan had said. She did not think she had ever seen her own grandfather laugh like that. Least of all at any sally a girl as young as that could make. He would be more likely to treat her to one of his withering stares and remove himself to the card room. 'He looks so jolly.'

'He looks,' Lord Ledbury retorted with disgust, 'like a man who is getting his own way. You should have seen the way he reacted when I asked if I might hold this house party and have a few of my friends to spend a few days here. He has very generously offered to run his eye over every female I have considered as a potential bride and give me the benefit of his advice. As if I was not perfectly capable of choosing my own wife!'

Some of Lady Jayne's tension dissolved at the realisation that not *all* of his anger stemmed from something she had done. In fact, she found it very encouraging that he was confiding in her like this. It proved that he found it as easy to talk to her as she did to him. Something inside her settled, like a knot coming unravelled. Even though they had quarrelled, he still considered her a friend.

But she was not going to offer him her sympathy. Apart from firmly believing he *was* going about finding a wife in completely the wrong way, the last thing he would want was to think she pitied him.

'Well, I must say,' she said quite frankly, 'judging

from the people you have invited, I tend to agree that you are in dire need of somebody's advice.'

'What do you mean? I have very good reasons for inviting each and every one of my guests.'

Not that he had any intention of explaining those reasons to her now, with so many of them within earshot. Possibly not ever.

For it was a bit galling to have to admit that Lady Susan and Lucy Beresford were the only two women he'd met so far this Season that he could actually remember anything about when they weren't in the room. Lady Susan was, in fact, exactly the sort of woman he'd had in mind before he'd met Lady Jayne. She was bright, witty, capable and well-connected. She was sure to leave her mark on the world.

And as for Lucy—well, as Berry's sister he couldn't very well *not* remember her. He'd decided he might as well invite her down here, to see if he could learn to find something about her to appeal to him as a man.

Which had led him to invite Miss Twining, too. For he had noticed that Berry was developing quite a tendre for the girl. Unfortunately she was so bashful it was well nigh impossible to tell whether she returned his regard. Only once or twice had he noticed her casting Berry glances that indicated his feelings might be reciprocated, if only he would pluck up the courage to make the first move. So Lord Ledbury had decided to give them a helping hand. A few days down here should resolve matters between them. Because between them he and his grandfather had organized a whole series of activities conducive to courtship.

That had made quite a small party, so he'd cast his net a bit wider and thought of Lord Halstead, who had apparently gone to Milly's assistance during the Lambourne masquerade. When he'd gone round to give Milly a piece of his mind for exposing Lady Jayne to danger by encouraging her to see Kendell behind his back, she'd angrily retorted that Lady Jayne had not been the only one who'd needed help that night. 'If it had not been for Lord Halstead I don't know how I would have got home safe. Not in that outfit.'

Not that he'd admitted to the fellow that was why he'd been invited. It was damned risky, having him here as well as Milly. He rubbed his hand over the crown of his head. Hopefully he hadn't seen Milly anywhere near Lady Jayne that night and would continue to think he'd been invited to make up the numbers. He certainly hadn't questioned the reason for his invitation at the time. Just jumped at the chance to spend a few days in the countryside on a repairing lease.

'More to the point,' he said to Lady Jayne, having shot a significant look in Milly's direction, 'I had very good reasons for *not* inviting others.'

She pursed her lips. She was doing it to express exasperation with him, no doubt, but to his way of thinking it looked just as though she was puckering up for a kiss.

'They are not good reasons,' she said mutinously. 'They are absolutely stupid reasons.'

He stopped wanting to kiss her. No, what he wanted to do now was grab her by the shoulders and shake her. Had she no idea what damage could be done to her reputation if it once got about that she had introduced his mistress into Society? Not that Milly *was* his mistress, but that was what everyone would think if they discovered his connection to her.

And he'd warned her that it was dangerous…. But

she'd said she didn't care. That was the thing about Lady Jayne. She was loyal to a fault. He could not fathom why she'd brought Milly here, and the cryptic remarks she'd made earlier about making him grateful had made no sense at first. But he was beginning to wonder if she didn't consider herself on some sort of crusade.

'We have got to have a serious talk,' he said grimly. 'Somewhere nobody else can overhear us, so that you can explain yourself. At the side of the house there is a shrubbery. You can get out to it by going out of the library doors and down the steps at the end of the terrace. Meet me there tomorrow, before breakfast.'

He turned and stalked off, having delivered his orders as though he expected her to snap to attention, salute and say, *Yes, Sir!*

Well, if he thought he could order her about like that, he had another think coming! Besides, she had no intention of getting into a potentially compromising position with him. The whole point of coming down here was to promote Milly's case with his family. If only she could have a few days' grace, to prove how well she could fit in, then he could announce that his search for a bride was over. Once they'd got to know her for the sunny, charming person she was, surely they would have no objections to him making her his countess? Why, in comparison with the other girls he'd brought down here Milly was like a rose among thorns.

Yes, within a few days he could introduce Milly to the world as the woman he loved, and they would all live happily ever after.

Well, Lord Ledbury and Milly would, anyway. She shivered as she had another vision of the bleak future awaiting her, and added an extra spoonful of sugar to her cup of tea. As she walked across the room to join Lady Penrose she consoled herself with the reflection that her chaperone lived alone, unmarried and was perfectly content.

She would be, too.

So long as she knew that Lord Ledbury was happy.

Chapter Ten

The next morning, when she went down to breakfast, she only had to glance at Lord Ledbury, who was savagely sawing away at a slice of sirloin, to see that he was furious with her for not keeping their assignation in the shrubbery. She lifted her chin as a footman held out a chair for her and took her place at the table. He would thank her one day. She just had to have the determination to ride out his annoyance and stick to her guns.

Why did one talk about sticking to guns? She had often wondered. It sounded like such an absurd thing to do. Guns recoiled after being fired, and if one stuck to them surely one would be flung about most uncomfortably? She would ask him to explain it to her one day. Since he had been in the army for such a long time he was bound to know what the expression really meant.

She lifted her head to look at him, anticipating the conversation, and was shocked by the chill with which he met her gaze.

Jolted by the searing pain that shot through her on receipt of that look, she lowered her eyes to her place setting. What if he never forgave her for meddling in

Play the Lucky Hearts Game

and get...
2 FREE BOOKS and
2 FREE MYSTERY GIFTS...
YOURS TO KEEP!

Yes! I have scratched off the gold card. Please send me my *2 FREE BOOKS* and *2 FREE MYSTERY GIFTS* (gifts are worth about $10). I understand that I am under no obligation to purchase any books as explained on the back of this card.

Scratch Here!
Then look below to see what your cards get you....*2 Free Books & 2 Free Mystery Gifts!*

246/349 HDL FJCQ

FIRST NAME

LAST NAME

ADDRESS

APT.#

CITY

STATE/PROV.

ZIP/POSTAL CODE

Visit us online at
www.ReaderService.com

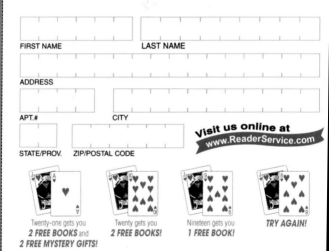

Twenty-one gets you
2 FREE BOOKS and
2 FREE MYSTERY GIFTS!

Twenty gets you
2 FREE BOOKS!

Nineteen gets you
1 FREE BOOK!

TRY AGAIN!

BUSINESS REPLY MAIL

FIRST-CLASS MAIL   PERMIT NO. 717   BUFFALO, NY

POSTAGE WILL BE PAID BY ADDRESSEE

THE READER SERVICE

PO BOX 1867

BUFFALO NY 14240-9952

NO POSTAGE
NECESSARY
IF MAILED
IN THE
UNITED STATES

his search for the perfect bride? He was the one person, apart from Milly, with whom she had ever been able to converse openly.

She spooned some jam disconsolately onto the side of her plate, though her appetite had vanished completely. She had meant well, but perhaps it would have been better not to have meddled in his love life?

Better for her. Yes, it would have been easier for her to just keep out of it. That would have been the sensible thing to do, and the course she had been tempted to take. But could she have lived with herself if she had stood back and let Lord Ledbury marry the wrong woman? No.

She firmed her mouth, picked up her knife and, with great deliberation, spread the jam onto a warm roll. Lord Ledbury deserved to find some happiness. And she would do whatever she could to help him achieve it.

'It looks as though the weather today is going to be fair and warm,' Lord Lavenham suddenly announced in a voice loud enough to carry above the muted conversations going on around the crowded breakfast table.

She would never have believed every single one of the girls invited would be such early risers. Clearly none of them had any intention of letting any of the others gain so much as five minutes' advantage in their pursuit of Lord Ledbury.

'I should be pleased to give as many of you as would care for it a tour about the estate. We shall convene in about an hour, in the stable block—if that gives you ladies enough time to get ready,' he said with a chuckle. 'I shall be able to match you all up with suitable mounts.'

The gentlemen, she assumed, would have brought their own horses.

'Now, I know that the ground will be a bit soft after all the recent rain, but I do not want you to worry about muddying your riding habits. For those of you who do not wish to ride this morning, I shall provide other transport.'

She met Milly's eye. What a stroke of luck! Milly did not know how to ride side-saddle, so the offer of a carriage ride to preserve the ladies' clothing was a wonderful cover for her lack of that particular accomplishment. So far, things could not be going better.

She felt more cheerful than she had for an age when she entered the stable block about an hour later. One of the things she had hated most about London was not being able to canter through the woods at Darvill Park in the misty dawn, or indulge in a breakneck gallop across open fields. In anticipation of just such a treat, when she had decided to come to this house party she had purchased a new riding habit. In honour of Lord Ledbury's military service she had gone for a severely tailored midnight-blue jacket with silver frogging round the buttons and silver-lace epaulettes. The hat she wore with it was one of those so popular at the moment, which looked a bit like a soldier's shako with a little white cockade.

Lady Penrose walked across to the barouche in which Miss Twining's chaperone was already sitting. The hood was pushed back, to allow them to get a good view of the estate, but it could be pulled up in the event of further rain.

Lady Susan, Miss Twining and Miss Beresford were already making their selection from the line of horses being held by some grooms. She had no idea how keen they really were on riding, but since the older ladies in the carriage would be obliged to stick to the roads, no husband-hunter worth her salt would pass up such a golden opportunity to shake off her chaperone. On horseback, the girls could disappear into a copse, or over the brow of a hill, for minutes at a time without incurring too much disapproval.

Lord Ledbury was lounging against the stable wall, his arms crossed, but when he saw her party he pushed himself upright and made towards them, his expression as forbidding as she had ever seen it.

Milly detached herself from Lady Jayne's side, made straight for the curricle in which Lord Halstead intended to drive himself and wasted no time in clambering up beside him.

Lady Jayne could not blame her. It would take a very brave person indeed not to quail before the look in Lord Ledbury's eyes as he stalked across the stable yard.

'Allow me to help you choose your mount,' he said through gritted teeth. When he crooked his arm, she dared do nothing but meekly take it and let him lead her across the yard to where the horses were lined up.

The other ladies looked daggers at her to see her receiving such special attention from their quarry. She looked straight through them. She did not care how much they hated her so long as she could prevent any of them from getting their claws into Lord Ledbury.

Since she was the last down to the stable yard there was little choice left. But the spirited-looking bay mare which Miss Twining had just rejected, after it had tossed its head and rolled its eyes when she reached out to pat its neck, looked as though it would suit her perfectly. The groom was having to hold its bridle with some determination to prevent it from skipping sideways across the cobbles. It was itching to get out and have some fun.

Well, so was she!

While she was making friends with the creature—whose name, the groom informed her with a meaningful look, was Mischief—Lord Ledbury strode away and, somewhat to her surprise, himself mounted up. True, the creature on which he was now sitting looked weary to the point of somnolence, but he was on horseback.

She had never seen him ride before. In fact, from the way he'd talked about his injuries, she'd suspected he might spend the rest of his life as a semi-invalid.

But he was fit enough to ride with them this morning. Which was absolutely wonderful.

She mounted Mischief and spent some time rearranging her skirts to give herself time to get her feelings under control. Had there been nobody else about she thought she might have rushed over and hugged him. Or broken out into a loud cheer. Or…something. She did not know what.

She had still not quite succeeded in regaining full control of her sheer delight by the time he positioned his beast beside hers as they began to exit the yard. In fact, she turned and beamed at him.

'How do you have the nerve to smile at me like that?' he snapped, dousing her joy at the sign of his return to health. 'Do you know how long I waited for you outside in the cold this morning? And don't tell me you never leave your room before breakfast. I know full well you can get up and dressed and go out to meet men when it suits you,' he finished bitterly.

There was nothing that would stop her from doing anything she put her mind to. He had seen her scramble up a tree like a monkey, having donned breeches under her dress, so that she could sneak out and dally with Lieutenant Kendell in the park at dawn.

'I could not help it,' she said, though she was not smiling any more. 'Are you not pleased to be on horseback again, too?'

He sighed. She had no idea how badly she had hurt him by not keeping their assignation. Well, it had taken him by surprise, too. Another proof, as if he needed any, that he was in love with her.

Falling in love was a damnable business, he thought, scowling. A bit like being at sea. When he'd seen her sauntering towards him in that outfit, with that smile on her face, his heart had soared. Then as abruptly plunged to his boots when he realized she hadn't chosen a military style for any reason that had anything to do with him. It was probably just the current fashion.

Yes, just like being at sea. Whether his mood was on the crest of the wave, or plunging into a trough, he never stopped feeling sick at heart.

Perhaps he ought to abandon this particular ship. He would certainly feel as if he'd got his feet back on firm ground if he stopped wondering whether he might ever induce Lady Jayne to marry him.

He could set off back on his original course. The one which would lead him to make a practical union with a woman who would bring lustre to the family line.

Only he'd lost any enthusiasm for going down that route. Oh, yes, he'd be on an even keel again. But he suspected it would be like slogging across a flat, barren, joyless landscape, with him frequently looking over his shoulder at what might have been.

'Pleased to be on horseback?' He turned his pessimistic mood on the poor unfortunate beast he'd just mounted. 'I would hardly grace this animal upon which I am sitting with the appellation of *horse*. In fact I do not think I have ever sat a creature which more nearly resembles an armchair in all my life. Even as a boy the first pony I was put up on by my groom had the energy to break into a trot upon occasion.'

Lady Jayne giggled. And it felt as though the sun had come out. It was the first time anything he had said had actually amused her. To hell with any thought of abandoning ship. This was progress. Real progress.

'Well, I expect it will be some time before your leg is strong enough to warrant mounting anything with too much spirit,' she observed, running her eyes along the length of his thigh.

Dear God, how he wished it was her little hands making the journey. He had never met any creature with more spirit, or more worth mounting, than the deceptively dainty-looking Lady Jayne.

To keep his mind off erotic images of Lady Jayne writhing beneath him with the kind of enthusiasm a man yearned for but very rarely found in his bed partner, he urged his recalcitrant mount into a forward motion.

Lady Jayne, by contrast, appeared to be exerting all her strength in holding Mischief back.

'Will it… I hope you do not mind me asking…. Will it mend completely, do you think? You do not limp as much as you used to. And you do not seem to need your cane very often now, either.'

'My leg wants only exercise to resume its former strength. Just like the rest of me.'

From the corner of his eye he saw her frown pensively.

'Yes, Milly told me you had a recurrent fever that laid you low throughout the winter.'

Hmm... The girls talked about him, did they?

'I cannot imagine a gently bred young lady being truly interested in hearing all the gory details of a protracted illness.' Unless she was interested in the patient.

'Oh, well...' She couldn't admit that she greedily devoured any tidbits Milly ever divulged about his past life. 'Do you object?'

Mischief shook her head irritably from side to side, indicating Lady Jayne's grip on the reins must have confused her.

'I suppose,' she said in a rather contrite tone, 'it must sound as though we have been gossiping about you. But, truly, neither of us meant any harm. It is just that sometimes, when we first met, you did not seem very well, and I did not quite dare ask *you*...'

She looked mortified, but he was heartened by her admission that she was, indeed, interested in the patient.

'When we first met,' he said, 'I was still far from well, it is true. Had I not felt it my clear duty to embark on the hunt for a wife I would not have attempted to take my place in Society at all this Season.'

He didn't look cross with her. So she plucked up the courage to add, 'You often looked very pale.'

'You noticed?' Lady Jayne had finally managed to settle Mischief to a walking pace his own mount was capable of matching. As they left the shelter of the last of the stable buildings he felt emboldened to admit, 'I thought I'd taken such good care to conceal my condition. I leaned on that cane and let people assume it was my leg that was the problem.' He laughed, a little self-deprecatingly. 'Rather that than risk my pride getting dented by passing out in the heat of a stuffy ballroom. But I don't mind admitting the truth to you, Lady Jayne.'

'You don't?'

The smile she darted at him put him in mind of a child who'd just been given an unexpected treat.

'No. I want you to know the truth about me, Lady Jayne. I want you to know who I am. All of me.' He frowned, as though choosing his next words carefully. 'The life of a soldier is harsh, Lady Jayne. Far harsher than a sheltered lady like you can possibly imagine. In summer we burn like biscuits in the heat of the sun as we march. In winter, if we cannot get shelter overnight, our blankets stick fast to the ground with ice. If we progress too fast, and the supply trains cannot keep up with us, we starve. And then, when it rains, we live in sodden clothing for days on end. Illness runs rife through the ranks, killing far more men than battles do. Even before I got my leg broken at Orthez, my constitution was pretty worn down. And then suddenly I had to stroll into ballrooms, and behave as though I was some great lord. I had never felt less like a lord in my life.'

No, she mused. He was far more like the corsair he'd dressed as the night of the masquerade. A man who helped damsels in distress to climb back in through their bedroom window rather than knock on the front door and hand them over in disgrace to their guardians.

'Th-thank you for telling me all that,' she said. He had paid her a very great compliment in confiding things to her that he deliberately concealed from everyone else. And his telling her about what it had been like to be a soldier helped her understand why he seemed so much more real than anyone she had ever met before. He had lived the kind of life most people only read about in books.

No wonder he often betrayed impatience with the pampered, shallow creatures who inhabited her world.

He heard her sigh, and saw her eyes filled with a look he found hard to interpret. Damn! He hoped he had not made her feel sorry for him. He had just wanted her to know him and…love him for himself? His mouth twisted in self-mockery. He was a lost cause. What was he doing, thinking he could win a prize like Lady Jayne with tales of warfare and injury? He wanted his head examining.

'I began to move in Society before I was ready, it is true,' he said. 'When I first went to Town doing hardly anything at all exhausted me to the point where I often went light-headed. But I have not needed that damn cane for the past couple of weeks.'

Now she came to think of it, that cane had been conspicuous by its absence on the night of the masquerade.

'The fact that you see me up on horseback, even though it is such a slug, is testament to my convalescence. The more exercise I can take, the quicker my weakened muscles will regain their full strength, I am sure.'

His full strength? What was that she had been on the receiving end of at the masquerade, then? When he'd picked her up and carried her into the conservatory it had felt as though she was wrestling with something very like a walking oak tree.

And yet he didn't consider himself to be back to his full strength?

Gracious.

And then, with a wrench—and because if she didn't

get back to the matter at hand she might spend the rest
of the ride gazing in fascination at the muscles of his
thighs, or remembering the feel of his arms clamping
round her as he'd lifted her effortlessly off her feet—she
said, 'M-Milly said that during last winter you were so
poorly she sometimes despaired...'

'Yes, yes,' he said impatiently, the mention of
Milly's name reminding him of the danger Lady Jayne
was courting. 'You don't need to remind me how much
I owe Milly. But that does not alter the fact that you
should not have brought her here. Which was why I
wanted to talk to you alone this morning.'

His expression turned so grim Lady Jayne's courage deserted her. She loved the way he'd opened up to
her. It made her feel as though she was special to him.
It would make his censure even harder to bear.

'Oh, dear,' she said, slackening her grip on the reins.
'I do not think I can...'

Mischief, sensing freedom, flung her head up and
down, curvetted, then shot away at breakneck speed.

She aimed her towards a long, slow rise, crested by a
belt of woodland into which she intended to disappear,
trusting that the horse Lord Ledbury was riding would
have neither the inclination nor the stamina to follow.

The dash up the hill took the edge off Mischief's
pent-up energy, just as she'd known it would, and they
entered the woodland at a steady canter. Even so, she
had to bend low over Mischief's neck to preserve her
hat from overhanging branches.

Since Mischief knew the terrain, Lady Jayne did not
attempt to guide the creature too strictly, and was soon
rewarded by her faith in the animal's instincts when

they emerged into a clearing on the far side of which was just such a broad ride as she had hoped to find.

But, instead of finding herself completely alone, she heard hoofbeats thundering up behind her. When she looked over her shoulder, to her complete astonishment she saw Lord Ledbury was only a few yards away. She could not believe he had managed to get that sluggish creature to keep up with Mischief!

Though she knew why he had done so. He was determined to give her a scold. Not only for bringing Milly into his home but also for letting him think she would meet him in the shrubbery and then cravenly staying away.

She wheeled Mischief round to face him.

'I know. I am sorry. I should have let you know I was not going to meet with you this morning,' she blurted, before he had the chance to reprove her. 'I know you must be furious with me. But think, my lord. You cannot possibly want to be caught in a compromising position with me.'

She meant, he thought moodily, that it was the last thing *she* wanted. She had not been so pernickety about getting caught out with Kendell.

'As if you care a rap for propriety!'

She flinched at his condemnation of her behaviour.

'Well, I do, actually,' she replied earnestly. 'Especially when it comes to you,' she admitted, blushing. 'I would never do anything to embarrass or hurt you.'

He allowed his horse to shudder to a standstill. It dropped its head to the ground, its flanks heaving wheezily.

'Are you telling me you had no intention of punishing me for the way I issued you with orders to meet me?'

'No! It was not like that. I did resent the way you spoke to me, but I had no deliberate intent to punish you. I suppose it cannot have been very pleasant for you, waiting outside for me.' She glanced at his leg, then at his face. 'I did not think.'

She looked so contrite that he could not doubt she spoke the truth. Though she was often impulsive and thoughtless, in all the time he had known her he had never seen her be deliberately unkind to anyone.

'Very well. I acquit you of attempting to punish me.' When her face lit up he almost forgot why he had been so determined to get her alone. It took him quite an effort to say, 'But that does not mean I am not still very angry with you for bringing Milly here, when it is the last place I ever wanted to see her.'

'No!' She looked shocked. 'You cannot mean that.'

'Of course I mean it!'

'Oh, but Richard, can't you see that once your grandfather has seen with his own eyes how lovely Milly is he can surely have no further objection to you marrying her?'

'What?'

Lady Jayne thought he wanted to marry Milly? And that his grandfather objected? How the hell had she reached such a staggeringly inaccurate conclusion?

He swiftly reviewed that initial interview, when he'd asked her to take Milly shopping a few times, and shook his head. Had he said something that had misled her?

He looked down into her earnest little face and something inside him settled. She had not brought Milly here to deliberately flout him. To show him that she would be friends with whomever she pleased and to hell with him...

Quite the reverse.

She thought she was assisting a pair of star-crossed lovers. She had spent hours teaching Milly how to look as though she was a real lady, or at least a woman who could pass as a lady's companion...when she had not, initially, even wanted to come down here. Because she wanted him to find the happiness that had been denied her and Lieutenant Kendell.

She had put her own problems to one side in order to try and solve his.

It didn't matter to him that she'd got hold of completely the wrong end of the stick. She'd flung herself into this madcap enterprise with the sole aim of making him happy. Nobody in his entire life had ever cared if he was happy or not. Let alone gone to such lengths to attempt to secure his happiness.

How could people think she was cold and call her such vile names? She was not cold. She was warm-hearted. And so beautiful, through and through.

There was a splash of mud on her face, and her hat had come askew at some point during her mad dash for the trees, releasing one golden curl from its confines. And there was nobody in the whole world to match her.

'You are such a darling,' he said huskily.

She was still looking at him warily, chewing on her lower lip.

That luscious lower lip.

Be damned to his ambition, and his search for a bride that would impress his family. Be damned to propriety, too. He wanted Jayne, and he was blowed if he was going to carry on resisting her allure for one more second.

He leaned across the space between their two mounts

and before she had time to guess his intention, before she had time to object or take evasive action, he kissed her.

He only managed to brush his lips across hers before Mischief fidgeted and jolted her out of his reach, but she felt it all the way down to her toes.

She had never dreamed one such brief kiss could do that to a girl.

She couldn't for the life of her think what on earth had prompted him to do it. But then her wits were so badly scattered that it was taking all her concentration to prevent herself from sliding out of the saddle and melting into a puddle on the forest floor.

Fortunately she was spared the necessity of having to attempt to make any kind of verbal response, because at that very moment Mr Beresford and his sister arrived on the scene.

'I say, Lady Jayne, are you unhurt?' called Mr Beresford.

'You must be terribly shaken after the way that horrid horse bolted with you,' said Lucy, looking, Lady Jayne thought, a little disappointed not to see her lying on the floor with at least one limb broken.

'Mischief did not bolt,' she returned coldly. 'I gave her her head. We both enjoyed the gallop. And now, if you will excuse me, my lord...'

Completely unable to look Richard in the face after that bone-melting kiss, she simply indicated to her mount that she was more than ready for some more exercise. He would not pursue her. Not even should he want to—which she doubted. How on earth he had managed to get such a turn of speed out of the horse he was on she would never know, but of one thing she was sure. He would not be able to reproduce such a miracle.

Mischief needed very little prompting. Glancing over her shoulder as she galloped out of the clearing and onto the broad ride, she saw Mr Beresford urge his own mount in hot pursuit—determined, she supposed, to do the gentlemanly thing by sticking close and thus being able to report the spot where she finally parted company with Mischief—leaving his sister alone with Lord Ledbury.

Not that it would do Lucy any good. His heart belonged to Milly.

While hers, she realized in a moment of startling clarity, belonged to him.

That was why she could not bear to think of him being miserable.

That was why she had visions of dwindling into an eccentric spinsterhood once she'd pictured him happily married off. It wasn't that nobody would want to marry her. It was that she couldn't imagine marrying anyone but him.

And *that* was why the merest brush of his lips upon hers had been enough to have her practically swooning, when all Harry's most vigorous efforts had done nothing but irritate her.

And was that the real reason she'd brought Milly here, too?

Was she so sure, deep down, that his family would never let him marry a girl from such humble origins that the only result of having Milly here would be to scupper his plans to marry anyone else?

Had she become so possessive of him that she could not bear to let any other woman take the place she had not admitted until this very moment that she wanted for herself?

And that awful sensation she'd had when she'd imagined him making Milly his mistress... Had that been jealousy?

She spurred Mischief on, needing speed to distract her from the dreadful pain of facing up to her deepest, most hidden desires. Desires she'd refused to acknowledge even to herself.

But now that she had acknowledged them she began to wonder when it had started.

From the first moment they had met, at that ridiculous come-out ball of Lucy Beresford's, where she had sat sulking on one side of the dance floor and he on the other, she had felt a connection. It hadn't been the fact that they were the only two there of comparable rank. No, she had sensed in him an irritation with the way people treated him that marched with her own.

And then he'd rescued her from Harry and taken her home when he could have landed everyone involved in hot water. And instead of bowing out he'd plunged right into the mess she'd been in with Harry and done his level best to prevent it all getting any worse. He'd been protective. And even when she'd interpreted that protectiveness as being overbearing and dictatorial, and told herself she resented him, she'd been *aware* of him. She always knew the moment he entered a ballroom without having to look up. And once he was there it was as if he and she were the only two people in the room. Nobody else had any real substance.

And since he'd held her in his arms as she'd gone to pieces over Harry's brutal honesty she could not stand anywhere near him without feeling the urge to…well, to wind her arms and legs right round him.

She'd told herself it was because of the comfort she'd found in his arms. And, despising herself for being weak, thinking she needed comfort, she'd ruthlessly repressed the urges and refused to so much as examine them.

But it wasn't comfort she wanted from him at all. The way her whole body had fizzed, then melted at the merest brush of his lips upon hers, had really opened her eyes.

Somewhere along the way she'd fallen in love with him.

She supposed she hadn't correctly identified the nature of her feelings because she didn't have any experience of love, first-hand. She'd thought that the fact that Richard stood in a class of his own, in her estimation, was because she'd never met anyone like him before—never had a relationship with anyone, male or female, with whom she'd shared so many intimacies or entrusted with so many secrets. She'd told herself that was why she thought about him so often. Why, when she wasn't with him, she wondered what he was doing. Why any event he attended stuck in her memory, and when he wasn't there the evening was unbearably flat.

But now that she knew the truth she did not know how she would be able to face him again.

Nor Milly. Her friend.

Her rival.

Chapter Eleven

She was avoiding him. Ever since she'd bolted from him Lord Ledbury had been kicking himself. He'd startled her with that kiss. And so, even though they were all confined to the house that afternoon because of the weather, in the end he had to recruit help to outmanoeuver her.

First he persuaded Lord Halstead that he would enjoy giving the ladies some instruction in billiards. As usual, Lady Susan and Lucy Beresford managed to exclude Miss Twining from the activity. And, after several minutes of watching from the sidelines, she was delighted to accept his invitation to take a walk in the long gallery so that he could show her the portraits of his many ancestors.

He heaved a sigh of relief as Miss Twining laid her arm on his sleeve and they set off. She was not given to conversation, which left him free to work out how to make Lady Jayne understand the almost blinding revelation that had led him to kiss her that morning. He had to explain that in that one moment he'd changed his mind about marrying some paragon who would impress his family for generations to come. He just wanted *her*.

No... That didn't sound right.

He would have to marshal his thoughts into better order before blurting out something clumsy like that.

Firstly, then, he would disabuse her of the notion he was in love with, or had ever been in love with, Milly— and, while he was at it, he needed to warn her that Milly was up to something. He wasn't sure quite what it was yet. But when he'd heard them singing that ballad he'd hardly been able to believe his ears. Oh, it was innocent enough on the face of it, but in their regiment they'd sung a version of it so bawdy it would have scandalised even the gentlemen present in that drawing room. He could have wrung Milly's neck. How could she repay all the kindness Lady Jayne had shown her by encouraging her to sing a song that would have made her a laughing stock if anyone with a military background had been there?

Admittedly, so far Milly had not actually done anything to harm Lady Jayne. But she could. Very easily.

Once he'd warned her that she ought not to be quite so trusting where Milly was concerned, he could move on to telling her that he'd changed his mind—no, that *she'd* changed his mind—about what he wanted from a wife. He'd been a stranger to love until he'd met her, so naturally he had not considered it as an important ingredient in any marriage he might contract. But she'd taught him it was vital. Vital. Yes, that sounded much better.

As he mounted the stairs he repeated the phrases in his head, hoping to fix them in his memory. At times like this he could understand what Berry saw in Miss

Twining. She was the most undemanding of women. They'd walked the entire way in complete silence, and she had not once attempted to interrupt his train of thought. He glanced at her as they reached the gallery, wanting to take note of her reaction when she saw Berry already there with Lady Jayne.

If he had not been paying close attention he would have missed it. It wasn't so much that she smiled, more that her whole face softened and her eyes warmed. And her fingers tightened on his sleeve, ever so briefly.

She was more than willing to accept Berry's suggestion that the men—as pre-arranged—should swap partners.

It was harder to read Lady Jayne's mood. Though she voiced no objection, neither would she take his arm as they strolled along the corridor. But still, by dint of stopping at each portrait to expound that person's life story, while Berry inexorably drew Miss Twining along to the next, it was not very long before he had managed to put some distance between himself and the other couple.

She was uneasy with him. But at least with Berry and Miss Twining within hailing distance she had no excuse for fleeing the scene altogether. And, since Berry wanted a modicum of privacy as much as he did, they were soon far enough away to converse without being overheard.

Which was good, because he had no intention of wasting this carefully staged meeting by sticking to polite nothings. He knew her well enough by now to see that the only way he would break through her reserve would be by a full frontal attack.

'It is no use,' he said firmly. 'I am not going to take the hint and pretend that kiss this morning never happened. You have been so distant with me ever since that I can only assume I offended you.'

'Offended me? Oh… No, not at all,' she said, so politely it made him grind his teeth.

'I must have done. It was not the act of a gentleman to take advantage like that.'

She still wouldn't look at him.

'Please believe me. I just couldn't help myself. No, dammit, that's no excuse, is it? When I saw Kendell pawing you about in the park I wanted to rip his arms off.'

They came to a standstill. He could not believe he had said that out loud.

She blushed and walked across the corridor, where she turned her back on him, ostensibly to look out of the window.

'It…' Eventually she managed to speak, in a very low voice. '…It was not at all the same.'

For one thing, she had enjoyed it. That slight brush of his lips had made her yearn for more. She had wanted him to put his arms round her and prolong the contact. She wouldn't have fought him off the way she'd fought Harry. Because he would not have crushed her. She couldn't imagine Lord Ledbury doing anything so maladroit when he took a woman in his arms. No, the woman lucky enough to have Lord Ledbury really kissing her would know only pleasure….

'It is generous of you to say so,' he replied, heartened by her verbal forgiveness, though she was still pretending to admire scenery that was scarcely visible through the rain-lashed window rather than facing him.

'Not at all. I could tell you were just overcome by… some momentary impulse…' A perplexed frown pleated her brow, as though she could not understand what on earth could have motivated him. 'Whereas when Harry kissed me it was all part of a deliberate, cold-blooded scheme….' She shuddered. 'Looking back, I could almost wish you *had* ripped his arms off.'

She turned and shot him a rueful smile over her shoulder.

Well, that was better. 'I am glad that I could not sleep that night, then, and decided to take a walk.'

He hitched his hip onto the windowsill, so that he could look at her profile, at least, since she had turned her head away again, and begun to fiddle with the tassels on the curtains.

'Actually, Lady Jayne, this is a good time to tell you that I have long since decided I am glad the solicitousness of those London servants drove me outside to seek fresh air, or I might never have met you.'

'I am glad, too. You came striding down upon us like some kind of avenging angel—even though, at that time in your life, you were still far from well.' She blushed again. 'D-do you still find it difficult to sleep? Or have you found some remedy for that particular ailment?'

Far from it. But the sleepless nights he'd suffered since had been mainly on her account.

He rubbed his hand over the crown of his head and got to his feet again. She was fencing with him. Deliberately keeping him at a distance.

'Lady Jayne,' he said, remembering his feeling that the only way to breach her defences was by full-frontal attack, 'I am trying to tell you something of great importance. I am trying to explain that I kissed you because… Well, the truth is that you have saved me from making a terrible mistake.'

He turned her round and took her by the hand, so that he could be sure she was attending carefully.

'When we first met, I told you about the kind of marriage I intended to make. Thinking like a soldier, I made a list of my objectives, drew up the plan of action most likely to achieve a swift outcome, moved myself into a strategic position, armed myself to the teeth and started making forays into what I looked upon almost as hostile territory. Before I met you it never occurred to me that I ought to feel more than respect for any woman I considered marrying. But over the last few weeks, and particularly since you have come to Courtlands, I...that is... You have shown me that a marriage without affection...that is...without...love would be...a travesty. Lady Jayne, you yourself said that love is the only reason a man and woman ought to marry...'

'Yes, I did, didn't I?'

She was pulling her hand away.

And it occurred to him that just because she wanted to make him happy, it didn't mean she was willing to sacrifice herself. She cared enough to see him happily married to someone else...which led him to the point he ought to have made first.

'Now, about Milly...'

She flinched, and began to chew at her lower lip.

'No, I am not about to scold you for bringing her here. You meant only to help, and although...'

She looked so uncomfortable he couldn't continue with the warning he'd meant to give her. In fact, it would be better to tackle Milly herself. Ask her what the devil she was playing at and warn her that if she ever did anything to harm or even embarrass Lady Jayne, their friendship, such as it was, would be at an end.

'Well, there is just one benefit of your bringing Milly to Courtlands,' he said, wondering where his plan to stick to his well-rehearsed script had gone. 'My former army servant, whom I left with her to see her settled into her new house, came here hotfoot to let me know she had run off.'

Fred had been frantic with worry over her apparent disappearance. He'd almost wept with relief to know she was safe and well.

'Fred *is* most welcome. He knows just how I like things done, and, since there is nothing for him to do in Town with Milly being here, he has agreed to stay and resume his role as my valet for the time being.'

'Fred?' She looked up at him with a puzzled frown.

He was almost as puzzled himself. He couldn't think how he'd ended up talking about his former batman when what he wanted to say was so important. He supposed it must have come from her asking about his inability to sleep....

But before he could wrest the conversation back into line, they were interrupted.

'Now, now—cannot have you monopolising Lady Jayne all day,' boomed the voice of Lord Lavenham.

He looked up with a flash of irritation to see his grandfather striding towards him, a brace of spaniels frolicking at his heels.

'Must mingle, my boy. Duty of a host to mingle. And numbers down in the billiard room are uneven. Get yourself down there and even them up, what? *I* shall show her ladyship the family portraits.'

'As you wish,' he said flatly, bowing and turning on his heel. He had not been making much headway with Lady Jayne anyway. He had started off well enough.

But then she'd started chewing her lower lip. And the ability to think about anything except kissing her had abruptly deserted him.

Time for yet another tactical withdrawal.

Lady Jayne noted the stiff set of his shoulders as he walked away and felt a surge of anger on his behalf. How *could* the old man treat him like an errant school-boy? Demean him like that in front of witnesses?

Lord Lavenham held out his arm with one of his genial smiles which, now she was on the receiving end of it, she beheld to be totally false.

She was not in the most receptive of moods to begin with, and over the course of the next half-hour, during which he not very subtly interrogated her upon her suitability to become the next Countess of Lavenham, she grew increasingly annoyed with him. But at least her irritation with his intrusive questions, coupled with the way he would keep running his eyes over her as though she was a brood mare, kept her from succumbing to the dreadful temptation to sit down, bury her head in her hands and burst into tears.

Lord Ledbury had decided to abandon his cold-blooded search for a titled, accomplished woman to marry. He was going to follow his heart instead. That was why he'd kissed her that morning. He'd had some kind of…epiphany. And it was all her doing. By bringing Milly down here she had in fact accomplished exactly what she'd set out to do. That was what he had been trying to say just now. Awkwardly, because he had been a soldier and was not used to talking about feelings of a romantic nature.

And when he'd said he was glad he'd met her it had not been because he found anything about her in the least bit appealing. Nobody could possibly just be glad to know her for herself. Had not the last few weeks seared that knowledge into her consciousness?

But she *had* shown Lord Ledbury that there was more to life than honour and duty. *That* was why he was glad he'd met her. She'd persuaded him that being in love with the woman he was going to marry was more important than any other consideration.

At the very moment she'd discovered she was in love with him herself, she was going to have to watch him casting everything aside in order to be with another woman.

She didn't know how she was going to bear it.

That evening Lord Ledbury went to his grandfather's study, where he knew he would find him taking one last drink before turning in for the night.

'Ah, Richard, my boy, take a seat.' He waved to the chair opposite the fireplace, where he was ensconced with a large glass of brandy. 'Come to discuss the girls, have you, now I've had a chance to look 'em all over?'

'Not exactly.' Not in the least. For he did not give a damn what his grandfather thought. He sat down, crossed his legs, and leaned back before saying, 'I just thought it would be polite to let you know that I've made up my mind regarding whom I intend to marry.'

'So soon? Well, whichever one it is, I must say I admire the way you've gone about the task I set you. No shilly-shallying.'

Well, that was hardly to his credit. He hadn't cared much who he might end up married to when he'd first accepted that his duty was clear. It had only been after Lady Jayne burst into his life like... Well, as he'd told her, just like one of Congreve's rockets, that he'd discovered there was only one woman with whom he wanted to spend the rest of his life.

'Miss Beresford, is it?' Lord Lavenham leaned back in his own seat and twirled his brandy round in its glass. 'Out of all the girls you've brought down here she is the one I can see making you the most comfortable sort of wife. You get on well with the brother, at least. Can be devilishly uncomfortable if you don't get on with the extended family.'

'No, not Miss Beresford. I intend to ask Lady Jayne to be my wife.'

Lord Lavenham looked up at him sharply.

'Lady Jayne Chilcott?' He shook his head. 'Richard, I can quite see why you considered her, given the qualities I urged you to look for in a bride. Highly born, and with a substantial fortune to bring to the table. And a good seat. Yes, I liked the way she handled Mischief this morning, and that's a fact. But you must have noticed how cold she can be?'

'Her manner may be cool, sometimes, but she is not cold at heart.'

'I have noticed that there is a distinct thaw in her attitude towards *you*. But I have to tell you, after spending half an hour in her company this afternoon I had to come in here and call for Watkins to light the fire.'

He shivered.

'Only met one person before with the capacity to freeze the blood in m'veins with one look, and that was her father. He was a cold-hearted blackguard, was the Marquis of Tunstall. Could be downright nasty if you got on the wrong side of him. Before your time, so you wouldn't know, so it's my duty to warn you, boy, to think very carefully before getting yourself hitched to any child of his.'

Richard sat forward, his hands clasped between his knees.

'I think I know what you mean, sir. I have watched her retreat within herself when she is upset or offended. But I find her dignified withdrawal far preferable to the behaviour of girls who lash out in anger when they are crossed. Or make spiteful remarks behind an unsuspecting victim's back.'

'Like Lady Susan.' His grandfather nodded. 'I am inclined to agree with you there.'

Well, that was something.

'If I can persuade Lady Jayne to accept me, I am confident that she will do her best to make me happy.'

Lord Lavenham frowned.

'So long as you have no sentimental expectations regarding a match with one of the Chilcotts, I suppose it might answer. And you don't strike me as being the sentimental sort, so... No, I suppose I cannot raise any objections.'

Expectations? No, he had no expectations. Expecting a woman to love him was not the same as hoping that one day she might feel something stronger than fondness towards him.

'When I set out to find a wife, you must know, sir, that sentimentality had nothing to do with it.'

'Indeed,' said the earl thoughtfully. Then he sighed. 'Well, whomever you marry, I cannot believe you could do worse than your own father, or either of your brothers.' His expression soured. 'They all disappointed me. Whereas you—' he looked at him squarely from beneath his beetling brows '—you never have. I have followed your career with great interest.'

'You have?' Why was this the first he'd heard of it? As far as he knew, his grandfather was only interested in his horses and his hounds.

'Yes. Upon several occasions your gallantry has brought distinction upon the name of Cathcart. Been proud of the way you earned your promotions. In short, I am not at all sorry that you will be the one to take up the reins when I am gone.'

At one time Richard would have given anything to know that one of his family was watching his military career. His father had acted as though he'd done him an immense favour by purchasing him a commission for his sixteenth birthday, but he'd always assumed the fact that it was in a regiment serving overseas had been a deliberate attempt to deal with the problem of the middle son for whom he could feel neither love nor hate. And he'd never, not once in his life, received a letter from his own mother—not once he'd left home. And he wasn't talking about his military service. She'd washed her hands of him the moment he'd gone away to school.

But his grandfather had followed his career? How he wished he had known that when it might have meant something. Now it was…not something that affected him as much as he would have expected.

When he'd vowed to do his duty by his family, in resigning his commission and marrying a woman worthy of raising the next generation of Cathcarts, he realized he'd done it because it was in his nature to do his best—not to win anyone's approval.

'Now, tomorrow,' said Lord Lavenham, 'I thought it

would be a good idea to take 'em all out to The Workings.'

'A good idea,' replied Richard, relieved that his grandfather was moving the conversation away from the personal to the practical.

'Chaperones in carriages. The rest of you on horseback. A pretty spot, some nice views, and you young things can all picnic. Play cricket in the afternoon if it is fine. Parlour games if not.'

Richard nodded. The Workings was an ideal location for an afternoon's entertainment during unsettled weather. Some twenty-five years previously his grandfather, this crusty old man who had such trouble talking about emotion of any sort, had built his own wife a substantial pavilion on the brow of a hill from which she could watch the progress of the canal which was being cut along one of the farthest-flung borders of the estate. It had been his way, Richard supposed, of showing her that he loved the woman his own parents had arranged for him to marry, since she'd become inexplicably fascinated with everything to do with the workings in the valley.

He'd even had the estate carpenter make her ladyship a working model of a lock staircase, though there was not one along this stretch of the canal. As a boy, Richard had loved going down to The Workings with a jug of water and navigating twigs, leaves or anything he could find that floated, through the series of locks. If the contraption still worked, it was just the sort of thing to keep all his guests amused for ages.

He left his grandfather's study wondering how, amidst all the bustle of the proposed activities, he would be able to draw Milly to one side and put a stop to her mischief-making.

Or, better yet, get Lady Jayne in some secluded spot where he might be able to coax her into letting him kiss her again.

Only this time it wasn't going to be a brief touch of lips. No, this time he was going to make sure she knew she'd been well and truly kissed. He was going to make such a thorough job of it that she wouldn't even be able to remember Lieutenant Kendell's name, never mind what he looked like.

He might have known she wouldn't make it easy for him. In fact, the day which he'd hoped would accomplish so much had been one of unmitigated torture.

Surrounded by chaperones, grooms, footmen with tables and chairs and boxes of other sundry equipment, maids with hampers of food, not to mention the other house guests all intent on getting a piece of him, Lady Jayne had had no trouble whatsoever avoiding him completely. To round things off nicely, now, when he'd rung for Fred, it had been Mortimer's valet who had answered his summons, with the intelligence that, so far as anyone knew, Fred had 'absconded to the nearest hostelry, in search of liquid refreshment.'

In one way, that news had come as no surprise. Fred had seemed ill at ease, if not downright morose, when he'd shaved him that morning.

For a moment he felt half inclined to go after him, so that they could drown their sorrows together.

Instead he dismissed Jenkins, deciding he would rather put himself to bed than endure his mealy mouthed ministrations.

But he got no further than pulling off his evening shoes, stockings and neckcloth before he sat down on the edge of the bed and buried his face in his hands.

Deciding to marry Lady Jayne was one thing. Telling his grandfather he was going to propose to her, no matter what he thought, was another. But actually saying the words to *her*...when like as not she would reject him...was turning out to be a great deal harder than he could possibly have imagined. How the hell did a man persuade a woman who was still recovering from a broken heart to look favourably on him? Last night it had sounded easy. Just kiss her and tell her he loved her. Or tell her he loved her, then kiss her and...

And that was the thing. He couldn't get the image of her struggling with Kendell, when he'd forced a kiss on her, out of his head. And she had loved *him* enough to agree to a secret assignation with him.

This kind of courting was damned complicated. He'd never been all that bothered about how the women he'd taken a fancy to might feel about him. A soldier took his pleasure where he could find it. But if he made one wrong move where Lady Jayne was concerned, and destroyed what goodwill she did appear to have for him, he did not know how he would bear it.

He shot to his feet, wrenching his shirt from his waistband and tearing open the neck, though the action gave him scant outlet for his frustration. He could not risk taking any course of action that might alienate her altogether. But if he sat about doing nothing she might still slip right through his fingers. He was going to have to—

What was that? He'd heard a most peculiar noise— a kind of rattling as of hailstones against the window, though there was not a cloud in the sky. It made the hairs on the nape of his neck stand on end, just as they always did when he scented danger.

Another, sharper sound, as of a bullet striking the masonry, had him flinging himself to the floor in a move so instinctive he was face to face with his chamber pot before he rightly knew what he was doing.

Who the devil could be taking potshots at him through a first-floor window, of all things? He swarmed on elbows and knees to his dresser, reached up and pulled his pistol from the top drawer, whilst wondering what kind of enemy would have waited until now to fire upon him, when he had been strolling about the park all day, a much easier target—especially when he had stood on the brow of the hill....

Well, he was not going to make it easy for him to put a period to his existence. He loaded his weapon, crawled to the window, sat up next to it and took a cautious peek over the edge of the sill.

Lady Jayne had been growing more and more miserable all day, waiting for Richard to propose to Milly.

But Milly still seemed to be under the impression he was angry with her, and had been keeping well out of his way.

Just as assiduously as she'd been avoiding Milly.

She should have gone straight to Milly yesterday and told her what Richard planned. But every time she braced herself to go through with it, and formed the words in her head, other words came welling up from deep, deep within. *Not you. He loves her, not you.*

And after the pain had come the shame that, instead of wanting Milly to be able to find happiness with Richard, she was all twisted up with jealousy inside. It was a rotten thing to do—fall in love with a man your friend wanted to marry.

It was no use telling herself she hadn't meant to do it. She *had* done it. And it made her feel like a traitor.

All day long everyone concerned had been utterly miserable.

She sighed.

Tomorrow. Tomorrow, if Richard had not managed it himself, she *would* tell Milly what she knew, and at least the two of them could be happy.

Only...

It sounded as though Milly was as unable to sleep as she, for some time now, had heard her moving about the room as though she was pacing up and down in agitation. In the end, though part of her wanted to pull the covers up over her ears and blot everything out, she pushed her own selfish desires aside, along with the bedcovers, got out of her bed, crossed the sitting room and tapped gently on Milly's bedroom door.

And stopped still on the threshold.

Clothes were strewn everywhere, as if somebody had got in and ransacked the room. But it must have been Milly who'd made all the mess. For she was standing amidst the wreckage, a small valise clutched in one hand, a bonnet in the other, and a mulish expression on her mouth.

And she was wearing a coat.

'Milly...'

Lady Jayne had been about to ask her what she was doing, but it was so obvious she intended to leave she would have felt foolish voicing the question.

'Milly,' she began again. 'Please don't leave. Not now, just when Richard—'

'This has nothing to do with him!' Milly's face hardened. She tossed the valise onto the bed and placed the bonnet on her head.

'Of course it has. Milly, I can see you must have given up hope to say such a thing, but—'

'There was *never* any hope for me with him,' she said as she yanked the ribbons into a bow under her chin. 'But at least now I've met a man who does see me as a woman. Tom's waiting for me right now. In the lane that goes up to The Workings. In his curricle...'

'Not... You don't mean Lord Halstead?'

'Why not Lord Halstead?'

'Well, because I...I can't believe he loves you. Not if he has asked you to run away with him like this.' She'd learned that much from her relationship with Harry. 'Besides, if you run off with another man it will break Richard's heart.'

'If you think anything I do might *touch* Richard's heart,' Milly said bitterly, 'let alone break it, you are very much mistaken.'

She turned to the bed and picked up her valise.

'Of course it will hurt him!' How could Milly be so obtuse? She had been devastated when Harry abandoned her, and she hadn't loved him at all. It was the betrayal, the lies he'd told. And it would be ten times worse for Richard, because he *did* love Milly. Was on the verge of proposing to her.

'Well, that only goes to show how little you really know him. That's 'cos he's only let you see him in the guise of a gentleman. But that's not really him. He's a soldier at heart. And an officer to boot. There's nothing soft about him to hurt. He's steel through to the core.'

'Even if that were true—' which she didn't believe for a minute '—you can't just go throwing your life away because you are upset.' It was the kind of thing she'd done in the past. Completely overreacted when she'd been hurt and angry. 'You don't really think Lord Halstead is going to offer to marry you if you run off with him tonight, do you?'

'Course not! What do you take me for?'

Lady Jayne gasped. She could just about see why Milly would have been content to become Richard's mistress. If a woman loved a man enough she might easily sacrifice her virtue. But this was not the same at all.

'Milly, have you taken leave of your senses? You hardly know the man!'

'I know enough,' said Milly defiantly. 'He's fun, at least. Since we've been down here I've had such laughs with him while he's been trying to work out if I'm really his Spanish lady from the masquerade. It was him as took me home, you know, after Richard spirited you away.'

'But...'

Milly's face softened. 'Look, I can see you're worried about what will become of me, but you needn't be. I'm not daft. I know this thing with Tom won't last long, but I'll survive. I've still got the house Richard gave me...'

'Milly! You cannot actually want to demean yourself by letting a man like that...use you? Then throw you away as though you were of no account?' For that was what men did with their mistresses, was it not?

Milly made an impatient gesture with her hand to silence her.

'Don't start preaching at me, Jayne. You don't un-derstand...*anything.* You cannot begin to know how awful it was, all those months when we didn't know if Richard was going to live or die. Fred was out foraging, and I was scrimping and saving and making do when his precious family wouldn't lift a finger to help. Es-pecially when you consider our regiment was having picnics and parties and balls all the way to Paris. And where was I? *Chatham!'*

She spat the word as though it was a curse.

'And then, when he did come into all this—' with a rather wild laugh she waved at the opulence of the room in which they stood '—and said he was grateful for all I'd done, and he was going to treat me right, I thought he was going to set me up in style. Give me a carriage and a pair of cream horses so I could go round the park like as if I was someone. Or a box at the theatre—now, that wouldn't have gone amiss neither. But instead of mak-ing sure I could start having some real fun he packed me off to Bedford Place and told me to be a good girl. But I'm not a girl,' she cried, stamping her foot. 'I'm a woman!'

Oh, how often Lady Jayne had wrought herself up to the same pitch as her friend was in now. Even though she could understand Richard's motives, she could *feel* every ounce of Milly's frustration. In just such a mood she'd vowed not to dance with a single man in London. In just such a mood she'd decided to go to that masquer-ade and meet Harry.

And who had been hurt? *Not* the person who'd pro-voked her into the act of defiance. Just herself.

'No!' cried Lady Jayne, stepping in front of Milly as she picked up her valise and made for the door. 'I won't let you do this. I can see you are very upset, but you have to stop and listen…'

'You really think you can stop me? I'm a head and a half taller than you, and far, far stronger if it comes to a fight. And I know tricks you couldn't even dream of.'

'I…I am quite sure you do,' she replied, lifting her chin. 'But I have something very important to tell you. It will change everything…'

But Milly did not stop. She did not listen. With a mulish pout, Milly simply pushed Lady Jayne aside and stalked into their sitting room.

She ran after her and seized her arm as she reached for the door handle.

'Milly, stop! I can't let you leave like this. I can't!'

'For heaven's sake, Jayney!' Milly dropped her valise, wrapped her arms round her waist, lifted her from the floor and flung her away from the door. 'Can't you see this will be to your advantage? Now you know I'm no competition, there's nothing to stop you going after Richard yourself.'

'What?' She straightened up, rubbing at her waist where she could still feel Milly's steely strong grip.

'Don't play the innocent with me. I've seen the way you come alive for him, when you can barely be bothered to be polite to any other man.' She thrust her face into hers. 'You go for the heroic type, don't you? That was what attracted you to your Hyde Park soldier. The uniform. The veneer of manliness.'

Lady Jayne retreated, shaking her head. It hadn't been like that with Harry at all!

'Well, take it from me, Richard is ten times the man Harry was. I've had my hands on every single inch of his body. And I can vouch for the fact he's got all the equipment necessary to keep a woman well satisfied.'

'Milly!'

'Even if it was true that my leaving might affect him, we both know he's on the hunt for a Society bride.'

'No! W-well he was, but he told me—'

'All you need do,' Milly interrupted, prodding her in the chest with her forefinger, making Lady Jayne take another step back, 'is flutter those great long eyelashes of yours, put your arms round his neck and let him kiss you. And I guarantee all will be right with his world again.'

'No. You've got it dreadfully wrong…' she protested, just as Milly shoved her hard in the chest and sent her reeling back.

And slammed the bedroom door in her face.

With every coarse remark, each jab of her finger, she had sent Lady Jayne retreating across the sitting room. She had been so shocked that Milly had known all along how she felt about Richard—especially when she'd only just untangled her web of emotions in his regard the day before—she had not noticed the moment she teetered on the threshold of her own room. But now she was on the wrong side of the door, while Milly was turning the key in the lock.

'Let me out! Milly! You must—' she slammed the palms of her hands against the locked door '—not leave!'

She grabbed the doorknob and tugged with all her might. It would not yield.

'Milly!' she yelled as loud as she could. But Milly's steps did not falter. And then she heard the outer door slam.

Oh, this was terrible. Not only was Milly ruining her

own future by acting on the kind of anger that Lady Jayne knew only too well, but she was also going to devastate Richard. This *affaire* would ruin any chance of him finding the happiness he'd only just started to reach for.

She kicked the annoyingly solid bedroom door just once, to relieve her feelings, welcoming the pain that shot through her toes. Because it was all *her* fault. If she hadn't gone to that masquerade Milly might never have met Lord Halstead. If she hadn't been such a selfish, jealous, coward she would have told Milly yesterday that Richard was going to propose, and then none of this would be happening.

There was only one way to make amends. With a determined glint in her eye, she marched across to the window.

Chapter Twelve

Lady Jayne opened the casement and leaned out, examining the climb she would have to make. For she had to get to Richard and warn him what was going on, and this window was the only way out of her room.

The apex of the *porte-cochère* was only a foot or so beneath her windowsill. The pitch of the tiles was quite steep and, since it had been raining earlier that evening, they were slick with moisture. The drop from the guttering that ran along the lowest edge of the slope to the ground looked to be another fifteen or twenty feet.

She had no fear of heights, since she had spent a great deal of her childhood, during the years when her father had just wanted her kept out of his sight, climbing trees. But this was not going to be an easy descent. That slippery slope had no handholds. And there was no way to avoid dropping the last bit.

She leaned out a bit farther. If she slid crabwise across the *porte-cochère,* to its lowest point, she might be able to find a toehold amongst the ivy. It covered the whole frontage of the house, and she knew from experience that a plant that vigorous would have some sturdy branches under all that thick foliage. Failing all else, she could grab a vine and let it slow her descent to the ground as it peeled away from the wall.

The image of getting a vine in her hand reminded her of a rope. A rope. Yes, if only she had a rope she could cling to it as she slid slowly down the sloping tiles. And then, even if it was not all that long, if she could hang from the end of it and reduce her fall by even a few feet it would make all the difference. If she only had to drop, say, ten feet, it would be like coming off a horse that was jumping a hedge, which she had done plenty of times.

You had to roll, her groom had taught her from an early age. Not just slam into the ground like a sack of potatoes, but crumple and roll. And then, though you still got bruises, you weren't so likely to break bones.

She turned round, scanning her room for something to fashion into a rope. Her eyes snagged on the plaited cords that tied back the silk damask hangings of her bed. She unlooped them and swiftly knotted them together as best she could. Then tied the end of the first one to the central stone pillar between her windows. Then gave a little tug, to make sure it was secure. She wished she had packed her breeches. But, since she had promised never to climb out of a window again, it hadn't occurred to her she might want them.

She clucked her tongue in annoyance. When would she stop making stupid, rash vows that she had no hope of keeping? Oh, dear. Was she doomed to end up like Milly? One day throwing her life away completely in a fit of…pique?

Not if she could help it. She firmed her lips and hitched her nightgown up round her thighs. She'd made mistakes in her past. Bad ones. But she wasn't so stupid she hadn't learned from them.

She knotted the yards of fine lawn in place with the belt of her dressing gown and swung her legs over the sill, clinging tightly to the plaited velvet cord.

There was a ripping noise.

She couldn't worry about whatever she'd torn just now. She had to concentrate on getting to Richard as fast as possible. To that end she turned to lie on her tummy on the tiles, skinning her knees in the process. Ignoring the pain, and the unpleasant sensation of wetness seeping through the front of her nightgown, she began to worm her way down.

It was when she was about halfway down that the rope went slack and then, to her horror, went slithering past her. Somewhere along its length it must have come untied.

Oh, why, she thought as she scrabbled in vain for purchase on the wet tiles, had none of those expensive tutors and governesses she'd had ever taught her how to tie knots?

After breaking several fingernails, she thought of kicking off her silk slippers. Maybe she could dig her toes into the steep and slippery slope. It didn't help at all. In fact, she felt as though she was sliding downwards even faster.

She shrieked as her feet went over the edge.

But then, by some miracle, she managed to grab hold of the limestone trough that acted as guttering. For a second or two she hung, suspended by her fingertips in midair.

And then she was falling through empty space.

Instinctively she curled into a ball as she hit the

gravel driveway. When she stopped rolling she lay quite still for a moment or two, taking stock and thanking providence for that groom. The one person who had taught her anything of real value.

It did not feel as though she had broken anything. With a determined grimace, she made herself sit up.

She was facing the massive, locked front door.

She could pound on the knocker, she supposed. Yes, and raise half the household. And then they would all know that Milly had run off with Lord Halstead after locking her in her room. Which was the last thing she wanted.

No, somehow she had to find Richard—and only Richard. Nobody else must ever know about this night's work.

She got to her feet and stood for a few moments, willing her legs to stop shaking, and wondered which out of the three storeys of closed, curtained windows this part of the house possessed was his.

And then she remembered him saying how hard he found it to sleep with the windows shut. But that Fred was here now. Fred who knew how he liked things done.

All she had to do was walk round the house looking for an open window. She didn't know anyone else who was likely to leave a window open at night, since most people believed that the night air was injurious to the health.

Although, she reflected as she made for the corner of the house, that did not stop anyone from staying out until dawn when they were in London. If night air was really that bad, surely it would be dangerous to go outside at night? She paused and scanned the windows on the west wing. All shut.

She set off again, going round to the back, where she came to a jumble of buildings that looked like kitchens and offices, which ran clear away to the stable block. He would not sleep down here.

So she retraced her steps to the front of the house, then continued round to examine the east wing, which had been tacked on to the earliest buildings at about the same time as the *porte-cochère,* by the looks of the stonework.

And felt a sense of jubilation when she spied, on the first floor, a single sash pushed up. It had to be Richard's room!

Only now that she'd found it how on earth was she to attract his attention? If she shouted for him she'd likely wake half the household.

She would have to throw something up at his window and hope it would wake him. She bent down, scooped up a handful of gravel from the driveway and flung it upwards.

Then squealed and scampered backwards as half of it came raining straight back down on her head. Gravel, she discovered, scattered in all directions when you threw it.

She'd have to find a pebble, then. But not too large a one. She did not want to run the risk of smashing anything. Broken glass would take too much explaining away in the morning.

A quick rummage through the urns that stood on the edge of the terrace proved unfruitful, the compost in them being so soft and crumbly she suspected it must have gone through a sieve. She trotted to the end, dived into the shrubbery and from beneath the very first bush managed to extract a couple of roughish small stones.

She threw the first one at the window, and almost stamped her foot with vexation when it went wide of where she had aimed it, striking the brickwork way to the left of the open window.

She stepped to the right half a pace and threw again. This time, to her immense satisfaction, the pebble flew right through the open window.

Only then there was a crash, as of breaking glass, and the sound of a man's voice cursing. Richard's head and shoulders appeared above the sill, as though he had been crouched beneath it.

'What the devil?' He stood up and leaned out. 'Lady Jayne? What do you think you are doing down there? My God! I almost shot you!'

'Oh, hush, Richard. Do not shout. Only come down quickly and let me in.' She gesticulated at a set of doors on the terrace. She thought she remembered him telling her they led into the library.

He nodded and disappeared.

She undid the belt of her dressing gown—the only knot that night that had held fast—so that her tattered nightdress covered the lower part of her legs once more. Then hopped from one bare foot to the other, wondering what they'd think when they cleaned the gutters out in spring and found a pair of ladies' slippers up there.

It seemed an age before the doors to the library swung open. When Richard stepped out onto the terrace, a furious scowl on his face, she wrapped her arms round herself in an involuntary gesture of self-defence. It was hard to be sure which aspect of the situation she found most intimidating. His scowl. The pistol he was still brandishing, even though he had warned her about the dangers of getting shot. Or the fact that he was bare-

foot and bare-chested, his open shirt billowing out behind him as he strode forward.

He'd looked very dashing at the masquerade, dressed
up like a corsair. But tonight, she thought as she gulped,
he looked as formidable as the real thing.

'What the hell is going on?'

'It's Milly.' Somehow she managed to drag her eyes
away from that fascinating expanse of bare male skin
and say, 'She's... I'm so—so sorry, Richard, b-but she's
run off with L-Lord Hals-tead.'

'You are freezing,' he said in response to her stam-
mered sentence.

Yes, she silently agreed. It was *cold* that was making her tremble all over.

'Let's get you back indoors and into the warmth, and
then you can tell me what on earth possessed you to go
running about in just your night things.'

'Yes,' she said as he ushered her into the library.
'B-but you must hurry, Richard,' she said as he shut
and bolted the doors behind him. 'If you get d-dressed
quickly there might still be time to stop them. It won't
take you long, will it? You already have your breeches
on,' she said, eyeing his behind as he bent to ram home
the floor bolts. 'You only need to do your shirt up and...'

She was gibbering. She could hear herself doing it.
But she was standing here wearing only her nightdress.
And everyone else in the house was asleep. Richard
had not paused to take hold of a candle when he came
down from his room, so the library was lit only by the
moonbeams shimmering in through the doors. And,
even though she could not make out very much of him
beyond shapes now, she could still see, in her mind's
eye, the wedge-shaped torso sprinkled with dark hair.

She'd never taken much account of the fact that a man's shape was so very different from her own. All hard, flat planes where she was soft, rounded curves...

'Stop them?' Why on earth would she think he wanted to stop them? If Milly had decided to throw herself away on a man like Halstead then there was nothing he could do about it. Good riddance to her! He had done all he could to ensure she stayed respectable. 'I know I can trust you not to make a whore of her,' her father had said. And he had not. *He* had kept his word.

But, no matter what hopes her father might have had regarding her future, Milly had a mind of her own. Of late she'd spent far too much of her time buying pretty clothes and showing them off at various pleasure haunts. Now it sounded pretty obvious that if virtue stood in the way of her enjoyment she had no compunction about shedding it.

But how could he explain that to an innocent like Lady Jayne?

'Look, let's get you back to your room, and we can talk about this in the morning.' By then he might have been able to think of some way to explain the way some women regarded relationships with men without shocking her.

'I *can't* go back to my room. It is locked. Milly pushed me inside and locked me in when I tried to stop her from leaving.'

'Then how the devil did you get down here? Don't tell me...' He made himself really look at her for the first time. He had been aware, from just one glance, that she was wearing only a nightgown. But he had tried to be a gentleman and not notice how wet it was, rendering patches of it transparent—how it clung to the swell of her belly and the fullness of her breasts. He forced his eyes not to linger on the dark shadows hinting at what lay beneath. 'Your dishevelled state tells its own story. You climbed out of the window.'

Why had she done that? Why had she thought it was so important to come to him, and...? Oh, Lord. He had never managed to explain properly that he was not in love with Milly. The darling little idiot had risked life and limb to come and warn him because she could not bear to think of him being hurt by Milly's defection.

Was there anyone so sweet-natured, yet so valiant?

Milly might have said she loved him, but he couldn't imagine her acting as selflessly or as recklessly as this. But then there was nobody quite like Lady Jayne.

'You might have broken your neck, you idiot,' he said, a shudder going through him just before he swept her into his arms and cradled her close.

'No, no, I would not. I am very good at climbing. I have had lots of practise.'

How could anything feel so wonderful when it was so wrong? It was her fault that Milly had run—both out of patience and off with Lord Halstead. And yet when Richard pulled her into his arms all she wanted was to put her arms round him and hug him back. Then press kisses onto the scars she had noted peppering the front of his left shoulder.

And it would not have been to offer him the comfort he was so obviously seeking in this moment of pain at Milly's betrayal. It was a purely physical response to being in his arms. Feeling his naked skin beneath her cheek. She just wanted him. In a way she did not fully understand with her mind. But her body—oh, her body knew what it wanted. It wanted more contact. Naked skin to naked skin. Her mouth wanted to taste and her hands to touch. It was all she could do to remain motionless in his arms, just breathing in the scent of him. It wasn't a scent she could put a name to. It was just… warmth and cleanliness and…Richard.

He felt her tense. 'Yes,' he said, relaxing his hold on her ever so slightly. 'All those times you climbed out of windows to meet with your Harry, I suppose.'

He had to rein himself in—and reminding himself she was still nursing a broken heart because of Harry was one sure way to do it. Though it was utterly delicious to feel her in his arms, now was not the time to let passion get the better of him.

She was not ready for moonlight kisses in the library. Especially not when they were both half-naked and he was growing steadily more aroused by the minute. It took every ounce of self-control he possessed, but somehow he managed to step back and let his arms drop to his side.

'Come *on,* Richard!' she urged him when he just stood motionless.

He clenched his fists. Lord, what would she do if she discovered how things really stood? He *had* to bring his arousal under control.

'You need to get back to your room and get some clothes on. Some boots on,' she corrected herself. 'And chase after her and stop her before it's too late.'

He didn't want to put his clothes back on. He wanted to take them off. And hers, too.

'Lady Jayne…' he grated. Now was the perfect time to tell her the truth. The bit that concerned Milly, at any rate. 'I don't really care if she has run off with Lord Halstead—' he began.

'You don't mean that! Richard, you mustn't give up on her! How will you ever live with yourself if you stand back and let her throw herself away like this?'

She seized hold of one of his clenched fists with both her hands.

'Don't you understand? She is not going to *marry* Lord Halstead. She... Oh, Richard, don't you see what will happen when he gets tired of her? She'll miss all the...what she calls *fun* she says she's been having with him, and she'll go out and get another...protector. And then another, and another.'

Her eyes were luminous with unshed tears.

'But she doesn't mean it. She isn't a bad person. She's just so angry and upset tonight that all she can think about is if she can't have you then why shouldn't she have cream horses and pretty clothes? Oh, Richard, you have to save her from making a mistake she will regret for the rest of her life.'

That was when it struck him that not all her distress was on his account. She was really upset at the thought Milly was making a mistake she would regret once her temper had cooled. A wry grimace twisted his mouth. If she were a man she'd already be down at the stables, saddling a horse and riding out after her. Once her friendship was given, she was loyal to the bitter end. And she would think less of anyone who demonstrated less than her own total commitment. Less of *him* if he stood back and did nothing to prevent Milly sinking into a life of vice.

'You are right,' he said. 'I must stop her.' Adding silently, *For your sake*.

'I *knew* that if only you could put aside your anger you would do the right thing. You always do.'

She was looking up at him as though he was some kind of...hero.

Even after she'd been betrayed by all the men in her life so far, she trusted him. She had complete faith in his ability to snatch Milly back from the abyss.

He felt ten feet tall. Because she believed in him.

'Very well,' he said, raising her hands to his mouth and kissing each one. 'Tell me where she has gone and I will go after her.'

Her whole body sagged with relief. 'She told me Lord Halstead would be waiting for her on the lane that goes up to The Workings. But she was on foot and carrying a bag. I'm sure you will be able to catch up with her.'

'Come on, then,' he said, grabbing her hand and heading for the door.

'Wh-where are you taking me?'

'Up to my room, for now.'

'Oh, there is no need for that. Just get after Milly.'

'As if I would leave you down here on your own— in the state you're in.'

He could hardly believe she would think he'd do that. What did she take him for? But one glance at her, and the way she was looking at him, was sufficient to re-assure him. It wasn't that she expected little from *him,* in particular, in the way of courtesy. That outlook had been drummed into her by the way everyone in her life had treated her so far. She simply did not expect *anyone* to care what became of her.

He felt a pang go through him. Lord, but he knew what that felt like.

He put his loaded pistol down on the table just inside the door when they reached his rooms, and led Lady Jayne to an armchair by the fire.

'Sit there while I fetch you a blanket.'

When he returned from his bedchamber she had drawn her knees right up to her chest and wrapped her arms round herself. But she was still shivering.

As he draped the blanket round her shoulders he noticed a bloodstain on her nightgown.

'You have cut your knee. And your poor feet,' he said, looking at the state of them. 'I should tend to your hurts. And get you some brandy…'

'Never mind me,' she said, grabbing the edges of the blanket and tugging them tight to her chin. 'I shall be all right. Just get after them. Hurry, Richard, hurry!'

Even now, she spared not a thought for herself. God, how he wanted to kiss her. But if he allowed himself to weaken now, while they were both wearing so little clothing, who knew where it would end?

Besides, by this time he'd come to the conclusion that she was right. It was essential for him to catch Milly and put a halt to her schemes. Otherwise, in the morning, everyone would hear that one of the young ladies—or at least a person they had all assumed was a lady's companion—had run off with one of the gentlemen. And it wouldn't stop there. Once the guests dispersed the scandal would be all over Town. It was just the sort of salacious gossip that people loved to spread: an apparent innocent seduced by a much older, experienced man at the house party where Lord Ledbury proposed to Lady Jayne Chilcott. And not just any innocent, but the girl who'd come as companion to Lady Jayne. And then how long would it be before someone unearthed the fascinating tidbit that Lord Ledbury had known said innocent even longer than he'd known Lady

Jayne? That he'd set her up in her own house, and given her an allowance?

It was the very scenario he'd been fighting to prevent ever since he'd introduced the girls to each other.

He would never forgive himself if it came to that.

'Help yourself to a drink, then,' he said gruffly, waving his arm at the table that held a decanter and glasses. 'While I go and get some boots on.'

By the time he returned to his sitting room, booted and half buttoned into his army greatcoat, Lady Jayne was sitting curled up in the armchair again, sipping a generous measure of brandy.

He went over and tugged the blanket back up round her shoulders snugly.

'I will be as quick as I can,' he told her. 'Just sit tight and keep warm. When I get back we'll see about cleaning up your cuts and scrapes and work out how to get you back to your room without anyone discovering you have ever been out of it.'

Then, because he couldn't hold himself back any longer, he bent down, seized her face between his hands, and kissed her hard—full on the lips.

'What did you do that for?' she gasped.

She looked puzzled, and a bit surprised, but not the least bit angry. Which filled him with elation. And hope.

'Because you are a darling,' he said, gently tracing the curve of her cheek with his forefinger. 'We shall have to have a serious talk when I get back. But in the meantime…' he bent and kissed her again '…behave yourself.'

And then he turned and left. Picking up his pistol on his way out.

Lady Jayne sat there in a daze. He had kissed her.

Twice. And called her a darling. She could still feel the imprint of his lips upon hers. And the echo of his hands cupping her face. A lovely, fuzzy warmth began to spread through her veins.

Only to come shivering to a halt when she recalled him adjuring her to *behave herself.*

He might be grateful to her for alerting him to Milly's flight, but he still only saw her as… Well, the best she could hope for was a friend. And he had not been able to resist saying something about her behaviour. He'd even brought up that dreadful episode when she had snuck out of Lady Penrose's house to meet Harry. The horrid, shaky feeling she'd had ever since she had fallen off the roof became a surge of real nausea.

She downed the rest of the brandy, then set the empty glass down on the floor by the chair with a snap.

Minutes ticked past.

It was awfully quiet, sitting up by the fire, in the middle of the night. She wondered where Richard was. Whether he'd caught up with them yet. And whether he'd shot Lord Halstead with that pistol he'd snatched up as he went out through the door. And whether Milly was flinging herself on his chest and weeping with gratitude…

She pulled her thoughts away from their reunion. Only to become increasingly aware of all the physical discomforts she'd told Richard did not matter. Her nightgown had absorbed a lot of rainwater when she'd slid down the wet tiles, so that in spite of the blanket round her shoulders she just couldn't get warm. Her knee hurt. As did the palms of her hands and her shoulders in the aftermath of hanging from the guttering. And her feet were filthy.

She'd feel much better if only she could have a wash and get into some clean, dry nightwear, rather than sitting here feeling sorry for herself because Richard had done exactly as she'd asked. Left her here alone, soaked, freezing and hurt, to go chasing after Milly.

But she could not go back to her room. Milly had locked her out.

No, she hadn't, though. She had locked her *in*. She had turned the key in the outside of the door. If she could just find her way back to the suite she would be able to get back in and, as Richard had said, nobody would be any the wiser.

Hitching the blanket round her shoulders, she tiptoed across the room and peeped out of the door through which Richard had gone. The corridor outside was pitch-black. Nobody would venture along here without a candle. And if she were to see any glimmer of light she could run and hide, surely?

She went and fetched a candle from Richard's bedroom. She felt a pang of guilt when she noted a mess of broken glass on his dressing table, where the stone she had flung had shattered the mirror. She also couldn't help noticing that his bed had not been slept in. He must have been getting ready for bed when she'd thrown the stone through his window. Which was why his shirt had been undone. Her mind flashed back to the sight of him, standing in the library doorway, barefoot and half dressed. And then her eyes fell to the rumpled coverlet of his bed. Had he been sitting just there, undoing his shirt, when her pebble flew through the window?

She backed hastily away from the bed, took the lighted candle from Richard's nightstand, and marched determinedly out of his suite of rooms.

If she turned to the left and walked until she came to the end of his side of the house, then turned left again, that would take her to the front of the house, where her own suite was situated.

The candlelight cast huge wavering shadows before her as she crept stealthily along the deserted corridors. How on earth did burglars have the nerve to creep through people's houses in the dead of night? By the time she reached the familiar sight of the door to the suite she had shared with Milly her heart was banging so hard against her ribs it was making her whole body shake.

She slipped inside, breathing a sigh of relief to think nobody had seen her, walked across to her room and stretched out her hand to unlock her door. But there was no key in the lock. Milly must have removed it for some reason, and she had not noticed because she had been making so much noise pounding on the door, demanding her release. With a sense of frustration she shook the handle, but it was no use.

There was nothing for it. She would have to go back to Richard's room and wait for him to return. It was what he'd asked her to do in the first place. If only she'd just stayed put!

She caught her lower lip between her teeth as she peered out into the darkened corridor. If only she'd just done as he'd requested, nobody would have known she was even out of bed. Richard would have got a spare key from somewhere and got her back to her room discreetly. But now, because she thought she knew best, she had doubled the risk of discovery by venturing along this same set of corridors twice over.

The nearer she got to Richard's room, the more nervous she became. She might have been able to explain away getting caught near her own room, but not all the way on the other side of the house.

When she finally reached the sanctuary of his suite she was shaking so badly there was nothing for it but to make straight for the brandy decanter. She sloshed a generous measure into the glass she'd used before, then sank onto the chair, draping the blanket she had left there round her shoulders—more for comfort than anything. Then she took a large gulp of the drink she'd poured, hoping the warmth that burned down her throat and into her stomach would soon radiate out through her limbs and help her stop shaking, as it had before.

Oh, what could be taking him so long? She peered at the clock on the mantelpiece. It was very blurry. She rubbed her eyes, but still could not make out the time. It was too dark in here. And her eyes did not seem to be able to focus on anything properly. And she was so tired.

She curled her legs up on the chair and tried to wedge her head against its high back, but it was very uncomfortable. It had not been so bad when she was moving about, but now she was sitting still she couldn't stop thinking about how cold and wet she was.

She wanted to lie down. And Richard's bed was just through that door. It had a huge bank of pillows where she could rest her head without getting a crick in her neck. And lots of blankets, topped with a quilt, that nobody was using right now. She picked up the candle to light her way into the room, the blanket slithering unheeded to the floor behind her.

She felt a sense of rightness when she returned the candle to the nightstand where she had found it. She ought to have just done as Richard had told her and waited for him here. And maybe used some of the water in that pitcher on his washstand to clean herself up a bit, instead of wasting all that time and effort running about all over the house.

She'd been really silly, tiptoeing up and down the corridors. She giggled as she recalled how, rounding one corner, she'd jumped when a grotesque shadow had loomed up—a shadow she'd created herself, because her hands had been shaking so much.

She threw the covers aside and saw the beautifully white starched sheets. It would be a terrible shame to soil them with all the slime and moss that was stuck to the front of her sodden nightgown. In fact, now she came to think of it, it was entirely the nightdress's fault that she was so cold.

'Ugh,' she said, pulling it off over her head. 'Nasty, wet thing.' She flung it away and then, completely naked, slipped into Richard's bed and pulled all the covers up to her ears. Oh, that was better. She would soon get warm now. She gave a huge yawn, shut her eyes and fell instantly into the deep sleep of total inebriation.

She had never partaken of spirits before. So she had no idea what effect two large glasses of brandy could have. She would never have dreamed that she might fall into such a deep sleep that not even dawn breaking could have the power to rouse her. Nor the sound of the maid coming in to draw back the curtains.

She did not even wake when the girl, spying a female head on her master's pillow, emitted a squeak of surprise. Not even when that girl, consumed by curiosity, tiptoed over to see if she could make out her identity, before gasping in amazement, and then running from the room, giggling.

Straight back to the servants' hall with the juiciest bit of gossip she'd ever had the privilege of broadcasting.

Chapter Thirteen

It was growing light when he got back to the stable yard, where he handed Ajax, a horse he'd inherited, like so much else, from his brother Mortimer, into the care of a sleepy groom.

He threw back his shoulders as he strode across the yard to the mud room.

He wouldn't have believed it would take so long. But he'd done it. He'd tied the entire affair up so neatly there would be no loose ends to come unravelled and bring so much as a thread of gossip to Lady Jayne's door.

And he'd learned something, too.

Shutting the mud-room door behind him, he bent to shuck off his boots. It had been when Milly had melted into Fred's arms the moment he'd confessed he was in love with her. If a confession of love was all it took to deal with all that spitting fury, all her rebelliousness, he'd thought, it was a great pity the idiot hadn't just told her he loved her months ago and saved everyone a whole lot of trouble. She didn't care a jot that the man had, as he'd put it in his own words, nothing to offer her but his heart. After all she'd said and done even

Milly could see that having a man who truly loved her was worth more than any amount of silk gowns a lord could give her.

Not a second later he'd seen that he'd been as much of an idiot as Fred. He'd thought he had nothing to offer Lady Jayne, either. But he did. His heart. It was hers. Had been completely hers from…well, to be honest, probably from the moment she'd begged him not to let her maid pay the price for her own misbehaviour.

His mouth firmed with determination as he removed his second boot and aligned it with precision next to its mate. The moment he got back to his rooms he was going to explain the situation with Milly in such a way that there would be no more room for misunderstanding. Then he was going to tell Lady Jayne straight out that he was in love with her. And ask her to marry him.

And if she refused—and he was almost certain she would the first time he proposed to her—then he was going to lay siege to her heart until she surrendered, however long it took. Because there was no question of him ever marrying anyone else.

He ran up the stairs two at a time, feeling as if he'd thrown aside a heavy cloak that had been hampering his sword arm. It had been as he was riding back to Courtlands that everything had fallen into place. He knew who he was at last. Not a soldier without a uniform. Or a lord with neither the training in estate management to be a success in the countryside nor the inclination to fritter his wealth away in the gaming hells of the capital.

No, he was just a man who was going to fight for Lady Jayne's hand, and her heart.

While he'd been removing his boots he'd been able to hear the rattle of pots and pans coming from the kitchens, and the smell of frying bacon assailed his nostrils.

It was going to be devilishly tricky getting her back to her own rooms undetected now that the servants were up and about their business. But he would make time to lay the bare facts before her, at least.

He flung open the doors to the suite that had once been occupied by his father, his eyes going straight to the chair where he'd left her.

She wasn't there. The blanket she had been using was crumpled on the floor, an empty brandy glass lying on its side next to it. But of Lady Jayne herself there was no sign.

Well, wasn't that just like her? The infuriating creature had slipped through his fingers yet again. He shook his head ruefully as he pictured her impatience mounting as the hours ticked by. Until she'd finally decided to take matters into her own hands. A slow smile spread across his face. He couldn't be annoyed with her for being resourceful and spirited. For behaving in the way that had made him fall in love with her in the first place. For being the ideal woman for him. Even if he'd still been a serving soldier she would have been perfect. The kind of dauntless woman who made an excellent officer's wife.

Well, since she was in no need of rescuing, he might as well go back to bed and catch an hour or two of sleep before breakfast. It went without saying that the pursuit and capture of Lady Jayne was going to be a challenging if not a downright exhausting business. But she was worth it.

He was still smiling as he went into his bedroom, shucked off his greatcoat and threw it over the back of a chair. He had not wasted time putting on a neckcloth before dashing off in pursuit of Milly, so all he had to do was undo the top few fastenings of his shirt and tug it off over his head.

He turned towards the bed as he unbuttoned the fall of his breeches, and froze.

Far from going back to her own rooms, Lady Jayne had solved her immediate problems by creeping into his bed. Seeking warmth and comfort, no doubt. He only had to look at her, with her hair in plaits, her hand tucked under her cheek, the very picture of innocence, to know she wouldn't have thought of anything else— more was the pity.

With deep regret, he refastened his breeches and went to wake her up. Much as he loved the sight of her lying in the bed where he'd spent so many hours dreaming of her, nobody else must ever know she'd been here.

He bent over her, a tender smile softening his features.

'Lady Jayne.'

The only response he got was a sigh redolent of brandy fumes. He winced, remembering the overturned glass on the sitting-room floor. How much more had she drunk while he was out haring all over the countryside? Quite a bit, to judge by the depth of her sleep.

He considered kissing her awake, like the prince in *Sleeping Beauty*. Only he didn't think he could be as restrained as a prince in a children's story. He wouldn't want to stop at just kisses.

He stretched out a hand to shake her instead. And paused, his hands hovering a scant inch over the curve of her shoulder.

Touching her, in any way, was just too great a risk

for him to take while she lay there looking so utterly tempting.

So he took hold of the coverlets instead, and swiftly twitched them off her, hoping the sudden cold might percolate into her consciousness.

And gasped.

She was completely naked.

For a moment he stood there, his fingers clenched on the coverlets, stunned to utter stillness by the perfection of her form. The early morning sunlight caressed the curve of her hip, slid lovingly along the line of her thigh, put a slight shadow between the bountiful fullness of her breasts…

He groaned as he went rock-hard.

And for the first time since Orthez he had complete confidence that, if she were willing, he could spend the entire day in bed with her without exhausting the possibilities.

He groaned again as he gently replaced the covers, in spite of wanting to just stand there, admiring her for as long as he could. She would be mortified if she ever knew he'd caught so much as a glimpse of her in all her natural glory. Which would not make her in the least receptive to a proposal of marriage from him.

Her eyelids flickered and half opened. She smiled up at him. And guilt assailed him. She would definitely not be smiling at him like that if she knew how long he'd been standing there, drinking in the sight of her without a stitch of clothing on.

'You're back,' she said. Then yawned, rolled onto her back and stretched her arms above her head. The covers slid down.

He grabbed them before they reached a point that

would have embarrassed her, and firmly tucked them up to her chin.

And backed away from the bed.

'Don't, whatever you do, sit up,' he warned her.

She frowned. 'Why?' A look of comprehension flitted across her face. 'Oh!' Her cheeks turned crimson. 'May I have my nightdress back, please?'

'If you tell me what you have done with it, I shall be only too happy to oblige.'

She pointed. He searched. And thrust the rather damp and grubby article of clothing into her outstretched hands.

'Cover yourself up quickly,' he urged her, turning his back, both to give her a modicum of privacy and to conceal his arousal. 'We need to get you back to your room before anyone notices you are missing.'

And they were running out of time. He ran his hand over the crown of his head, inwardly cursing at the realisation that explaining anything to her now, let alone proposing to her, was out of the question.

'Have you got a key, then? Tried to get back in on my own. Couldn't find the key.'

'Damnation!' He should have stopped off at the housekeeper's room and got a spare.

'Don't want to wear this.'

He looked over his shoulder to see Lady Jayne throwing the nightdress back onto the floor, her nose wrinkled in distaste.

His annoyance evaporated at the sight of her snuggling back down among the pillows, closing her eyes and sighing. She obviously had not quite slept it off, but damn if she wasn't the most charming drunk he had ever encountered!

He couldn't help smiling, but he still had to get her back to her room.

'If you don't like your nightdress, and I can hardly blame you,' he said, recalling the green smears coating the front of it, 'then you will have to make do with one of my shirts.'

He went to his clothes press and picked out a silk shirt.

'Come on, sleepyhead,' he said, giving her shoulder a nudge. 'Put this on and get up.'

'No,' she protested, squeezing her eyes tighter shut. 'My head feels funny when I move. I need to stay in bed.'

'Not in my bed, you don't.'

'No, Richard…' she protested feebly as he sat her up and began to try and thread her arms through the sleeves of his shirt. It might not have been so difficult if he had not felt obliged to keep her decently covered by the sheets at the same time.

'This is like wrestling a greased pig,' he chuckled as he pulled the edges of his shirt together under the sheets. Only that kind of activity would not have left him with such a painfully urgent erection. He might not be able to see anything beneath the level of her shoulders, but his hands could not avoid trespassing into forbidden territory. Besides, he knew she was naked. He had seen every glorious inch of her.

It was an exquisite form of torture, getting her decently covered in his shirt when all his instincts were clamouring for him to strip off his own clothes and join her in bed.

Especially when she flopped back onto the pillows the moment he let go of her and closed her eyes again.

No—*she* was the exquisite form of torture. Since the moment he'd met her she'd blown all his carefully constructed plans to smithereens, invaded his thoughts, robbed him of sleep, got him so tied up in knots he forgot what he was saying halfway through a sentence.

And made him feel more alive than he'd ever thought possible.

He stood looking down at her for a moment or two, hands on his hips. She had no idea what mayhem she was causing just by lying there. Tempting him.

Trusting him.

Hell's teeth—the only way to get her back to her room would be to carry her. Which would mean dealing with all that nakedness...

He swallowed hard.

'I'm going to pick you up now,' he warned her, just before rolling her over and over so that several blankets, as well as the eiderdown, enveloped her completely.

'Good.' She sighed as he hefted her into his arms. 'You are very strong,' she observed as she wriggled one arm free and looped it around his neck. 'Is this a dream? Are you going to kiss me again?'

She looked at his mouth and ran her tongue over her lips. And lowered her eyelids seductively.

There was only so much temptation, Lord Ledbury discovered, that a man could resist. With her still cradled in his arms, he bent his head and kissed her.

The little whimper of pleasure she gave ricocheted from his mouth to his groin, and the erection which had barely subsided since the moment he had seen her naked greedily sucked all the blood from the rest of his body, making his head spin.

He was shaking so much that he barely managed to

stumble into the sitting room before collapsing onto the armchair with her on his lap, though he did manage to keep their mouths fused together the whole time.

'We have to stop this,' he moaned eventually, tearing his mouth free. 'It is madness.'

'Don't be a spoilsport.' She pouted. 'It's lovely.'

And then her inquisitive little hand began to explore the breadth of his chest, and all the reasons why he ought not to make love to her, right there and then, flew out of the window.

He burrowed through the layers of bedding and slid his hand inside his shirt.

The one that *she* was wearing.

Her breast fitted the palm of his hand perfectly.

'Oooh…' She sighed, arching up into his caress. 'More of that, please.'

She wanted more? He would give her more. Pushing the silk aside, he bent his head and laved her nipple with his tongue. It was like having his dreams come true. Better. Tasting her for real exceeded all his fantasies. Soon he was lost to all but the feel of her under his hands and in his mouth, and the sound of her breathy little moans urging him on. So he sucked her nipple, rigid now after the attention he'd paid it, deep into his mouth. She let out a yelp—but it was of shocked pleasure, not protest.

At that precise moment the door to his suite flew open.

'Lord Ledbury!' a woman's voice screeched.

'Damn you, Richard, what do you think you are doing?'

He looked up to see Lady Penrose and his grandfather standing side by side, just inside his room. Lady

Penrose was white-faced and trembling. His grandfather red-faced and quivering.

He removed his mouth from Lady Jayne's left breast, thinking it must have been quite obvious what he was doing. He was wearing nothing but a pair of breeches, while Lady Jayne was... *Damn*. She'd somehow managed to kick aside every one of the blankets he'd so carefully wrapped her in.

Mindful of her dignity, he pulled the edges of his shirt together over her breasts, then grabbed the coverlet, draping it over the pale length of her legs.

Then Lady Jayne set the seal on things by looking at them in a bewildered fashion, and asking, 'What are you all doing in my room? And where is Milly?' She frowned up at Richard. 'Did you find her?'

'She's gone.'

'You mean you could not stop her? Oh, no!'

'Oh, I stopped her all right,' he said grimly. 'But I don't think this is the time to be talking about *her*.'

'Well, you are right about that much!' said his grandfather, giving Lady Penrose a shove between the shoulder blades that sent her tottering farther into the room, before turning and slamming the door shut.

'Put. Her. Down,' said Lady Penrose indignantly. 'Take your hands off her and put her down. This instant!'

'Just one moment,' said his grandfather. He strode across the room and into the bedroom. He did not stay in there long.

Richard groaned, knowing what he would see there. Tousled sheets. A torn, bloodstained nightdress lying on the floor. More bloodstains on the sheets. Which, he had noted when he picked her up, meant he ought to have taken care of that cut on her knee and her poor little abused feet before he went out. But which his grandfather was bound to take as evidence of a night of wild debauchery.

'You damned fool!' Lord Lavenham stood framed in the bedroom doorway, his face now mottled with purple.

'This is worse than mere foolishness,' said Lady Penrose, pointing at the overturned glass on the floor.

'You got her drunk?' Lord Lavenham bellowed. 'And then seduced her?'

He had thought it could not get any worse, but Lady Jayne set her hand to her head.

'Oh, please stop shouting,' she moaned. 'It goes right through my head.'

'Lady Penrose,' said Lord Lavenham, turning to her with a grim expression. 'You have my abject apologies. I did not believe that this one of my grandsons was as much a libertine as the others.'

'He is not a libertine,' Lady Jayne protested. 'He has not done anything that I did not ask of him…'

'That is quite enough!' Lady Penrose screeched, grabbing her hand and tugging her off Lord Ledbury's lap.

She stumbled on the mound of blankets strewn around the chair.

'I accept your apology, my lord,' Lady Penrose said stiffly to Lord Lavenham, whilst deftly rearranging the folds of the coverlet she'd snatched up with the expertise of one well used to ordering the demi-train of an evening gown. 'I could not believe it at first, either, when my maid came to me with the tale which she claimed is titillating the entire servants' hall. It was only when

I discovered that my charge was not in her room that I gave it any credence. In the same way, you needed to see the evidence with your own eyes.'

'What evidence?' Lady Jayne was blinking from one of them to the other. 'Why is everyone so cross?'

'The only thing to do is announce their engagement at once,' put in Lord Lavenham.

'Engagement? Why? We were only...'

'Be quiet, you foolish girl,' snapped Lady Penrose. 'There is no excuse for such carryings-on, even if the pair of you do wish to marry. Unheard of!'

'No...' protested Lady Jayne again. 'You have got it all wrong....'

She felt as though she was emerging from a lovely, vivid dream into a viciously muddled nightmare, where everyone was accusing Richard of the most vile behaviour. They seemed to think he had got her drunk and deliberately seduced her.

'Richard, tell them...' She turned to look at him. And her blood ran cold. If anything had the power to sober her up it was the sight of him, sitting on the chair, his head in his hands, his shoulders bowed.

The picture of despair.

As Lady Penrose seized her wrist and dragged her from the room she realized that she'd ruined his life.

Snatches of things that had happened flashed through her mind as she stumbled along the corridors in her chaperone's outraged wake. The look of shock on his face when he'd found her naked in his bed. The harshness of his voice as he'd ordered her to cover herself up. It had all been a bit hazy, but the next thing she knew he'd been grimly wrestling her into one of his shirts. And then he'd picked her up and forcibly carried her

from his bedroom. Her cheeks flamed red as she recalled her wanton behaviour over the next few minutes.
Having all that naked chest within reach had been more
temptation than she could resist. She had rubbed herself
up against it like a cat. Almost purring with pleasure.

And then she'd begged him to kiss her.

Well, he need not have complied quite so enthusiastically, the voice of reason reminded her. But then her
love for him surged back with the excuse that *any* red-
blooded male, propositioned by a naked woman who
was running her greedy little hands all over his naked
torso, might have succumbed to a momentary lapse of
judgement.

But, oh, how badly he was regretting that lapse now!
She only had to think of the way she had left him, sitting with his head in his hands, after learning that he
was going to have to pay for what he'd said at the time
was madness with a lifetime of wedlock to her!

The moment they reached her rooms she whirled
round and said, 'Oh, please, you must not think Richard could possibly have done what his grandfather accused him of. None of what happened was his fault. It
was all mine!'

Lady Penrose sat down upon a chair by the window that overlooked the *porte-cochère,* her back to the
window.

'Indeed? Would you care to tell me what really happened?'

Lady Jayne sank onto the sofa and, pausing only
once or twice to take sips of water to ease her parched
throat, haltingly recounted the events of the previous
night.

When she had finished, Lady Penrose made a gesture of annoyance.

'What on earth possessed you to drink so much brandy?'

'It—it was only the two glasses,' replied Lady Jayne, slightly mystified. She had done so many dreadful things during the course of the night that it seemed very odd that her duenna should take her to task for her consumption of alcohol. 'I have often seen gentlemen drink far more without it affecting them in the slightest.'

'They are well used to it, though. And before last night, to my knowledge, you have never been allowed to taste more than just a few sips of champagne.'

'That is so, but...'

'And it was Lord Ledbury who gave you that first glass. Did he make you drink it all?'

'No! No...' She frowned, trying to recall the exact sequence of events. 'In fact he did not give me a drink at all! I helped myself while he was getting dressed to go after Milly.'

'And I suppose you filled the glass to the top and drank it down as though it were a nice cup of tea? Now I can quite see how you came to think it was perfectly logical to remove every stitch of your clothing and get into Lord Ledbury's bed,' said Lady Penrose acidly.

Put like that, it did sound terribly wicked. Shamefaced, she nodded her head.

'Where you promptly fell asleep. And spent the rest of the night. Alone.'

She nodded again.

'And you still maintain that the bloodstains on the sheets must have come from the cut you sustained to your knee sliding down the roof.'

'Yes.' She drew aside the coverlet to reveal her grubby grazed knees.

'I have to say that your explanation is the only one that makes complete sense. The others completely failed to account for the rope, and the fact that your room was locked from the outside.'

'The rope? It is still there?'

'Yes.'

For some reason the knowledge that the rope had not disintegrated completely was strangely comforting. Even if it was only in that one tiny detail, she had not made a *complete* mull of the whole affair.

'Your Josie came to my room in a dreadful state first thing, before I had even had my chocolate, with some wild tale about you eloping with a mysterious lover by knotting the curtain ties together to form a rope. Well, naturally I discounted that story straight off. If you had eloped you would have locked the door from the inside, to prevent your disappearance from being discovered as long as possible.'

'Wait a minute... How did Josie get into my room? I tried to return last night and the key was not in the door.'

'No, it was lying on top of the dresser next to it.'

'Of course! Why did I not think to look there?'

'Because you had already had one large glass of brandy,' snapped Lady Penrose. 'It was enough to dull your intellect to the point where all the subsequent choices you made were the wrong ones. Though for the life of me I cannot see what possessed you to climb out of your window by means of a makeshift rope in the first place. Why on earth did you not simply ring the bell for Josie to come and let you out?'

'I was trying to be discreet.'

Lady Penrose winced and closed her eyes. 'God help us all if one day you actually *try* to cause a scandal.'

Lady Jayne felt about two inches tall.

Lady Penrose's eyes flicked open and bored into her as she said, 'And then, of course, my own maid came in with my chocolate, full of the gossip that was raging below stairs about how you had been found, dead drunk, in Lord Ledbury's bed, following a night of torrid passion. Which was another story I could not credit, knowing the pair of you as I do. Besides there being no reason for it.'

A maid had seen her? 'Oh, no...' she moaned, burying her face in her hands. Gone was any hope of trying to persuade Lord Lavenham and Lady Penrose to keep the whole incident between themselves. 'I have been such a fool. And Lord Ledbury is going to have to pay the price....'

'Do not for one moment succumb to any sympathy for that young man! His behaviour has been disgraceful!'

Lady Jayne looked up, bewildered. 'But I thought you said you believed me...'

'I do believe you. And I therefore acquit Lord Ledbury of deliberately getting you drunk and seducing you. But do not forget the scene which met my eyes when I came in and found you together was very far from innocent. You were sprawled across his lap half-naked—both of you. And he was taking full advantage of your helpless condition. Had we not arrived when we did, I have no doubt he *would* have accomplished your seduction.'

'No. Not Lord Ledbury. He wouldn't...'

'Of course he would. He's a man. And they are all

governed by the basest of urges. No matter how cunningly they conceal the fact.'

She pulled herself up with what looked like a considerable effort.

'But that is all beside the point. You were caught in his room, half-naked, having clearly been there all night. You will have to marry him. And that is that.'

Defeat washed over her. *He* would have to marry *her.* That was what Lady Penrose meant. He was going to have to pay a terrible price for an incident that was entirely her fault.

'You will get dressed now, if you please, and we shall go downstairs for breakfast, where we shall announce your betrothal. You will *not* behave as though you have done anything to be ashamed of. And let anyone make any conjectures about what happened last night if they dare!'

Chapter Fourteen

It was too much to hope that even *one* of Lord Lavenham's house guests might be unaware of the gossip.

But they were all at the breakfast table when she went down. And all looking far more alert than she felt.

The shock of realising she had trapped Lord Ledbury into a betrothal he didn't want had dispersed the haziness left over from the brandy. But she still had a pounding headache. And her knee and shoulders hurt like the very devil. When she lowered herself into a place beside Lady Penrose at the table she did so gingerly, trying hard not to jar any of the myriad scrapes and bruises she had sustained from her barely controlled descent from the roof.

Lady Susan smirked and made a comment behind her hand to Miss Twining, who was sitting next to her, which made Miss Twining blush and stare very hard at her plate.

And Lady Jayne realied that to any onlooker the stiffness of her movements as she took her place at table must have made her look exactly like a young woman who had just spent the night being thoroughly ravished.

While she was still thinking about how close Lady Penrose considered she had come to that, the door opened and Richard walked in. There was a distinct air of expectancy around the breakfast table, rather like that in a theatre on the opening night of a new performance. Everyone was either looking at her, or at him, or from one to the other. And, in spite of Lady Penrose's warning not to look as though she'd done anything to be ashamed of, she felt her cheeks heat. It didn't help when Lord Lavenham stalked in, not two paces behind Richard, with a face like thunder. She couldn't believe how angry he still was. That he could have condemned Richard's behaviour without even giving him a fair hearing in the first place. Why, Lady Penrose, whom she had known for only a few months, had been willing to hear *her* side of the story—yes, and had believed her, no matter how unlikely it must all have sounded.

But Richard behaved as though he didn't care what anyone in the room might be thinking of him. With a breezy smile he walked straight to her, and wished her a cheery good morning.

She could not hold his gaze for more than a split second. One look at him was all it took to remind her that not two hours since he'd had his hands all over her. That smiling mouth had suckled at her breast. How could he just saunter in, looking all cool and collected, when she was so flustered she hardly knew what to do with herself?

When he took her hand and planted a kiss on her knuckles, like a practised lover, it struck her that this was the difference between them. He almost certainly *was* a practised lover. He'd likely had his hands all over lots of other women in his time.

The image that conjured up didn't help at all.

'May I get you some toast?'

'Toast?' She was almost dying with mortification, and he was talking about toast?

'Or eggs, perhaps?' He summoned a footman. 'Peters, why have you not poured Lady Jayne a cup of tea?'

'I was just about to my lord,' said the footman, hastening to fetch a teapot.

He had not let go of her hand. And he did not look as though he was the least bit cross with her. From the ease of his manner, anyone would think that marrying her was his fondest wish.

It was so...*decent* of him to shield her from public censure by putting on this show. He didn't seem to bear her any ill will at all now that he'd recovered from the initial shock of finding himself forcibly engaged to her. But then he knew she hadn't meant to bring all this down on his head. That she'd just been trying to help and, being the idiot she was, made a total hash of things.

She returned the pressure of his hand, finally finding the courage to look into his eyes. He smiled, pulled up the chair next to hers and sat down.

'I expect we should tell everyone our news. Though it looks as though they all suspect something anyway.'

He gave a devil-may-care grin that sent a pang straight to her heart. Perhaps he really didn't care. He had already accepted he was going to have to marry for duty. She could just imagine him shrugging fatalistically as he shaved and deciding that, after all, she was no worse than Lady Susan or Lucy Beresford.

'I have the privilege,' he said, looking round the table with a glint of challenge in his eyes, 'of being able to announce that Lady Jayne and I are to be married. Is that not so?' He gave her hand a squeeze. 'My love?'

It was her cue to back him up.

She opened her mouth to agree. But the power of speech seemed to have deserted her. She had never been at such a loss. Normally she had no trouble maintaining a cool facade. Where was it now that she so desperately needed it?

She looked at him and nodded. It was the best she could do. But it seemed enough for Richard, who smiled at her with all the tenderness anyone could expect from a newly engaged man.

She wanted to weep for him.

'Well, then, congratulations, I suppose,' said Berry, a little doubtfully.

Lucy stayed silent, but the spark of jealousy in her eyes said it all.

And Lord Lavenham made an angry sort of growling noise as he took his seat at the head of the table.

Lady Jayne bristled. She knew he had never liked her. And now he probably thought she was some kind of a drunken…slut, who could only get a proposal by creeping into a man's bed at night. And the glower on his face as Watkins hurried over to pour his coffee would only confirm everyone's suspicions about what had gone on the night before. And tell them that he thoroughly disapproved.

It was the outside of enough. If Richard did not care, then neither would she give a fig for what any of them thought. Anger gave her the strength to lift her chin and freeze them all out.

Richard watched her pulling on her public armour

with disappointment. He much preferred her all flustered and shy.

But he had seen pain flit across her face, too. She
hated the thought of having to marry him. He only had
to think of how many times she had protested when
both her chaperone and his grandfather had insisted it
was the only way out of the mess.

He might be getting his heart's desire, but it was
coming at a very great cost to her.

Being discovered together like that had solved the
problem of how he was going to get her to marry him.
But he had wanted to win her heart, not force her compliance. He wanted her to be thrilled at the prospect of
marrying him. Not looking haunted. Ashamed.

He glared at the other occupants of the breakfast
table, who were adding to her distress with their mixture of avid curiosity and blatant disapproval.

For two pins he would throw the whole pack of them
out of the house!

But there were another two days to go of this house
party. And the matter between Berry and Miss Twining was not quite settled. Besides, if he turned them out
in anger they would all go straight back to Town and
start spreading the kind of malicious gossip about Lady
Jayne that would taint their marriage for years to come.
It would be better to carry on as normal.

'Do we have anything in particular planned for our
guests' entertainment today?' he asked his grandfather.

Lord Lavenham glowered at him for a moment, before replying, 'With the weather being so unpredictable,
I thought to have some targets set up on the lower lawn
for some archery. Not too far for the ladies to run back
to the house if it rains.'

Under cover of a muted chorus of approval, Richard leaned and whispered in Lady Jayne's ear.

'Since nobody else is likely to want to brave the weather, I think we should go out for a ride together. I need to talk to you privately. Will you meet me at the stables?'

It was so different from the way he'd ordered her to meet him clandestinely before. And her feelings about doing so had completely changed. She *needed* to speak to him. If they put their heads together, surely they could come up with some way to extricate themselves from this unholy mess.

'Of course,' she said.

If nothing else, she owed him an apology.

Several apologies.

'You look lovely,' he said, when she walked into the stable yard an hour later, wearing the same riding habit he'd admired so much before. The military style of it reminded him, again, that she would have made a wonderful soldier's wife. Though if he had still been a serving soldier—a pang shot through him—he might never have met her. He thanked God, for the first time, that he had been obliged to sell his commission. What would his life have been like had she never come into it? It didn't bear thinking about.

Lady Jayne was eyeing Ajax with a troubled expression as his groom led him to a mounting block.

'Is he safe for you to ride?' she asked, as the beast flung its head up and down, then skittered sideways on the cobbles in his delight at getting out of his stall.

'Oh, yes. He's just eager to get going. He will enjoy our gallop as much as we shall.'

'Gallop? Are you sure? Richard, last time we went out you were on that awful slug of a horse...'

'Last time *I* went out,' he corrected her, 'Ajax and I came to an understanding.' He clapped the horse on the neck. 'Didn't we, old boy?'

'You rode Ajax last night? When you went after...?'

Richard shot her a look, warning her not to discuss last night's events in front of the grooms. Then he swung himself up into the saddle with an athletic grace that almost made her gasp.

A groom helped her mount, and they had hardly passed out of the stable yard before Richard turned to her with a grin and said, 'Race you?'

'Do you mean it?' She had never had anyone willing to race with her before.

'Why not?'

'Well, because...' She nibbled at her lower lip. When she had gone to live with her grandfather he had decreed it was unlady-like to go careering all over the place astride her pony, and had set a groom to teach her the technique of riding side-saddle. It had been one of the worst restrictions he had enforced upon her behaviour.

But Richard wanted to race?

'Where to?'

'The Workings,' he said, and dug his heels into Ajax's flanks.

'That is not fair!' she cried as he set off.

And Mischief seemed to agree. For the next few minutes both she and her horse were equally determined to catch up with the males of the party. By the time she reined in at The Workings she was so exhilarated she scarcely felt any of the aches and pains that had so plagued her at breakfast.

'Oh, you beast!' she said, laughing down at Richard, who had already dismounted and was unlocking the door to the pavilion. 'You cheated.'

He came and helped her to dismount.

'You would surely not wish me to *let* you win a race, would you?' He took Mischief's reins and led her to the iron ring set in the wall to which he'd already tethered Ajax.

'No, but neither do I think you should take unfair advantage. I was riding side-saddle, you know, which is very far from easy.'

'But I have a wounded leg, which cancels out the disadvantage of your awkward saddle.' Having securely tethered both horses he turned and made his way back to her.

'But you still set off without giving me due warning,' she protested. 'And anyway, you said your leg was not that bad.'

'I do not think riding side-saddle is that bad, either. I have seen ladies riding side-saddle leading the hunting field. Looking quite magnificent.'

He ran his eyes over her figure in a way that made her acutely aware of the fact that he'd already seen most of it naked. She felt herself blushing with pleasure at his blatant appreciation. Not only had that statement indicated he didn't object to behaviour her grandfather decried as hoydenish, but Richard also seemed to have pleasant memories of that morning's interlude.

Pleasant enough that he was not dreading consummating their marriage, anyway.

'I think you are getting away from the whole purpose of coming out here,' she said, before his kindness went to her head and she started to entertain the misapprehension that he actually *wanted* to marry her.

'The purpose?'

The whole purpose of coming out here had been to get her alone and hopefully persuade her that marrying him was not such a bad idea. The way she'd run straight to him when she'd been so frantic about Milly proved she trusted him. And the fact that some of her concern was for his feelings also indicated that she cared for him to some extent. For a while there, last night, he had begun to hope she was beginning to feel physically attracted to him, too... But then, when she had looked so appalled at the prospect of marrying him, he had worked out what must really have been going on in her head. Alcohol often had the effect of making people feel amorous. And half-asleep, and probably waking from a dream about the man she *did* love...

The guilt he'd felt then had all but crushed him. How could he have taken advantage of her trusting nature? How could he have deceived himself into thinking she was truly responding to *him* when she had been so sleepy, so befuddled...?

'Is this a dream? Are you going to kiss me?'

He had only to recall the shock on her face when she'd fully woken—the number of times she had said *no!*

She had not really been aware of what she was doing. Or, more importantly, *with whom.*

'You must tell me what has become of Milly,' said Lady Jayne earnestly. There was a tension in the air between them she did not know how to deal with. A look on his face she wanted to dispel. 'She has not come back. And neither has Lord Halstead. Yet nobody seems to have got wind of the fact they ran away together.'

'Well, apart from the fact that they did not, they have far more juicy gossip to discuss today, do they not? Our supposed night of drunken debauchery.'

She hung her head. 'At least my foolish behaviour has resulted in some good, then. Everyone is so busy sniggering at me they have hardly noticed Milly is missing.'

'Well, nobody is ever very interested in the fate of a lady's companion. And Lord Halstead had the foresight to leave a message to the effect that he had been called away on urgent business. But they will never connect her disappearance with that of Lord Halstead anyway—not once she has married my valet.'

'Your valet? I don't understand. Why would she do something like that?' As if it wasn't bad enough for Milly to run off with another lord, now he was telling her she was marrying someone else entirely.

He glanced up at the sky. 'Shall we go inside? It looks as if it's going to rain any minute.'

He opened the door for her and she preceded him into the summer house built to take advantage of the view down into the valley and the canal that ran along its floor.

'Yes, thank you, Richard. But... Well... Though I can see that marriage was a better option for Milly than...' She trailed off uncomfortably and walked across to the window. 'But to your valet?'

'Don't you recall me telling you that the man came hotfoot from London when he thought Milly had disappeared? It turns out that the poor sap has been head over ears in love with her for months, but never dared speak up because he thought he had nothing to offer her. Which showed me that—'

'Wait a minute… That is the end of the tale, to be sure. How did you prise her away from Lord Halstead?'

'With remarkable ease. He took one look at my face, understood I meant what I said, and beat a hasty retreat.'

'I suppose the pistol you took with you had nothing to do with it?'

He grinned. 'I might have had it in my hand when I told him I took exception to his sneaking off in the middle of the night with one of my guests.'

She could just picture the scene. Richard could be downright intimidating when coming across couples meeting clandestinely—even without a pistol to back up his words.

'And then Milly decided she'd rather accept your valet's proposal?' She frowned in perplexity.

'Not quite. To start with I was just seeking a way to get Milly out of Courtlands. I was so angry with her. I decided to track Fred down and get him to take her back to Town. She didn't want to go, needless to say. She even tried to make me believe it would break her heart to be forced to leave my side,' he finished, with a distinct curl to his lip.

'You didn't believe her?'

'I have known for some time that she doesn't love me.'

'No!' She walked over to him and seized his hands, her eyes full of sympathy.

'Oh, yes. In fact I think she said it at first in a blind panic. You know—when I told her and Fred that because I'd come into the title I would have to remove to Lavenham House and find a suitable wife. I think she really thought I would just turn my back on the pair of them. And she employed the one weapon she knew I was powerless to resist.'

'Oh, yes,' she breathed. 'I know *just* what you mean. If someone says they love you, when nobody else ever has, it gives them a terrific hold over you…'

'Exactly so.' His voice gentled. He took her to the window seat and they sat down, still holding hands. 'She had got to know me well enough by then to understand the power of such a declaration. But even when she first made it I wasn't completely sure I believed her. I had always thought I was…well, her ticket out of a nasty situation. We were about to push into France. She'd seen how brutally the Portuguese and Spanish peasants treated the French soldiers and anyone associated with them. She was just starting to become a woman, and a target for men's lust. Her father wanted her safely out of the way in case the French populace gave a similar reception to English troops. I don't blame him for that. Or her for going along with his plans. I couldn't have asked for a better nurse, or a more cheerful companion through all the months I spent recovering. But she never wanted me for myself. Only what I could provide for her.'

'Cream horses and a box at the theatre,' put in Jayne. 'She was just the same over the red-satin dress. She'd seen one once, and promised herself if ever she had the means she'd get herself one just like it. Without once thinking about how inappropriate it was, or what she might have to do to earn it.'

'She came to her senses when she saw the state Fred had drunk himself into after he'd not been able to dissuade her from running off with Lord Halstead. That reached her in a way perhaps nothing else could have done. He absolutely worships the ground she walks on. And it turns out she needs a man to worship her more than cream horses or red-satin dresses. Though it helped when I promised to secure their future prosperity by buying them a tavern for a wedding present,' he added dryly.

'A tavern?'

'Yes. It is every soldier's dream to leave the army and own his own tavern. By the time I left Milly was full of plans for their new venture.'

'She will make a great success of it, I'm sure,' said Lady Jayne bleakly.

Milly was a competent person. Richard had told her once before that she was well able to look after herself. And she could just see Milly ordering supplies, bustling about and charming her customers.

'But I warn you,' he said sternly, 'I don't want you to go seeking her out and having any kind of association with her in future. She is capable of causing you no end of trouble.'

'I don't care about that!' She reined in her flash of temper, lest he think it was directed at him. 'I just don't think I will ever be able to forgive her for the way she used you and betrayed you.'

His heart swelled with love. Though he was not going to read too much into her reaction. She considered him her friend. He looked down at their linked hands. She would feel as outraged on behalf of anyone she considered her friend. It was the kind of person she was.

'I am so sorry, Richard, for the way it has turned out,' she said, looking at his downbent head. 'It is humiliating to discover that a person who has said they love you has only been using you all along.' And then to find himself compromised into marriage, while he was still trying to recover from Milly's perfidy.

She wanted to put her arms round him and kiss away his hurt. Milly had said all she would have to do would be to offer him that sort of physical comfort and all would be right with his world.

But then Milly hadn't really been in love. She didn't understand that there was no substitute for the person you loved. Besides, she didn't want to be a substitute for anyone else. She didn't want Richard to be thinking of Milly when he kissed her.

'We're trapped in such a terrible situation.' She let go of his hand to rub at her forehead.

He looked up at her sharply.

'I only wish I could think of some way out.'

Panic chilled his gut into a block of ice. She was so resourceful she would soon come up with dozens of ways to wriggle out of this marriage—if he didn't put a stop to it right now.

'There is none. So do not even bother trying to think of escaping,' he said sternly. 'Your reputation would never recover if I did not put a ring upon your finger now. And mine would be irrevocably tarnished. People would think I was the kind of man who would turn my back on a woman after seducing her. Do you think I want that kind of notoriety?'

'N-no. Of course you don't. But it is so unfair! You did not seduce me. And I do not want you to have to pay the price for my own reckless…stupid… Oh!' She leaped to her feet and began pacing up and down in agitation. 'There must be *some* way out.'

'Well, there is not one. We have announced our

betrothal to our guests. In spite of his protests my grandfather will even now be sending the official announcement to the papers. It is too late to stop him.'

She stopped pacing and hugged herself round the middle, head bowed. He got to his feet, turned her round and laid his hands on her shoulders.

'Will it be such a terrible fate, Lady Jayne?' he asked her gently. 'Don't you think you could get used to being my wife? Could you not—' he squeezed her shoulders '—make the best of it?'

It would not be the least bit terrible being married to him—if only he did not think it was a situation *he* had to *get used to*. Her lower lip began to tremble. She caught it between her teeth.

He made a strangled sound in his throat, before grating, 'Now, now, don't cry.'

He put his arms right round her awkwardly and she sagged against him in despair. It was a pathetic parody of the kind of embrace a man ought to give the woman to whom he had just become betrothed.

'We have come to know each other pretty well over these past few weeks,' he said in such a reasonable tone it made her want to scream with frustration. 'I am sure we will be able to rub along tolerably well together, if only we put our minds to it.'

Rub along tolerably well? Oh, it hurt so much to hear his opinion of what their marriage would be like that it was actually growing hard to breathe.

She kept her face buried in the front of his waistcoat, since she could not bear to see the look of stoicism that must be on his face.

'I know you are a brave girl,' he said, running his hand up and down her spine in a soothing gesture. 'I know you have experienced a bitter disappointment quite recently, and that it is too soon to talk of anything more than friendship between us. But we have become quite *good* friends over the past few weeks, have we not? We have learned that we can trust one another. At least I trust you, Lady Jayne. I know that once we are married you will stay true to your vows. And I promise you I will be faithful to mine.'

It was no consolation at all to hear him declare that he intended to stay faithful to his vows. It was the kind of thing an honourable man did. Stuck to vows made in church.

But she wanted him to love her so much he would not *dream* of looking at another woman.

'We can make it work, this marriage of ours. I am sure we can. In fact, if you tell me what you want, I swear I will do all in my power to give it to you. What do you want from marriage?'

'Me?' She blinked up at him wide-eyed. Nobody had *ever* asked her what she wanted from marriage. Only insisted that it was her duty to marry well.

No wonder she couldn't help loving him.

'When Grandpapa sent me to Town to find a husband, I was so determined to thwart him that I never thought about what might actually tempt me into taking such a step. Though I have always known,' she said on a surge of certainty, 'what I don't want. And that is to end up living in a state of open warfare, like my parents did.'

He frowned. 'I have heard that your father was not the most pleasant of fellows.'

'He was perfectly beastly to Mama. He despised her for her inability to give him the heir he felt she owed him. She became dreadfully ill, with all the miscarriages she had. As long as I can remember she was practically an invalid. But she refused to lie down and die, and leave him free to marry again. I'm sure it was only her hatred of him that kept her going. For she did not outlive him by more than a few weeks.'

'That is appalling.' God, what she must have suffered as a child. 'I thought my own parents' marriage had been a disaster, but that…'

'Your parents' marriage was unhappy?'

'It was a pale imitation of your own parents', in some ways. My father was an incorrigible womanizer and my mother soon grew to despise him. And, then… Well, because he adored my older brother, his firstborn and heir, she despised him, too. But for some reason she took a shine to my baby brother. Which made my father, in his turn, despise Charlie. So it wasn't just the two of them involved in the battles, but the entire family.'

She noted he'd left himself out of the picture, and asked in a soft voice, 'Which of them either loved or despised you, Richard?'

'Me? Oh, neither of them bothered about me in the least,' he informed her, in a matter-of-fact tone that she could tell concealed a world of hurt.

For she remembered him saying that nobody had come to his aid when he'd been so ill—and the look on his face when he'd told her about all those letters that had gone unanswered while he lay hovering between life and death.

'They were quite wrong to treat you so,' she said indignantly.

'They were quite wrong to make my other brothers pawns in their ongoing war, as well. But never mind them. One thing I can certainly promise you. We won't end up like any of our parents. I…I like you too much to ever treat you with the disrespect my father showed my mother. In fact, I…' He took a deep breath.

Was now the time to tell her he loved her?

He hesitated. She'd said that having someone say the words gave them a kind of power over you. A kind of power she clearly didn't like.

And she'd already had one man tell her he loved her and prove false.

Dammit, if he'd only paved the way for such a declaration he might have stood some chance she would believe him. But as things stood… He would hate doing anything that might make her look upon him with suspicion, instead of the trust that was blazing from her eyes right now. Besides, every time he'd tried to start telling her how he felt he'd made a complete mull of it. Making plans and barking orders at troops were a far cry from uttering words of love. Especially when he was so unfamiliar with the emotion. When it made him never sure whether he was on his head or his heels.

He shook his head. He might have decided he was going to tell her how he felt today, but with everything that had happened since he'd made that decision he had a very strong suspicion that it might be counterproductive.

'I admire you very much,' he finished.

That was a start. She might not believe him if he blurted out some clumsy words that would, knowing him, be open to misinterpretation anyway. But if he demonstrated by the way he treated her, by the care he took of her, that she meant the world to him… After all, actions spoke louder than words. This building in which they stood was testimony to that. His grandfather had shown the wife his parents had chosen for him that he loved her by building this place just to keep the rain off her while she watched the progress of the canal being dug through the valley.

Since they were going to be married he had a lifetime to convince her of his utter sincerity by the way he pampered and cosseted her. His spirits lifted.

'Now, you say you had not thought about what you wanted from marriage. But—forgive me if you find this an insensitive question—you *would* have married Lieutenant Kendell if you had been able to. So what was it about him that made you willing to flout all the rules?'

She blushed and lowered her head. When she looked back on her behaviour with regard to Harry it made her cringe. She had not loved him at all! Nor wanted to marry him—not once he had kissed her. But it would be too humiliating to admit that.

Though she did want to be able to tell Richard the whole truth one day. Perhaps after they'd been married a few months, and she'd had a chance to prove she wasn't the silly girl she'd shown herself to be in all their dealings thus far.

'You have to understand what my life has been like.' For today, it would have to be enough to explain some of the steps that had led her into the tangle with Harry. 'When I was a little girl, you see, nobody much cared what I did as long as I stayed out of the way. So I ended up left in the care of a groom, mostly, haring about all over the estates. But then my parents died, and Grandpapa took me to Darvill Park. He was so shocked by my uncouth ways that he spent the next few years beating them all out of me.'

'He beat you?'

'No. Not physically. But I felt…trampled on. I was watched every moment of the day. And drilled relentlessly. And I was never allowed to mix with anyone he had not first approved. Eventually, after years and years of imprisonment on the estate, he thought he had succeeded in making me behave like a *proper* young lady, and allowed me to go to a few local assemblies. Well, he could hardly not! Not when other girls my age, from good families in the area, were going to them. It would have looked like failure. And Grandpapa never fails!

'Anyway, Harry came and asked me to dance without first getting approval from my chaperone. He asked *me* if I wanted to. He looked so dashing in his uniform. I felt so daring when I said yes without checking first. And when Grandpapa forbade me to see him again, I… dug my heels in. You see, no matter how hard I tried, I never managed to please him. So I decided to stop trying.'

Richard flinched. God, he knew exactly what that felt like! The letters he'd written home when he'd first gone away to school that nobody had ever replied to. The creeping realisation that nobody cared where he was so long as he wasn't underfoot.

'I just could not stand it any more. The confinement. The rules and restrictions. I just had to make a stand over Harry. Do you see?'

'Only too well.'

'And then when Harry followed me to London I was completely overwhelmed by what I thought was his devotion. Nobody had cared so much for me before. Not my parents. Not my grandfather, who disapproved of everything about me. And I had never had any friends that I had chosen myself. But there was Harry, telling me he would risk everything to be with me, and I...I lost my head.'

Her shoulders slumped. 'Of course, it turned out not to be me he wanted at all, but only my money. I do not know why I did not see that from the start.'

Richard hugged her. No wonder she had fallen prey so easily to a glib, personable fortune-hunter. Nobody else had ever shown her a scrap of affection. She had no means of telling the genuine from the counterfeit. He had almost made the same kind of mistake with Milly—although, having been an officer, he had a sight more experience of spotting a lie when it was told him.

'My poor darling,' he said.

He was glad now that he had not spoken words to her that had been used to deceive her in the past. It would be better to *show* her what real love was all about. Day by day, month by month, year by year, he would love her so wholeheartedly that it would wipe away all the years of hurt and neglect she had endured thus far. Seeing to her welfare, ensuring her happiness, would be his prime objective.

To his last dying breath.

Chapter Fifteen

When she got back to the house, Lady Jayne found a very tense-looking Lady Penrose waiting for her in her rooms. With some very surprising news.

'My dear, your grandfather has arrived.'

'How did he know that—?'

'Oh, he did not know anything about last night—how could he? No, he came because he was angry to find, when he returned to Darvill Park, that you were not in London, waiting for him as instructed. He was quite furious when he got here...'

Her heart sank. 'And now, of course, he must be even more angry...'

'No! Far from it.' Lady Penrose's lips twitched with wry amusement. 'The news that you are betrothed went a long way to appeasing him.'

'Oh. Of course.' For as long as he'd had control of her life he had been training her to become a fitting wife for a man of high station. Lord Ledbury was exactly the kind of man of whom he would approve. Catching him would atone for any number of other transgressions. 'Does he know...everything?'

'Unfortunately, yes. That buffoon Lord Lavenham gave him the scurrilous version of events.'

'And how did he take it?'

Lady Penrose sobered. 'You will find out for yourself when you see him. He is waiting for you in Lord Lavenham's study.'

Knowing that his temper would only increase the longer she kept him waiting, she hastily changed from her mud-spattered riding habit into a gown more becoming for a meeting with her formidable guardian.

Her heart was hammering as she made her way down the stairs, even though Lady Penrose was at her back, providing much welcome support.

She hesitated outside the door, making sure her emotional armour was in place before facing him. But when she went in the first person she saw was Richard. She did not know how he had managed to get there before her, but she was incredibly grateful that, for the first time in her life, she was not going to have to face her grandfather's wrath alone.

Part of her wanted to run straight to his side. But she detested revealing any form of weakness to her grandfather. So she stiffened her spine and turned towards the chair upon which Lord Caxton was sitting. She dipped a curtsy and then, when he motioned her to approach, bent to bestow a dutiful kiss, as though she had nothing whatsoever to fear.

At the last moment he raised his hand to his face, as if he was suddenly recalling something. And that was when she noticed he had three nasty-looking gashes on his face. It looked like something, perhaps a cat, had raked its claws across his skin.

He turned his other cheek for her to kiss, and then,

when she would have straightened up, grasped her hand in his. 'Do you *want* to marry this young man? Will he be able to make you happy?' he asked.

When she could not hide her astonishment that his first words were not a reproof, his expression turned wry.

'What? Has it never occurred to you that your happiness is of great importance to me? It is all I have ever wanted for you.' He grimaced. 'All I ever wanted for all my girls. I dare say you think I have treated you harshly in the past. But you were such a wild little creature when you came to me. I thought my primary duty was to tame you. For there is a streak of rebelliousness in you to which, alas, the Vickery women seem particularly prone.'

Tears sprang to his eyes as he said in a quavering voice, 'I was afraid that if I did not subdue it you would end up just like your aunt. And I could not have borne to lose you to some adventurer, as I lost her.'

She had never seen him looking so emotional. She had always thought him such a rigid disciplinarian. Yet all the time he had been concealing a deep abiding fear that she would turn out like her Aunt Aurora.

Her aunt's elopement and subsequent estrangement had clearly cut him much deeper than he had ever let anyone suspect. She had always thought he refused to let her name be spoken because he was angry with her. But that was not the case at all. It was because it hurt too much.

Suddenly she understood him as she had never done before. Because he was acting in exactly the way *she* would have behaved. People accused her of being cold, because she could fix her expression into a mask that concealed what she was feeling. The more she hurt, the colder she looked. They had said she got that trait from her father. But now she saw how absurd it was for them to say that. He had *never* bothered to conceal his feelings. Particularly not the contempt he'd felt for her, nor the hatred he had borne for her mother. His pride had been of the kind that made him impervious to what anyone thought of him.

Her pride was the pride of the Vickerys, which made it an absolute necessity never to let anyone suspect they might have wounded her. She was a Vickery through and through, she realized on a wave of relief. Not a Chilcott after all.

For the very first time she felt a real connection with this proud old aristocrat sitting before her. And the minute she understood that she was far more like her grandfather than she'd ever suspected, she saw what her refusal to welcome his long-lost granddaughter back into the family must have done to him.

'I am so sorry I did not obey your summons to meet my cousin, Lady Bowdon. I hope she was not offended.'

Or perhaps hurt. Oh, how ashamed she was of flouncing off in completely the opposite direction from where he'd ordered her, without considering what effect it would have on her poor cousin. She caught her lower lip between her teeth. She might at least have written to Lady Bowdon. But she'd been so angry it just hadn't occurred to her.

To her surprise, instead of following up her apology with a stinging rebuke, as was his wont, Lord Caxton smiled, a soft faraway look in his eyes.

'We can make all right with an invitation to your wedding now. I cannot begin to express my relief that you have found a man of substance to marry. A man who will be able to care for you when I am gone.'

She caught a quick, searching look in his eyes which prompted her to say, 'Yes, indeed he will.' For had not Richard promised as much? He would do his best, he had told her, to make sure they never became enemies—which, considering the way this betrothal had come about, was much more than she deserved.

Her eyes flew to Richard's. He was staring into a glass of what looked suspiciously like brandy with a wooden countenance.

'You will be married from Darvill Park, of course,' said Lord Caxton. 'Lady Bowdon and her husband will come to stay beforehand, which will give us all time to get to know one another before the ceremony.'

From that moment on he and Lady Penrose practically ignored her while they discussed arrangements.

At first Jayne was inclined to bridle at the way he had walked in and simply taken over. But she very soon realized that she had no real objections to any of the plans they were making on her behalf. She *would* be only too glad to get to know her cousin and her husband, and any friends of theirs, before her own wedding. It would just be less annoying if they at least pretended to consider her wishes.

Besides, she could see that Lord Caxton was really looking forward to hosting the wedding of the Season. He seemed to grow younger and more animated by the second. And letting him enjoy himself like this felt like a good way to atone for having so badly misjudged him all these years. She had been so used to unkindness from her parents that she hadn't understood he'd been trying to eradicate the effects of all those years of neglect and abuse.

It was Richard's grandfather who injected the only jarring note into the proceedings, by rather caustically pointing out that it might be better to get a special licence.

'You don't want to delay the ceremony for too long. Since they have already anticipated their vows.'

Her own grandfather looked at him down the length of his long, aristocratic nose, his nostrils pinched.

'I will not have my granddaughter married in some secretive, hasty fashion which will give others leave to suspect she has done something of which I disapprove,' he said in a withering tone. 'I intend to tell anyone who is vulgar enough to enquire—should they hear any of the gossip that is running rife through *your* household— that they are so much in love with each other they simply could not wait. And that I have decided to forgive their youthful impetuosity. If *you* are foolish enough to imply that this is anything other than a love match, all you will achieve is to drag the names of both our families through the mud.'

Lady Jayne could hardly believe it. For the first time in her life, her grandfather had spoken in her defence.

Lord Lavenham got to his feet and glared at Lord Caxton, his face suffused with purple. Lord Caxton lounged back in his chair, a slight sneer curling his lip. For a second or two the others all held their breath. It was rather like watching two stags preparing to lock horns.

The battle that might have ensued would no doubt have been of epic proportions had not Lady Penrose defused the situation by bringing them all back to practicalities.

'So we are agreed. Lady Jayne will leave here tomorrow and go to Darvill Park, so that the banns can be read at the parish church this Sunday. Three weeks should give us enough time to organize everything.'

Lord Ledbury's heart sank into his boots. He felt just as he had when his own cavalry had ridden over him at Orthez. Only this time he was not in physical pain. But in mental agony.

They were taking Lady Jayne away to Kent, to prepare for their wedding, just when he most needed to keep her at his side and convince her that marrying him was not such a terrible fate. He had begun to hope, that morning, that he had made some progress with her. She had agreed that they were already friends, at least. Nor had she objected to letting him hold her, for a few moments, in a comforting sort of way. But then for some reason she'd pulled away and dashed outside. He hadn't been too worried then. He'd thought he would have plenty of time to find out what had spooked her and soothe away whatever insecurities still plagued her.

But now he felt hope slipping through his fingers, leaving him grasping at air. Why couldn't anyone else see how suspicious it was that from the moment Lord Caxton had set foot in Courtlands she had turned back into that expressionless little porcelain doll, meekly agreeing with everything they decided? *Look at her!* he wanted to shout. Couldn't they see that the way she was sitting, with her hands folded neatly in her lap, that expression of polite acquiescence on her face, was a pose to hide what she was really thinking?

It was a trick he'd learned himself, when hauled up

before a commanding officer to answer for some misdemeanour. *All* soldiers perfected the knack of keeping a wooden countenance whilst internally cursing the pompous ass who was dressing them down.

God, what was she *really* thinking? What did she *feel* about the arrangements they were making on her behalf?

And, more importantly, what was she planning to do about it?

He should never have let it come to this. When she had come to him last night he should have escorted her straight back to her own room and let Milly go to the devil her own way. Except that Lady Jayne had been so upset at the thought of her friend's ruin. And he couldn't bear to think of her living with that distress for the rest of her life.

And what had happened to all those fine decisions he'd made on his way back? About how he was going to tell her everything, lay his heart bare before her, and then lay siege to her heart until she surrendered?

He'd seen Lady Jayne naked, that was what had happened, and it had all gone to hell in a handcart.

It was all he could do not to groan out loud. Nobody else was asking her what she wanted, but *he* had to know. He had to straighten things out between them or he was going to spend the next three weeks worrying that when he got to the altar his resourceful bride would be miles and miles away.

No doubt in the mistaken belief that it was for his own good.

Lady Jayne blew out her candle and flopped back onto her pillows. If she had been the kind of girl who got headaches she was sure she would have one now, even though her grandfather's timely arrival seemed to have nipped the threat of scandal in the bud.

She had been amazed, at dinner that night, how much the atmosphere had changed since breakfast. Even Lady Susan had remarked, albeit rather waspishly, that she had seen from the start that she and Richard had only ever had eyes for each other. Not that she believed that tale for a minute. The chaperones had probably counselled all the disappointed contenders for Richard's hand that it would be far wiser to stay on good terms with the scions of two such influential families than say anything to precipitate a complete breach.

She was sick of all the pretence. In some ways she would be glad to leave Courtlands in the morning. If only it did not mean that she would not be seeing Richard again for more than three weeks. He had tried so hard to make everyone believe he was perfectly content to be marrying her. But she hadn't been able to help noticing that he was looking more and more strained as the day wore on. After three more weeks of contemplating the marriage to which her thoughtless actions had condemned him he might well have built up quite a store of resentment.

If only she could—

What was that? It sounded as though something large and heavy had just landed on the roof of the *porte-cochère*.

She sat up and stared at the window, even though the darkness and the drawn curtains prevented her from seeing out.

Then there was a scraping noise...as though something metallic was sliding across the tiles.

She got out of bed just as something rattled down the roof and then smashed onto the gravel path beneath. One of the tiles, by the sound of it.

She had just put her hand to the curtains, to draw them back so she could look out, when there was a rasping sound, and then a click and then the casement creaked open.

Someone was breaking into her room!

She dashed back to the bed, looked wildly around for a weapon, and seized upon the candlestick.

She turned round, half crouched defensively, to see a man's booted leg, which he had clearly just been thrown over the windowsill, appear through the curtains.

Swiftly followed by...

'Richard!' She stood up straight. 'What on earth do you think you are doing?'

'Climbing up to your room, obviously,' he said, pushing the curtains aside so that he could get his other leg over the windowsill and stand up.

Immediately shafts of moonlight silvered the scene, taking her back to the time they had been alone in the library.

Her heart, which had been beating fast with trepidation just a moment previously, hesitated and then settled into a heavy rhythm which had nothing to do with fear at all. She was wearing only her nightdress. And he was dressed in a uniform which had clearly seen better days. There were patches, and holes with charred edges all over it. And as for his boots—they were the very antithesis of the highly polished Hessians he wore about Town. They were scuffed, and creased round the ankles, as though they were far too comfortable for him to throw away even though they looked so shabby.

It reminded her of how rakish and daring he had looked on the night of the masquerade. Only tonight he was not in costume.

This was the real man. The man he had told her about. The soldier who had marched across scorching plains and slept on frozen ground.

The man who climbed into a lady's window and... what?

'What do you want?' Her voice had gone breathy, and was barely more than a whisper as she asked, 'Why have you come?'

He stalked across to where she stood, his mouth curving into a grin. 'That's my Jayne,' he said approvingly. 'Straight to the point. No vapours or feeble feminine protests about impropriety.'

'Well, there would be little point, would there? Everyone already thinks I am ruined.'

He grimaced, coming to a halt only an inch or so from her.

She could feel the heat from his body through the flimsy material of her nightgown. He was breathing heavily from his exertions, and a faint sheen of sweat made his brow glisten. Was he going to ruin her properly tonight? Lady Penrose had said if he had not been interrupted he would have done so that morning. And at The Workings this morning he'd looked for a moment as though he'd been thinking about what they'd started.

Her tummy flipped with excitement.

Then from his cross belt he plucked out two roses that had been tucked there. A white one, and she thought a red one—though the moonlight had robbed it of its colour.

'You climbed up to my room...to bring me roses?'

It was a lovely, romantic gesture. But she couldn't understand why he should think that at this stage it was necessary. Unless… Perhaps he thought it would make it easier for her to become reconciled to this forced betrothal if he gave her some reassurance? Looking back over the day, she realized she'd done nothing but talk about finding ways out of it.

Yes, that was just the sort of thing he would do to ease her over what he thought she saw as a dreadful hurdle.

She laid the candlestick down and took them from him.

'And to tell you that to me,' he said with deliberation, as though he had rehearsed what he was about to say, 'you are as lovely as any rose. I know you can be a little unapproachable at times. I think you have deliberately cultivated a hedge of thorns about yourself, to stop anyone from getting too close to you and hurting you.'

'You…you think I am prickly?'

'You know very well you can be, my lady.' He stepped closer still, his voice low and urgent as he said, 'But it does not lessen my regard for you. A rose is a wonderful flower. Nothing can compare with its voluptuous, velvety petals.'

He reached out and twined one curl, which had escaped her plaits, round his forefinger. She caught her lower lip between her teeth.

'Or the heady perfume it gives off,' he grated. 'Lady Jayne, will you…? I came here to ask you…' He was staring at her mouth. 'Whatever it was has gone completely out of my head now,' he said irritably. 'All I can think about is how much I want to kiss you.'

'You want to kiss me?'

'God, yes,' he said, his voice throbbing with yearning.

Then, slowly, he began to lower his head towards hers. Giving her the chance, she realized, to refuse him. But she did not want to. So she tipped her head back, offering him her lips.

And he did kiss her.

Not swiftly, as he had done just before going out to chase after Milly. Or with that edge of desperation he had displayed when he'd come back. But slowly, as though he had all the time in the world and intended to savour every minute. He slid his arms round her waist and pulled her close. She clung to the facings of his jacket. The scent of roses filled the air as the flowers were crushed between their two heated bodies. Indeed, by the time he finished she felt as though she was melting.

But still a faint feeling of unease nagged at her.

'You don't need to do this. I don't want you to pretend something you don't feel for me, or—'

'Very well, then,' he said raggedly, stepping back. 'Listen to me, Lady Jayne. I am not pretending any more. I'm done with pretence. I have to tell you…'

'Yes?'

'That nightgown of yours is virtually transparent,' he groaned. 'Don't stand just there in the moonlight, please, or I won't be able to think of anything but how beautiful your breasts are. How much I want to see them again, taste them again…'

She went weak at the knees as her memory supplied the feel of his hands cupping her breasts. His tongue lapping. His teeth nipping.

The roses fell from her hands as they flew instinctively to her neckline.

He sucked in a short, sharp breath as she loosened the ribbons of her gown with trembling fingers.

'Maybe I don't want you to think about anything else,' she said, pushing the fine lawn from one shoulder, revealing the upper slope of her left breast. But then her courage ran out. He had not seemed to like it when he found her naked in his bed. Would he lose all respect for her if she fully exposed her breast to his gaze? Would he think she was wanton?

She was just about to cover herself up again when his hand shot out and stayed hers. Then, very gently, he stroked the fabric of her gown aside.

For a moment he just stood there, breathing heavily as he gazed at her. His hand hovered an inch above her flesh so that she could feel the heat of it, tantalizingly close. The tremors that ran through his body made it look as though he was exerting all his willpower to hold himself back.

So she stepped forward, pushing her breast into his outstretched hand. Her nipple beaded into his palm immediately.

And then it was as if whatever had been holding him back snapped. He tore open enough fastenings to expose both breasts. His mouth swooped to suckle feverishly on one while his hand caressed the other. The sensation was incredible. And it was not restricted to the area where he was touching her, but flooded the whole of her being with heat and yearning and wonder.

'I want you,' he said.

'Y-you do?' she gasped.

'More than anything. Oh, Jayne,' he murmured, running kisses along her collarbone and up the side of her neck. 'Jayne.' He sighed into her ear.

'Oh, yes, Richard, yes.'

'Yes? You mean that?'

'Mmm…'

She wanted to reach up and put her arms round his neck, to show him that she was a more than willing participant in whatever was going to happen. But her nightgown had slid down to her elbows, imprisoning them at her sides. And it suddenly felt much more satisfying to leave him entirely in charge. To know that whatever followed was all going to be exactly as *he* wanted. She did not want to feel any guilt, any shadow of doubt about who had seduced whom. Not tonight.

He walked her backwards to the bed, hastily undid the rest of her ribbons and slid her nightgown down over her hips. Then he picked her up and laid her gently down on the bed.

She felt very shy about being so exposed while he was still fully dressed. But he only stood looking down at her for a moment before joining her on the bed. He paid such sweet homage to her—with his hands, his lips, his tongue—that it was as though he was worshipping her body. He made her feel like a goddess as he bestowed reverent kisses upon every inch of her. He untied her plaits, sifted her hair through his fingers as though it was some rare treasure, then spread it out across the pillows. He stroked her flanks as though enchanted by the curve of her hips, the indentation of her waist. And whenever he encountered a bruise or a scrape he placed a particularly tender kiss there.

But eventually he began to restrict his attentions to the parts of her that were crying out for attention the most. Pretty soon the sensations he evoked were so intense she had no power left to think, only to feel.

And what she felt was beautiful. Men had told her before that she was beautiful. But she had dismissed their words as just that. Mere words. Only Richard could make her *feel* she really was beautiful. To him.

Yet though it was glorious it was not enough. She needed to touch him, too. Needed to kiss him.

'Richard, please,' she whimpered, reaching for him. 'Kiss me.'

At her pleading, he rolled her onto her side so they were face to face and did as she bade, kissing her long and languorously. Prising open her mouth with the insistent probing of his tongue and thrusting it inside when she opened to him.

It felt incredible, having his fully clothed body all along the length of her sensitized skin. The roughness of the material of what she was certain was the uniform in which he had served created such delicious friction.

She raised her leg, rubbing her foot along the supple leather of his boots, feeling the material of his breeches abrading the soft skin of her inner thigh.

He pushed her onto her back, reared up and pulled off his jacket.

'Buttons,' he muttered. 'Don't want to hurt you.'

And then he was back, kissing her with a feverishness that was even more glorious than anything that had gone before. For even in her inexperience she could tell his passion was raging almost beyond his control. The satisfying proof of that came when he fumbled open his breeches, pushing material out of the way, and nudged her legs apart.

And then suddenly he froze.

'I should not be doing this,' he said through gritted teeth. 'Lady Jayne, can you ever forgive me?'

When he made to roll off her she let out an indignant squeal and locked her hands behind his neck. 'I shall never forgive you if you stop now—and that is a promise!'

'It is wrong,' he insisted, though she noted with satisfaction that he wasn't trying all that hard to pull away from her. 'I did not come here for this.' He groaned. His whole body was shaking. 'I must not force myself on you like this….'

'You think you are forcing me?'

'Yes.' He lay down and pressed his face into the crook of her neck. 'You have to marry me, Jayne. I want you so much…too much,' he murmured.

His breath was hot on her ear. And the weight of him on top of her, with her legs spread like that, made it hard to concentrate on his words. She could only feel.

'Richard, please stop talking and just take me.'

'You are still that wild little creature your grandfather described this morning,' he said softly as she butted her hips up against his pelvis with a little whimper. 'You think right now that this is what you want because you are being ruled by your senses. But in the morning, when you think about it…'

'I shall be glad that you made me yours completely,' she declared. 'I shall ride back to Darvill Park in the carriage, hugging the knowledge that you saw something in me that made you climb up to my room and behave completely disgracefully, for once.'

And with that she spread her legs wider and hooked her ankles round the backs of his knees. The slight shift in position brought his member to the exact spot where she needed to feel it.

'Oh, God,' he groaned. 'I cannot fight you any more.'

He reached between her legs. Stroked along the slick folds of skin with his fingers. Then repeated the action with his rigid length. Sliding repeatedly towards the place where she felt an aching need to have him. The need increased as he continued to tease her until she was writhing beneath him, clawing at his back and panting, 'For God's sake, Richard, now. *Now!*'

And at last he pushed up, and in, and he was there, seated deep within her. Exactly where she needed him.

For a few glorious moments they both went wild. He plunged and she bucked. She clung and he grasped. He suckled on her neck. She sank her teeth into his shoulder. She flung her head back to cry out her ecstasy. He buried his face in her hair to groan out his, his fingers kneading into her buttocks so hard she knew she would still feel the imprint in her flesh the next day.

'You are mine now,' he panted. 'You will *have* to marry me.'

'And *you* will have to marry me.' She sighed with utter bliss. 'You are too much the gentleman to abandon a woman you have so thoroughly ravished.'

He winced. 'A real gentleman would never have done what I just did.'

'I don't think I will ever have much use for a real gentleman.' She sighed, running her hands up his shirt, which was stuck to his back with sweat. And then she giggled. 'I cannot believe you climbed up here and made love to me without so much as taking your boots off!'

In the silvered light that shimmered across her bed she saw a look of anguish flit across his face before he said, 'I wanted to show you who I really am. I came to you in my uniform because deep down I'm just a soldier, Jayne, not a lord. But I never intended to rob you of your innocence. I…I only meant to take you out for a moonlit picnic at The Workings. So I made a grappling hook to fix into the ridge tiles, and brought a rope ladder for you to climb down so you wouldn't graze your knees like last time. To demonstrate that if you need to climb out of a window for a little adventure I will be right there with you, making it better than anything you could have on your own. But the minute I saw you standing there bathed in moonlight,' he said huskily, 'I just couldn't resist you.'

He shook his head ruefully and rolled to one side, holding her tight, as though he was determined not to let her go even though they were no longer conjoined.

'No, it was before that. When you nibbled on your lower lip.' He sighed, tracing it with his thumb. 'That *always* has the effect of making me almost forget my own name. Though that's no excuse. I should have stuck to my plans tonight, our last night together for weeks, when it was so important that I bared my soul to you. Instead of which I was still…trying to protect myself.'

He shut his eyes, as though he was ashamed to meet her gaze.

'I have been a soldier most of my life, and soldiers get battered about. My leg, especially, is not a pretty sight,' he said sombrely. 'But then nor is a great deal of the rest of me. I made love to you with most of my clothes on because I didn't want you to see my scars. For you are so breathtakingly lovely. A vision.' He opened his eyes and tangled his fingers into her tousled curls. 'Far too beautiful to have to be tied to a wreck of a man like me.'

'Oh, Richard,' she said, 'what you look like has nothing to do with how I feel about you.'

'I know, I know,' he said swiftly. 'You are very far

from being vain or shallow, like most of your sex. But, even so, I am not quite what you wanted from a husband, am I?'

Before she could refute this allegation he had propped himself up on one elbow and was looking down into her face with such an earnest expression that she did not have the heart to argue with him. Whatever it was he was about to say was coming from some deep place in his heart, and she knew she needed to let him say it.

'Jayne, I love you. I love you so much that I won't ever try to repress any aspect of your nature. That is why I climbed up here tonight. I wanted to persuade you that we are made for each other. To tell you that I adore you exactly as you are. To show you that I don't want to *tame* you, like your grandfather has tried to do. Well,' he said ruefully, 'that is only half the tale. To be completely truthful I wanted to climb up after you through your bedroom window that first night we met.'

'You love me?' she gasped. 'You have wanted me since *that* night?'

'Yes. Even though I knew you were in love with Harry. I even started plotting ways to get rid of him. I grew so desperate. The only thing holding me back was knowing you would never forgive me....'

'Oh, how I wish you'd told me. Richard, I *never* loved Harry. I tried to explain to you this afternoon that he was just a rebellion against my grandfather's tyranny. I didn't realize that myself until he kissed me and it was so disgusting. After that, all I could think of was how to get rid of him, too.'

She checked at the look of astonishment on his face. And suddenly, from feeling like some kind of goddess, she shrank back to being just a child on the verge of a scold again.

'Does that make me a bad person?'

'No. Quite the reverse. You told me earlier, remember, that his declaration of love gave him a hold over you? And you are such a warm-hearted person that I can understand exactly how hard it must have been for you to find a way to break it off with him without hurting him. Even though it was all lies. But, Jayne, I am not lying to you. I really do love you.'

She looked at him doubtfully. 'How can you? Milly only ran away yesterday...'

'Ah, but I never loved Milly, either.'

'What? Never?'

'No. I admired her greatly for her courage and resourcefulness. I wanted to be sure she was going to be happy when we had to go our separate ways. But...'

'But she said...'

'I am sorry she misled you. But, Jayne, I had no idea you thought I was in love with her until you told me yesterday when we were out riding. I did try to explain, several times, but something always got in the way.' His eyes dropped to her mouth as she took in a great, shuddering breath.

'You didn't love Milly at all?'

'Not one bit.'

'All this time,' she said, 'I have been doing my utmost to make things work out for the pair of you. Because I thought if *I* could not have your heart, the least I could do was ensure you could marry the woman you did love, and not one of those dreadfully *accomplished* women.'

'Well, I *am* going to marry the woman I love, so...

Wait a minute—that sounded as though… What you said… Do you…?'

'Yes. I love you, Richard. I have been so miserable because I thought you could never love me.'

'How could you think that?' He closed his eyes and winced. 'No, I know only too well *exactly* why you felt unworthy of love. Your wretched childhood. And then Harry's lies on top of it all.'

'Richard,' she said in wonder. 'I don't think there is anyone in the whole world who would just *understand* me the way you do. And still…I…like me.'

He smiled tenderly. 'I more than like you. And the best of it is we have the rest of our lives to get to know each other even better.'

'Then would you mind explaining why you thought I would ever want to climb out of a window again when I have all I need right here?'

'Well, I didn't know you loved me then.'

'*Your* wretched childhood,' she said, quick as a flash, and hugged him hard.

'And as I've already said,' he murmured, burying his face in her curls, 'I couldn't let you leave without telling you how desperately I do want to be your husband. The moonlight picnic was supposed to give me the chance to lay my heart bare before you went away.' He pulled back abruptly. 'It's still there, laid out for us to enjoy. And there are two horses saddled and ready to go…'

'Richard,' she said tenderly, reaching up to stroke his scarred face, 'I don't really want to have to climb out of a window ever again.'

'You don't?'

'No. I've already told you. I have all I need right here. Except…'

'What? Tell me what you want. Anything, anything…'

'For what I have in mind you need to stop talking, Major Cathcart.'

She gave a sultry smile and settled back against the pillows.

'And take off your shirt.'

* * * * *

REQUEST YOUR
FREE BOOKS!

 HARLEQUIN® HISTORICAL:
Where love is timeless

2 FREE NOVELS PLUS 2 FREE GIFTS!

YES! Please send me 2 FREE Harlequin® Historical novels and my 2 FREE gifts (gifts are worth about $10). After receiving them, if I don't wish to receive any more books, I can return the shipping statement marked "cancel." If I don't cancel, I will receive 6 brand-new novels every month and be billed just $5.19 per book in the U.S. or $5.74 per book in Canada. That's a savings of at least 17% off the cover price! It's quite a bargain! Shipping and handling is just 50¢ per book in the U.S. and 75¢ per book in Canada.* I understand that accepting the 2 free books and gifts places me under no obligation to buy anything. I can always return a shipment and cancel at any time. Even if I never buy another book, the two free books and gifts are mine to keep forever.

246/349 HDN FEQQ

Name	(PLEASE PRINT)	
Address		Apt. #
City	State/Prov.	Zip/Postal Code

Signature (if under 18, a parent or guardian must sign)

Mail to the **Reader Service:**
IN U.S.A.: P.O. Box 1867, Buffalo, NY 14240-1867
IN CANADA: P.O. Box 609, Fort Erie, Ontario L2A 5X3

Not valid for current subscribers to Harlequin Historical books.

Want to try two free books from another line?
Call 1-800-873-8635 or visit www.ReaderService.com.

* Terms and prices subject to change without notice. Prices do not include applicable taxes. Sales tax applicable in N.Y. Canadian residents will be charged applicable taxes. Offer not valid in Quebec. This offer is limited to one order per household. All orders subject to credit approval. Credit or debit balances in a customer's account(s) may be offset by any other outstanding balance owed by or to the customer. Please allow 4 to 6 weeks for delivery. Offer available while quantities last.

Your Privacy—The Reader Service is committed to protecting your privacy. Our Privacy Policy is available online at www.ReaderService.com or upon request from the Reader Service.

We make a portion of our mailing list available to reputable third parties that offer products we believe may interest you. If you prefer that we not exchange your name with third parties, or if you wish to clarify or modify your communication preferences, please visit us at www.ReaderService.com/consumerschoice or write to us at Reader Service Preference Service, P.O. Box 9062, Buffalo, NY 14269. Include your complete name and address.

HHI1B

When Lady Deborah Napier blackmails notorious London thief Elliot Marchmont into becoming his accomplice, the thrill of adventure is *nothing* compared to the sudden rush of intoxicating passion that he incites within her….

"If I take you, it will be because I want to."

The words made Deborah shiver. Did he want her? Want *her?* No one had ever wanted her like that. "And do you—want me?"

Looking around swiftly to check they were quite alone, Elliot pulled her to him, a dark glint in his eyes. "You are playing a very dangerous game, Deborah Napier. I would advise you to have a care. For, if you dance with the devil, you are likely to get burnt. You may come with me, but only if you promise to do exactly as I say."

"You mean it!" *Oh God, he meant it!* She would be a housebreaker. A thief! "I'll do exactly as you say."

"Then prove it. Kiss me," Elliot said audaciously, not thinking for a moment that she would.

But she did. Without giving herself time to think, her heart hammering against her breast, Deborah stood on tiptoe, pulled his head down to hers and did as she was bid. Right there in Hyde Park, in the middle of the day, she kissed him.

She meant it as a kiss to seal their bargain, but as soon as her lips touched his, memories, real and imagined, made the taste of him headily familiar. His lips were warm on hers, every bit as sinfully delicious as she'd imagined, coaxing her mouth to flower open beneath his, teasing her lips into compliance, heating her gently, delicately, until his tongue touched hers.

It was a kiss like none she had ever tasted, heated by the

bargain it concluded, fired by the very illicitness of their kissing here in a public space, where at any moment they could be discovered. She could not have imagined, could not have dreamed that kissing, just kissing could rouse her in this way.

"Are you quite sure you want to do this?" he asked.

"Oh yes," she said, "I'm sure."

Elliot *always* gets what he wants. But will this most accomplished thief steal his greatest prize to date—Lady Deborah's heart?

Find out in
OUTRAGEOUS CONFESSIONS OF LADY DEBORAH
by Marguerite Kaye,
available from Harlequin® Historical in August 2012.